Advances in
REPRODUCTIVE PHYSIOLOGY

Advances in
REPRODUCTIVE
PHYSIOLOGY

Edited by
Anne McLaren

Institute of Animal Genetics
Edinburgh

LOGOS PRESS
ACADEMIC PRESS

Published by
LOGOS PRESS LIMITED
in association with
ELEK BOOKS LIMITED
2 All Saints Street, London, N.1.

Distributed by
ACADEMIC PRESS INC.
111 Fifth Avenue, New York, N.Y. 10003
and
ACADEMIC PRESS INC. (London) LIMITED
Berkeley Square House, Berkeley Square, London, W.1.

Library of Congress Catalog Card Number 65-27403

Paper supplied by Robert Horne and Company Ltd.
London
Printed in the Republic of Ireland by Hely Thom Limited, Dublin

CONTENTS

CONTRIBUTORS

ANTONIE W. BLACKLER

Division of Biological Sciences, Cornell University, Ithaca, New York, U.S.A.

J. D. BIGGERS and R. A. MCFEELY

School of Veterinary Medicine, University of Pennsylvania, Philadelphia, U.S.A.

PATRICIA A. JACOBS

Medical Research Council Clinical Effects of Radiation Research Unit, Edinburgh 4, Scotland.

P. E. LAKE

Agricultural Research Council Poultry Research Centre, King's Buildings, West Mains Road, Edinburgh 9, Scotland.

J. L. HANCOCK

Animal Breeding Research Organization, Edinburgh 9, Scotland.

W. K. WHITTEN

National Biological Standards Laboratory, Canberra, Australia.

K. P. BLAND and B. T. DONOVAN

Department of Neuroendocrinology, Institute of Psychiatry, Denmark Hill, London S.E.5., England.

M. J. R. DAWKINS

late of Institute of Child Health, Hammersmith Hospital, London W.12, England.

G. R. VENNING

G. D. Searle & Co. Ltd., High Wycombe, Buckinghamshire, England.

EDITOR'S FOREWORD

The Book of Life begins with a man and a woman in a
garden. It ends with Revelations. (Oscar Wilde, 1893)

This book begins with primordial germ cells in Amphibia; it ends
with the world population explosion and its control. The degree to
which two such apparently diverse subjects are related constitutes
the degree to which the physiology of reproduction deserves to be
considered as a subject in its own right, and the justification for the
appearance of yet another series of review volumes. It also reflects
the remarkable degree to which theory and practice are linked in this
field – more so, perhaps, than in any other field of biology. Some
may be concerned to increase fertility, others to reduce it; few can
claim to be uninterested in the practical implications of their work.

The group of articles by Blackler, Biggers and Jacobs raises at the
most fundamental level the question of what makes the two sexes
different. Primordial germ cells in Amphibia develop into sperm and
eggs in accordance not with their own genetic constitution, but with
that of the gonad in which they lie. In Man, the inclusion of the short
arm of a Y-chromosome in most cells of the body appears to be a
necessary, though not perhaps a sufficient, condition for the development of maleness; but this may not be true of goats. What happens
in sex chromosome mosaics is still an open question; perhaps the sex
of a gonad is determined by the 'majority vote' of its cell population.

Turning to the results of sex determination, Hancock's article il-
luminates the awe-inspiring complexities of microanatomy of the
mammalian spermatozoon. The 'homunculi' of the early microan-
atomists could hardly be more remarkable than the revelations of
electron microscopy. Lake deals with the equally impressive biochemical complexities of poultry semen and spermatozoa. The development of a satisfactory technique for the use of frozen semen in
artificial insemination in poultry is apparently still to come; but the
volume of background work is such that one feels it cannot be far
away.

Hormones form such a vital part of almost all reproductive phenomena that for many, reproductive physiology is coextensive with
endocrinology. Bland and Donovan describe how the ovary and uterus
function as an integrated unit, and speculate on the endocrinological

control mechanisms which make this possible. Whitten shows that chemical signals enable the female mammal not only to organize her own internal economy, but also, in the form of pheromones, to respond to relevant aspects of her environment, such as males. For readers interested in the comparative approach, there is an excellent article by C. G. Butler, entitled 'Pheromones in Insect Reproduction', in the Entomological Society's Symposium No. 2.

Our last two articles deal with the results of sexual reproduction. Dawkins' review of 'The Hazards of Birth' leaves one astonished that any infants at all survive the ordeal; enough do in fact survive to constitute what many believe to be the greatest problem facing our species today. Venning outlines the problem, and surveys what present-day contraceptive methods can and might do to solve it.

Control mechanisms, in the sense of positive and negative feedback mechanisms, are essential in any form of communication which is to function effectively. Review journals are no exception. We hope that this volume will be the first of a series; we hope too that our readers will ensure that the series improves as it goes along, by sending us their criticisms and comments, and their suggestions for further subjects that should be dealt with and authors that might deal with them.

ANNE MCLAREN
Summer 1965

Michael Dawkins died suddenly, at the age of 34, shortly after completing his article on 'The Hazards of Birth'. Proofs of the article were kindly corrected by his friend and colleague, Dr. Peter Gruenwald. By permission of the British Medical Journal we are reprinting their obituary notice, since we feel that anyone who reads his article will wish to know more about the life and work of this outstandingly able man. In his few years of research, he had already contributed much to our understanding of the physiology of the newborn; it is saddening and tantalizing to speculate on how his interests might have developed had he lived longer.

1

EMBRYONIC SEX CELLS OF AMPHIBIA

Antonie W. Blackler

Division of Biological Sciences, Cornell University, Ithaca, New York, U.S.A.

A. INTRODUCTION

Investigation of the embryological origin of vertebrate sex cells has always been hampered by the absence of any notable and enduring cytological character which would enable the sex cells to be distinguished in embryonic material. The lack of such a diagnostic character has been the source of various controversies that have arisen in this field.

The older literature has been adequately covered in a number of reviews (Bounoure, 1939; Everett, 1945; Nieuwkoop, 1949; Johnston, 1951). The present article will be concerned chiefly with recent studies on gonocyte origin in the Amphibia, which differ from earlier investigations in three important ways.

First, in at least one group of the Amphibia, the Anura, there exists in the developing embryo a unique cytological marker, present exclusively in the germ line of cells, thus identifying these cells in a non-equivocal manner. The marker can be traced throughout the course of development from the fertilized but uncleaved egg up to the establishment of the early larva: that is, up to that moment when the gonadal rudiments are formed. Subsequent development of the gonocytes can be followed by ordinary histological means without too much difficulty. The discovery and description of the 'germinal cytoplasm' were the work of Bounoure (1934). Bounoure analysed, for the European frog *Rana temporaria*, the whole series of cytological events during early development in which this germ-plasm is involved. He went on to argue convincingly that this special cytoplasm was probably the determining principle which distinguishes the embryonic sex cells from the somatic cells.

The use of experimental interference is the second feature which distinguishes Amphibian studies from almost all work on other vertebrates, in which the emphasis has been largely histological. The third feature is that the experimental attack has been reinforced by the use of a number of genetic markers, which have the substantial virtues of constancy and predictable behaviour.

B. DESCRIPTIVE

1. *History of the sex cells in Anura*

When the frog or toad egg has been deposited and fertilized, the first signs that activation has occurred are the production of the second polar body, the free rotation of the egg within its vitelline membrane, and the movements in the cortical layer which result eventually in the appearance of the grey crescent. About forty minutes after the penetration of the sperm in *R. temporaria* (Blackler, 1958), small islets of 'germinal cytoplasm' begin to appear just below the cortex of the lower third of the egg. In eggs which possess little vegetal pigment (for example, the eggs of *Xenopus laevis*), the islets can be seen as grey patches with the aid of a low-power microscope. They are free of yolk inclusions but contain copious mitochondria and basophil cytoplasm; at least part of the basophily is due to the presence of ribonucleic acid. These constituents of the 'germinal cytoplasm' enable it to be coloured in sections by such stains as

Altmann's acid fuchsin, azure A, and even Heidenhain's azan, although pre-treatment with potassium dichromate is usually necessary.

As the moment for the first cleavage division of the egg approaches, the islets of germ-plasm begin to move toward the vegetal pole and to coalesce as they do so. After the first two divisions have been completed, the germ-plasm is distributed in approximately equal quantity between the four blastomeres. At the same time, it has been migrating toward the animal pole by 'sliding' along the cell membranes in the egg axis. These movements are presumably part of the general phenomenon of polar ingression, first described by Schectmann (1934) and later confirmed by other authors (Bounoure, 1935; Nieuwkoop, 1947).

During the formation of the blastula the germ-plasm may or may not be further divided. The degree to which the germ-plasm approaches the animal pole also varies according to the species examined. In Ranids the plasm-bearing cells may be found quite superficially in the floor of the blastocoel, while in *Xenopus* these same cells rarely ascend more than a third of the distance between the egg poles. In both *Bufo* and *Discoglossus* the cells with the 'germinal cytoplasm' are extremely superficial and in some eggs part of the plasm may actually be extruded into the blastocoel itself. The number of cells with germ-plasm at this time is rather variable. In *Discoglossus* there are about a dozen, in *Rana* and *Bufo* as many as a score, while in *Xenopus* the number varies between 2 and 14. Hammer's studies suggest that the actual number is in some way predetermined, since it varies according to which particular female has laid the eggs.

In the late blastula the germ-plasm undergoes a remarkable intracellular change of position (Plate 1). Up to this moment the 'germinal cytoplasm' has always been adherent to the cell membrane, but it now leaves this site, traverses the cell cytoplasm, and applies itself to the nuclear membrane. Here it may form a cap, or may completely envelop the nucleus. From the time that the germ-plasm reaches the nuclear membrane, the cells that contain it cease to divide.

During gastrulation the cells with germ-plasm are moved by the morphogenetic movements, so that by the neurula stage they are situated deeply within the endodermal material. In *Rana* the cells tend to be scattered among the endodermal cells, but in *Xenopus* they are much more closely aggregated. When neurulation has been completed and the elongation of the embryo is under way, the cells with germ-plasm migrate to the dorsal part of the endoderm and eventually reach its crest, passing each side of the archenteric slit in doing so (Plate 2). The migration is viewed by Bounoure as being amoeboid, and is apparently facilitated by a general loosening of endodermal cell adhesion at this time.

The plasm-bearing cells now leave the endodermal crest and become attached to the dorsal angles of the developing dorsal mesentery. Peritoneal cells gradually mix with the special cells and eventually isolate them from the body cavity. When this event is complete, the gonadal rudiments have been constituted. Their subsequent history has been too well documented (e.g. Witschi, 1929) to need further description. However, one subsidiary event that may occur during the formation of the germ ridges is worth mentioning. Occasionally the dorsal mesentery appears to form rather too rapidly for all of the plasm-bearing cells to reach its dorsal angles; some get trapped in the roof of the endoderm and later become part of the intestinal wall (where their subsequent fate is uncertain, although certainly some degenerate). During the formation of the germ ridges, the 'germinal cytoplasm' loses its affinity for the stains used; and the cells can then be seen to start dividing again. Fortunately, their content of yolk platelets (which persists for some time after the yolk has been 'used up' in adjacent cells) allows their fate to be followed, and many of the older accounts claim that their transformation into oogonia and spermatogonia can be followed without difficulty.

'Germinal cytoplasm' has been found in *R. temporaria* (Bounoure, 1927, 1934; Blackler, 1958), in *R. pipiens* (DiBerardino, 1961), in *R. esculenta* (Hammer, unpublished), in *Bufo bufo* (Blackler, 1958), in *Discoglossus pictus* (Gipouloux, 1962a), in *X. laevis* (Nieuwkoop, 1956a, b; Blackler, 1958), and in other species of *Xenopus* (Hammer, unpublished). Thus there is sufficient evidence to indicate the universal existence of 'germinal cytoplasm' in Anura. This plasm is, as far as I am aware, the earliest evidence of chemical differentiation found in any vertebrate.

2. History of the sex cells in Urodela

The presence of 'germinal cytoplasm' has not been claimed for any Urodele egg, so that our knowledge of the early events is defective. Almost all of the histological studies have dealt with developmental stages in which the gonadal rudiments have already been formed. The interpretation of these studies closely parallels the findings from Anuran material.

The earliest tracing of embryonic sex cells has been accomplished by Humphrey (1925), who was able to distinguish them in tail-bud and later stages of *Hemidactylium*. Humphrey claims that the gonocytes can be recognized by virtue of such characteristics as the large spherical nucleus and the finely distributed chromatin (the mesodermal cells at this time have smaller and rather flattened nuclei, while the nuclei of the endoderm cells are large but irregular in shape). Similar characteristics are shown by Anuran gonocytes; indeed, were it not for the presence of the germ-plasm in frog eggs, identification of the sex cells would have to rest on such criteria.

According to Humphrey, the embryonic sex cells are associated with the sheet of lateral plate mesoderm, and in particular with its more dorsal regions. In embryos of 3–7 somites, the gonocytes are located about midway between the last somite and the anus. Recognition at the neural plate stage proves impossible, because the criteria used to identify the sex cells are now shared by many other cells of the embryo. The number of gonocytes present at this time is about 20 to 100, and a significant detail is Humphrey's statement to the effect that mitosis is found in the sex cells only after the embryo has reached an age of 31 days or more.

3. Commentary on descriptive studies

The descriptive studies in both groups of Amphibia demonstrate that the embryonic sex cells do not originate in the gonads, but have a longer developmental history than these organs. The sex cells, at least in Anura, appear to be constituted during the late blastula stage and thereafter exist as a continuous line of cells. It is tempting to suppose that the 'germinal cytoplasm' plays a determinative role, although only experimental studies can reveal the truth or falsity of this supposition (see section C1). Nonetheless, it is clear that cells of germinal *potentiality* exist even before the blastula stage.

Is the embryonic sex cell differentiated or not? If the presence of the germ-plasm is taken as the criterion of the embryonic sex cell, then it follows that the fertilized egg is itself a sex cell. It is only when the third cleavage (horizontal) has taken place that a somatic line of cells is constituted. In this context the term 'germ cell', used so often in texts as being equivalent to 'egg cell', gains an added meaning. Since the embryonic sex cell includes a cytoplasmic differentiation that other cells of the embryo lack, in this sense the sex cell is a 'differentiated' cell. On this basis, what occurs during cleavage is the establishment of somatic cells from the primary sex cell, by means of a synchronous 'de-differentiation' of the somatic cells.

However, one can take a different view. Any one of the first four blastomeres has both germinal and somatic *potentiality;* that is, it is not a 'pure' cell and is therefore not *developmentally* differentiated. On this view we are forced back to considering the late blastula as marking the moment in development when true sex cells originate. Again, whether or not the sex cells at this time lack developmental potential can only be answered by an experimental analysis (section C5).

In conclusion, attention can be drawn to the tissue in which the embryonic sex cells are first located: mesoderm in Urodeles, endoderm in Anurans. This difference in position probably has no real developmental significance, for we have seen that in Anura the association of the sex cells with the endoderm is purely secondary. It is more reasonable to consider the gonocytes as specific elements whose history merely happens to coincide with one or other of the germ layers.

C. EXPERIMENTAL

1. The question of sex cell origin and continuity

The presence of the 'germinal cytoplasm' in frog eggs raises the question of its possible determinative significance. Two experimental techniques have been used in seeking an answer: the destruction of the germ-plasm by ultra-violet light (UV) and ablation of the plasm by surgical means.

Bounoure and his co-workers (Bounoure, 1937, 1950; Aubry, 1953; Bounoure, Aubry and Huck, 1954) were the first workers to irradiate the vegetal hemispheres of uncleaved eggs of *R. temporaria* in an attempt to provoke sterility. In larvae derived from eggs that survived the UV treatment, the number of gonocytes in the gonads was always reduced and, in the later studies, was reduced to zero. In the best series, 60% of the larvae were completely sterile.

The most critical stage for maximal UV effect seems to be immediately before the first cleavage. Padoa (1963, 1964) has irradiated the eggs of *R. esculenta* at this stage and obtained up to 85% total sterility. In the interpretation of his results, Padoa draws attention to the ribonucleic acid component of the 'germinal cytoplasm' and believes the sterilizing effect of the UV to be due to selective absorption by RNA. Padoa has also raised the possibility, based on the absence of germ-plasm in unfertilized eggs and its appearance between sperm entry and the first cleavage, that the germ-plasm contains messenger RNA. Irradiation early enough may therefore prevent protein synthesis and upset the presumed nucleo-cytoplasmic relationship that leads to sex cell formation. On this basis, the failure of UV to provoke sterility when applied after the critical stage can be explained. New experiments to explore this possibility are current in Padoa's laboratory.

The idea of messenger RNA being implicated in sex cell formation is sophisticated, and a simpler explanation can be advanced to account for the variability in results of UV experiments. Immediately before the first cleavage occurs, the 'germinal cytoplasm' is in its phase of greatest coalescence and is superficial. Thus UV irradiation should have maximum effect if applied at this moment. After the first cleavage, some of the germ-plasm will be lying much deeper in the egg interior and will therefore be less accessible to the UV. Moreover, Nieuwkoop (1947) advances the argument that in Bounoure's experiments the UV may be deleterious not only for the germ-plasm but also for the egg itself. In his view, increase in dose of the UV will create progressively unfavourable conditions for sex cell formation.

A feature missing from the studies of both Bounoure et al. and Padoa is a cytological analysis of the *immediate* effects of the UV treatment. In this connection the experiments of Hammer (unpublished) are interesting. Using *Xenopus* material, Hammer obtained up to 75 % sterility in embryos treated with UV, but also observed in sectioned material that the somatic events leading to gonad formation, and the physical appearance of the 'germinal cytoplasm', were not disturbed by the treatment. It was only during later cleavage that abnormalities arose in the establishment of the sex cells.

In another study of determination, Nieuwkoop and Suminski (1959) pricked the vegetal poles of four-cell stages of *Xenopus*, thereby causing loss of some of the vegetal material. They found no subsequent sterility, and therefore concluded that the 'germinal cytoplasm' was not an indispensable ingredient of the embryonic sex cells. Here again, however, the experiment was not controlled by sectioning eggs after healing, in order to verify that ablation of the germ-plasm had been achieved. The descriptive studies show that at this time the islets of germ-plasm are closely associated with the egg cortex; since this is quite viscous *in vivo*, the extruded material may have consisted wholly or mostly of the liquid endoplasm. Further experimental analysis of the role of the 'germinal cytoplasm' is clearly still required.

Apart from the above studies in Anura, Nieuwkoop (1947) has performed experiments on Urodeles which he interprets as demonstrating that the sex cells require an inductive stimulus by the dorso-caudal endoderm in order to differentiate. The experiments involved extirpation of the whole endoderm from early neurulae of *Triturus taeniatus*, which led to a considerable reduction in the number of sex cells at later stages. When Takamoto (1953) came to repeat these experiments, using middle and late neurulae of *T. pyrrhogaster*, he could find no sex cells at all in surviving larvae. Asayama and Amanuma (1957), in a study of induced secondary embryos in the same species, considered that the sex cells which they found in the secondary embryo had had no association with the dorsocaudal endoderm. The question of stimulus being in some doubt, Amanuma (1958) excised the posterior endoderm from the early neurula of *pyrrhogaster* and later found sex cells in surviving larvae. The studies with the newt *T. pyrrhogaster* are thus cited as evidence against Nieuwkoop's interpretation.

Turning now to the question of sex cell continuity, we may consider at the same time the experimental proof of sex cell origin as indicated by the descriptive studies.

For the Anura, experiments have been performed which demonstrate that the embryonic sex cells are indeed the ancestors of the gametes (Blackler, 1962; Blackler and Fischberg, 1961). In *Xenopus*, as mentioned above, the embryonic sex cells of the neurula are closely aggregated. Regions containing the gonocytes can therefore be transferred from one neurula to another, and animals which survive the operation can be raised to sexual maturity.

In grafts of this kind, it is of course necessary to distinguish grafted gonocytes from unextirpated sex cells and other cells of the host. Such distinction was achieved by using a genetic marker, the so-called 'Oxford' mutant (Elsdale, Fischberg and Smith, 1958). In non-mutant *Xenopus laevis*, the cells are potentially 2-nucleolate: many nuclei contain two separate nucleoli, while the rest contain a similar amount of nucleolar material fused into a single body. The 'Oxford' mutant, in the heterozygous condition, causes all cells to carry one nucleolus only. The mutant acts in a simple Mendelian manner: a 2-nucleolate animal ($2nu$) mated to an 1-nucleolate animal ($1nu$) yields progeny of which half are $1nu$ and half $2nu$.

In the graft experiments, all donor neurulae were $1nu$ and all

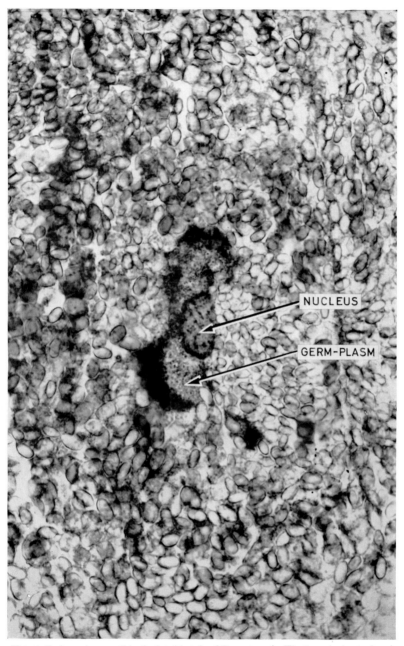

Plate 1. Embryonic sex cell in the late blastula of *R. temporaria*. The 'germinal cytoplasm' has left the cell membrane and is beginning to envelop the nucleus. Granular material between the bow-shaped germ-plasm and the nucleus is pigment.

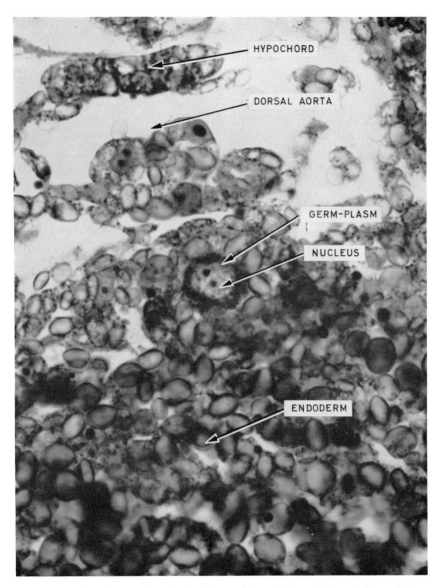

Plate 2. Embryonic sex cell at the dorsal crest of the endoderm in the early larva of *R. temporaria*. The nucleus of the cell, which shows two prominent nucleoli, is surrounded by a corona of 'germinal cytoplasm'.

recipient neurulae were 2*nu*. If we take the experimental situation in which donor sex cells were successfully transferred but not all the host sex cells were removed, the results of mating the grafted animals with normal individuals can be represented as in Fig. 1. Any 1*nu*

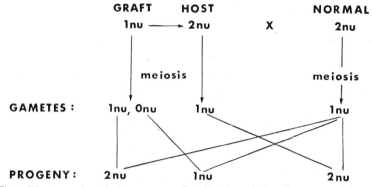

Fig. 1. Diagram to show the consequences of mating a 2-nucleolate *Xenopus* containing sex cells derived from a 1-nucleolate animal, with a normal 2-nucleolate individual. It is assumed that not all the host 2*nu* sex cells were removed in the transfer operation. All 1-nucleolate progeny must be derived from graft material.

individuals found in the progeny must have involved a gamete of graft origin, and in addition to these an equal proportion of the 2*nu* forms must also have been associated with the graft (although these 2*nu* animals are indistinguishable from 2*nu* animals derived from the host's sex cells). Therefore the percentage of 1*nu* offspring can be used to calculate the ratio of graft-derived to host-derived gametes. When the percentage of 1*nu* offspring is 50%, only graft-derived gametes have been produced by the experimental animal.

Experiments of this kind have shown beyond question that sex cells do indeed exist in neurulae, and are the direct ancestors of functional gametes. The success of transfer is usually between 80 and 100%. Parallel experiments in which the 'Oxford' marker has been used in conjunction with another marker ('pale' and 'dark' eggs) have yielded more or less identical results.

The experiments do not, of course, demonstrate that the sex cells seen in sectioned material are necessarily the same as those transferred by surgery. However, it must be emphasized that the design of the experiment was based on the siting of the embryonic sex cells by the descriptive method. Moreover, if the sex-cell region is excised from a neurula and replaced *not* by the same region of another neurula but by endoderm, which is expected, on descriptive grounds, to be devoid of gonocyte material, only two kinds of *Xenopus* result:

completely sterile animals, and animals producing gametes of host type only.

In other experiments on Anura, Gipouloux (1962b) and Monroy (1939) extirpated the endoderm from neurulae of *Discoglossus* and found sterility of gonadal rudiments in surviving larvae. This result is entirely in line with the *Xenopus* result, and suffers only from the shortcoming that the *Discoglossus* embryos could not be cultured for very long after the operations.

For the Urodela, Humphrey (1927, 1929) and Nieuwkoop (1947) have confirmed the mesodermal site of the embryonic sex cells by exchanging lateral plate mesoderm material between late neurulae and late gastrulae of *Ambystoma* and *Triturus*. Unfortunately, precise markers were not available at the time that these studies were performed, although Nieuwkoop was able to recognize host and graft sex cells by their different content of pigment granules. The papers cited also recount mesoderm deletion experiments which resulted in sterility.

In a recent study, Smith (1964) has transferred lateral plate material between mid-gastrulae of *Ambystoma mexicanum* which were genetically marked, and has raised the experimental animals to maturity. The marker used affects the colour of the axolotls beyond the larval stage. It appears that the normal black of axolotls is due to the dominant gene D, either in homozygous or heterozygous combination. White axolotls are all homozygous recessives (dd). Matings between black and white animals involve simple Mendelian segregation. Thus, for this Urodele, Smith has used the colour marker in an analogous manner to the use of the nuclear marker in *Xenopus* (Fig. 2).

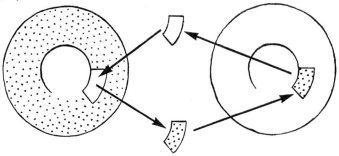

"BLACK" (DD)   **"WHITE" (dd)**
GASTRULA   **GASTRULA**

Fig. 2. Operation scheme for the reciprocal transfer of 'black' and 'white' presumptive lateral plate mesoderm between axolotl gastrulae (after Smith, 1964).

In the black-to-white combination (DD or Dd→dd), 19 adults survived in which the graft could be seen to be located partially or wholly within the gonadal region of the host; when these were mated to white animals (dd), 14 of them gave rise to at least some black offspring, proving that some of the gametes produced must have been of graft origin. Again the experimental method shows that embryonic sex cells are present in early embryonic stages, and that they are the ancestors of the functional gametes.

In concluding this section, we cannot fail to be impressed by the perfect harmony that exists between the experimental data for the Anura and Urodeles and the results of descriptive studies.

2. The question of the secondary origin of sex cells

Many authors in the past have flatly denied the existence of embryonic sex cells and have considered the gametes to be entirely derived by transformation of some of the somatic elements of the gonads in the adult animal. In the light of the experimental evidence, this point of view can no longer be upheld. On the other hand, there has long been controversy over the view advanced by other writers that while the existence and continuity of the gonocytes is accepted, their number is augmented by metaplasia of gonadal somatic cells in later development. Against this concept one may cite the deletion experiments of Humphrey, Nieuwkoop, Monroy and Gipouloux (see above). Unfortunately, other experiments made during the past decade by Japanese workers have given different results.

Deletion experiments by Asayama (1950) and Amanuma (1957) did not lead to sterility. Moreover, when Kotani (1957, 1958) replaced lateral plate mesoderm in early T. pyrrhogaster gastrulae by ectoderm, he reported that sex cells were later to be found in the germ ridges, suggesting a transformation of ectodermal cells into sex cells. The weakness of these studies is that none of the experiments involved markers, so that the sex cells could not be definitely shown to have had ectodermal origin.

In this context, another of Smith's (1964) experimental series has fundamental importance. Again using the colour mutant, Smith transplanted presumptive epidermis from 'black' (DD or Dd) gastrulae into the lateral plate region of 'white' (dd) gastrulae. When embryos surviving this kind of experiment (Fig. 3) were raised to adults and then mated to normal white animals, none of 18 grafted animals gave progeny in which black individuals were included. Transformation of ectoderm is thus refuted.

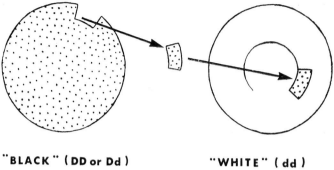

"BLACK" (DD or Dd)
GASTRULA
　　　　　　　　　　"WHITE" (dd)
　　　　　　　　　　GASTRULA

Fig. 3. Operation scheme for the transfer of 'black' presumptive epidermis into the 'white' presumptive lateral plate mesoderm region in axolotl gastrulae (after Smith, 1964).

Additional evidence against the hypothesis of secondary origin of sex cells comes from Smith's lateral plate exchanges in *Ambystoma* and Blackler and Fischberg's endodermal exchanges in *Xenopus*. In all experiments of this character, a good proportion of the grafted animals have yielded gametes solely of graft origin. With deletion studies, it could be argued that any power the somatic part of the gonad might have to form sex cells is abrogated by absence of the primary sex cells; but with exchange experiments, this objection does not arise, since primary sex cells of donor origin are present.

One gains the impression, from appraising the experimental results in both Anura and Urodela, that the more exact and sophisticated the design of the experiments becomes, the less plausible is the concept of secondary origin of sex cells. This view is in complete accord with the evidence from experimental studies carried out on birds and mammals.

3. The question of sex cell movements

We have seen that the movements of the 'germinal cytoplasm' in the Anuran egg during cleavage is part of the more general phenomenon of polar ingression. The displacement of the embryonic sex cells between the late blastula and early neurula stages is likewise a passive movement, since the cells are caught up in the general morphogenetic movements inherent in the gastrulation process. On the other hand the intracellular movement of the germ-plasm in late blastula cells, as well as the migration of the sex cells from a deep endodermal position in the neurula to the gonadal rudiments of the early larva, cannot be explained on such a basis.

Of the intracellular movement of the 'germinal cytoplasm' nothing is known, but the final migration of the sex cells has been subject to an extended analysis by Gipouloux (1962c; 1963a,b,c; 1964a,b). This worker has based his studies on the premise that the sex cells do not have an innate tendency to migrate dorsally, but that they are directed to do so by the embryonic axial material.

In a first series of experiments, Gipouloux grafted together *Bufo* neurulae by their ventral surfaces, and then removed the whole of the dorsal axis (notochord, somites and nephrotomes) from one of the embryos. As might be expected, the survival rate was poor; but in the animals which did continue to develop Gipouloux found that the fertile region of the gonadal rudiments was longer than in control larvae of the same age, and contained more sex cells (up to 39 cells as against the normal 24 cells). No sex cells could be detected in the partial embryo. The conclusion from these experiments was that the augmentation of sex cell number must have been due to migration of the sex cells of the partial embryo in a direction diametrically opposite to the normal direction. Unfortunately no marker was available to confirm that the extra sex cells were indeed derived from the partial embryo.

In an attempt to confirm this result, a further series was performed in which the whole endodermal mass, including the roof of the archenteron, was rotated about its axis through an angle of 180°. Survival was achieved only at the expense of considerable loss of endoderm before the ectomesodermal coat had healed, but nevertheless in the few surviving animals gonadal rudiments were found which had incorporated an average of six sex cells. This result was thus in line with the result of the earlier studies.

When the notochord and/or the nephrotomes were extirpated, three types of embryos continued to develop. The individuals lacking notochords were poorly elongated but normal germ ridges were formed, bearing the normal number of sex cells (24). The animals lacking nephrotomes also bore normal germ ridges containing the usual number of sex cells. However, when both tissue types were simultaneously extirpated, no germ ridges were formed although the sex cells migrated as usual and could be found at the root of the dorsal mesentery or in the dorsal crest of the endoderm. The absence of notochord and/or nephrotomes does not therefore disturb the dorsal migration of the embryonic sex cells. On the other hand, while germ ridges can be formed in the absence of one or other of these tissues, they cannot differentiate in the absence of both of them.

Gipouloux has gone on to new studies (Fig. 4), involving removal

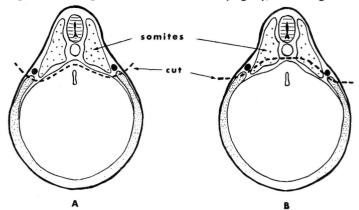

A   **B**

Fig. 4. Operation scheme for demonstrating the influence of the somites on sex cell migration (after Gipouloux, 1964a). In A, all the dorsal axial material is removed, and in B, only the ventral regions of the somites are left in place. After removal of material in both A and B, the wound is covered by body ectoderm to facilitate healing.

of all the dorsal tissues from early tail-buds of *R. esculenta* (A), or removal of most of the dorsal material, but leaving the ventral parts of the somites in place (B). Healing of the wounds was encouraged by covering them with general body ectoderm. When the animals were fixed 17 days later, controls showed germ ridges with about 35 sex cells, but none of the experimental animals had developed germ ridges. In individuals from (A) operations sex cells were never found, but individuals derived from (B) operations showed 13–18 sex cells in the endoderm immediately under the remaining piece of somite.

In the most recent experiments of Gipouloux, a suspension of somitic mesoderm cells has been prepared and incorporated in agar. Pieces of this agar have then been grafted into the ventral regions of neurulae which have been deprived of the whole of their dorsal material. When the embryos were killed and sectioned 12 days after operation, up to six sex cells were found in the immediate vicinity of the agar. This indicates some chemical attraction of the embryonic sex cells by the somitic material during neurula and tail-bud stages of Anura.

4. The question of regulation of sex cell number

As we have seen previously, irradiation with ultra-violet light of the vegetal pole of the egg just before the first cleavage provokes either severe reduction in number of the sex cells in the gonadal rudiments, or total sterility. The completely sterile animals are naturally the more interesting from the point of view of the investigator interested in the function of the 'germinal cytoplasm' and the problem of secondary sex cells, but the partially sterile gonads sometimes manifest a phenomenon not encountered in normal larvae, namely, frequent mitoses in those sex cells that remain in the gonad. For the frog *R. temporaria*, Bounoure (1964) quotes some interesting figures which indicate that the frequency of mitosis bears some relationship to the number of sex cells present in the depleted gonads. Whereas in the gonads of normal larvae less than $\frac{1}{2}$% of the sex cells are in active mitosis, in experimental larvae containing between 50 and 100 sex cells about 8% of the cells are in mitosis, and in larvae carrying between 15 and 25 gonocytes the percentage of cells in division is increased to about 30%. Active regulation thus occurs in the germ line of cells to compensate for the destruction of potential sex cells by the ultra-violet light.

Manifestations of numerical regulation have also been noted in irradiated *Xenopus* material (Hammer, unpublished) and in sex cell transplantations in which few graft cells have been successfully transferred and few host cells left in position (Blackler, unpublished). However, in other cases few sex cells are present in the gonad but numerical regulation does not take place. Preliminary counts of the sex cells in these indicate that the number of cells is rarely more than 20. Moreover, in matings of normal *Xenopus* carried out under laboratory conditions up to 2% 'sterility' may be detected among the offspring. This 'sterility' is made up in part of genuinely sterile animals and for the rest of animals bearing between one and twenty sex cells. Possibly differentiation of the gonad requires the initial presence of a certain number of sex cells of early origin. This 'threshold' number may show species differences.

5. *The question of sex cell potentiality*

Once the embryonic sex cells have achieved a gonadal position, the descriptive studies imply a regular sequence of events taking place in the cells, resulting eventually in the production of gametes. However, the level of differentiation of the sex cells can only be investigated by experimental analysis. It appears that the gonocytes are not *sexually* differentiated during early development, notwithstanding the existence of the so-called sex chromosomes in the nuclei of the embryonic cells. It has been known for some time, from studies which have involved parabiosis, transplantation of presumptive gonad material and treatment with sex hormones, that the direction of sexual differentiation in sex cells can be reversed (e.g. Burns, 1930; Humphrey, 1933, 1948; Gallien, 1956). The results of transferring gonocytes between neurulae of different sexes in *Xenopus* (Blackler, 1965) have substantiated this conclusion. It seems that it is the sexual nature of the gonad in which the sex cells take up residence which determines whether they will form spermatozoa or eggs.

Sex reversal of gonocytes has also been employed to create sex genotypes that do not normally exist in nature (Humphrey, 1957; Mikamo and Witschi, 1963; Blackler, 1965). The interest of these studies lies in the demonstration that the sex chromosomes, while normally important in steering the development of the animal in one of two alternative sexual paths, are not indispensable for gametogenesis. Thus, for example, the normal female of *Xenopus* has a genetic sex constitution ZW, but females can be artificially created of constitution WW; when the sex of these unusual females is reversed they give rise to functional W sperm (normal sperm carry only the Z sex chromosome).

Transplantation of embryonic sex cells between neurulae of different subspecies (Blackler, 1962) and species (Blackler, unpublished) in *Xenopus* has demonstrated, however, that while the course of sexual differentiation of the grafted sex cells can be altered by the somatic environment supplied by the host neurula, other donor characteristics cannot. This is perhaps best illustrated in the transfers between the species *X. laevis* and *X. tropicalis*. The egg of *laevis* measures about 1.5 mm. in diameter, is coloured a dark brown in the animal hemisphere, and its development shows characters not seen in the development of *tropicalis* eggs. The egg of *tropicalis* is much smaller (0.7 mm. in diameter) and coloured with a distinctive black speckling. When reciprocal transfers of embryonic sex cells are made between neurulae of the two species and the experimental animals raised to sexual maturity, females will lay eggs identical in size, colour and development with those of the species which provided the grafted material. Here is a convincing demonstration that the 'foreign' environment has not induced any change in the potentiality of the sex cells to determine species characteristics.

6. Commentary on experimental studies

Taking together the various experimental studies that have been performed with amphibian sex cells, the following general conclusions emerge:

(*i*) Embryonic sex cells are formed very early in the life history of the animal, at least as early as the mid-gastrula in Urodeles and the neurula in Anura. These sex cells persist in the embryo and eventually differentiate into the functional gametes of the adult animal. In Urodeles the sex cells are initially associated with the dorsal parts of the lateral plate mesoderm, but in Anura they are lodged in the endodermal material.

(*ii*) It has become increasingly probable that *all* the gametes of the adult are derived from the embryonic sex cells and that augmentation of sex cell number by transforming somatic cells does not occur. Moreover, gonocytes are not transformed into somatic cells except during the transition from one generation to the next.

(*iii*) At least in the Anura, the early movements of the sex cells within the egg are almost certainly passive. During the migration of the cells into the gonads they move independently of the surrounding cells. The direction of movement appears to be dictated by a chemical attraction emanating from the axial somitic mesoderm.

(*iv*) Embryonic sex cells do not have a stable sexual character in spite of the presence of sex chromosomes. It is the sexual character of the gonad in which the gonocytes will differentiate which decides whether they are to form spermatozoa or eggs. The genotype of the sex cells does, however, determine many characteristics of the eggs they can form.

REFERENCES

Amanuma, A. (1957) Effects of extirpation of the presumptive intermediate mesoderm upon the differentiation of the primordial germ cells. *Zool. Mag.*, **66**, 276-8.

Amanuma, A. (1958) On the role of the dorso-caudal endoderm in the formation of the primordial germ cells. *J. Inst. Polytech.*, *Osaka*, **9**, 211–16.

Asayama, S. (1950) The developmental potencies of the intermediate mesoderm of *Triturus pyrrhogaster* when transplanted into orthotopic or heterotopic sites in the body wall of another embryo. *J. Inst. Polytech.*, *Osaka*, **1**, 13–26.

Asayama, S. & Amanuma, A. (1957) On the primordial germ cells of the secondary embryo induced by the organizer. *Zool. Mag.*, **66**, 279–82.

Aubry, R. (1953) Analyse de certaines conditions expérimentales favorisant la stérilisation *ab ovo* de la grenouille rousse. *C. R. Soc. Biol.*, **147**, 893–4.

Blackler, A. W. (1958) Contribution to the study of germ cells in the Anura. *J. Embryol. exp. Morph.*, **6**, 491–503.

I am grateful to Dr Hammer for permission to quote from unpublished studies.

Blackler, A. W. (1962) Transfer of primordial germ cells between two subspecies of *Xenopus laevis*. *J. Embryol. exp. Morph.*, **10**, 641–51.

Blackler, A. W. (1965) Germ cell transfer and sex ratio in *Xenopus laevis*. *J. Embryol. exp. Morph.*, **13**, 51–61.

Blackler, A. W. & Fischberg, M. (1961) Transfer of primordial germ cells in *Xenopus laevis*. *J. Embryol. exp. Morph.*, **9**, 634–41.

Bounoure, L. (1927) Le chondriome des gonocytes primaires chez *Rana temporaria* et la recherche des éléments génitaux aux jeunes stades du développement. *C. R. Acad. Sci.*, **185**, 1304–6.

Bounoure, L. (1934) Recherches sur la lignée germinale chez la grenouille rousse aux premiers stades du développement. *Ann. Sci. natur. Zool.*, 10e sér., **17**, 67–248.

Bounoure, L. (1935) Sur la possibilité de réaliser une castration dans l'oeuf chez la grenouille rousse; résultats anatomiques. *C. R. Soc. Biol.*, **120**, 1316–19.

Bounoure, L. (1937) Les suites de l'irradiation du déterminant germinal, chez la grenouille rousse, par les rayons ultraviolets: résultats histologiques. *C. R. Soc. Biol.*, **125**, 898–1000.

Bounoure, L. (1939) *L'origine des cellules reproductrices et le problème de la lignée germinale*. Masson et Cie., Paris.

Bounoure, L. (1950) Sur le développement sexuel des glandes génitales de la grenouille en l'absence de gonocytes. *Arch. Anat. micr. Morphol. exp.*, **39**, 247–56.

Bounoure, L. (1964) La lignée germinale chez les batraciens anoures. In *L'origine de la lignée germinale*, ed. E. Wolff. Hermann, Paris.

Bounoure, L., Aubry, R., & Huck, M-L. (1954) Nouvelles recherches expérimentales sur les origines de la lignée reproductrice chez la grenouille rousse. *J. Embryol. exp. Morph.*, **2**, 245–63.

Burns, R. K. (1930) The process of sex transformation in parabiotic *Amblystoma*. I. Transformation from female to male. *J. exp. Zool.*, **55**, 123–70.

DiBerardino, M. (1961) Investigations of the germ-plasm in relation to nuclear transplantation. *J. Embryol. exp. Morph.*, **9**, 507–13.

Elsdale, T., Fischberg, M. & Smith, S. (1958) A mutation that reduces nucleolar number in *Xenopus laevis*. *Exp. Cell Res.*, **14**, 642–3.

Everett, N. (1945) The present status of the germ cell problem in vertebrates. *Biol. Rev.*, **20**, 45–55.

Gallien, L. (1956) Inversion expérimentale du sexe chez un anoure inférieur, *Xenopus laevis* D. Analyse des conséquences génétiques. *Bull. Biol.*, **90**, 163–81.

Gipouloux, J–D. (1962a) Mise en évidence du 'cytoplasme germinal' dans l'oeuf et l'embryon du Discoglosse: *Discoglossus pictus* Otth. *C. R. Acad. Sci.*, **254**, 2433–5.

Gipouloux, J–D. (1962b) L'ablation précoce de l'endoderme provoque la stérilisation de la larve chez le Discoglosse (*Discoglossus pictus* Otth.). *C. R. Acad. Sci.*, **254**, 4081–2.

Gipouloux, J–D. (1962c) Les tissus mésodermiques dorsaux exercent-ils une action attractive sur les gonocytes primordiaux situés dans l'endoderme, chez l'embryon du Crapaud commun *Bufo bufo* L.? *C. R. Acad. Sci.*, **255**, 2179–81.

Gipouloux, J–D. (1963a) Les gonocytes primordiaux peuvent subir une migration intraendodermique en direction opposée à la direction normale; démonstration expérimentale chez le Discoglosse, *Discoglossus pictus* Otth. *C. R. Acad. Sci.*, **256**, 2028–30.

Gipouloux, J–D. (1963b) Influence de la corde dorsale et des uretères primaires sur l'édification des crêtes génitales et la migration des gonocytes primordiaux: démonstration expérimentale sur le Crapaud commun, *Bufo bufo* L. *C. R. Acad. Sci.*, **257**, 1150–2.

Gipouloux, J. D. (1963c) Confirmation, au moyen de greffes, du rôle joué par la corde dorsale et les uretères primaires dans l'organogenèse de la gonade du Crapaud commun (*Bufo bufo* L.). *C. R. Acad. Sci.*, **257**, 2719–20.

Gipouloux, J–D. (1964a) Les somites attirent les gonocytes primordiaux situés dans l'endoderme: Démonstration expérimentale chez la grenouille verte *Rana esculenta* L. *C. R. Acad. Sci.*, **258**, 1066–8.

Gipouloux, J. D. (1964b) Une substance diffusible émanée des organes mésodermiques dorsaux attire les cellules germinales situées dans l'endoderme: démonstration expérimentale chez le crapaud commun *Bufo bufo* L. *C. R. Acad. Sci.*, **259**, 3844–7.

Humphrey, R. R. (1925) The primordial germ cells of *Hemidactylium* and other amphibia. *J. Morph.*, **41**, 1–42.

Humphrey, R. R. (1927) Extirpation of the primordial germ cells in *Amblystoma*. Its effect upon the development of the gonad. *J. exp. Zool.*, **49**, 363–99.

Humphrey, R. R. (1929) The early position of the primordial germ cells in Urodeles: Evidence from experimental studies. *Anat. Rec.* **42**, 301-14.

Humphrey, R. R. (1933) The development and sex differentiation of the gonad in the wood frog (*Rana sylvatica*) following extirpation or orthoptic implantation of the intermediate segment and adjacent mesoderm. *J. exp. Zool.*, **65**, 243–69.

Humphrey, R. R. (1948) Reversal of sex in the females of genotype WW in the axolotl (*Siredon* or *Ambystoma mexicanum*) and its bearing upon the role of the Z chromosome in the development of the testis. *J. exp. Zool.*, **109**, 171–85.

Humphrey, R. R. (1957) Male homogamety in the Mexican axolotl: a study of the progeny obtained when germ cells of a genetic male are incorporated in a developing ovary. *J. exp. Zool.*, **134**, 91–101.

Johnston, P. M. (1951) The embryonic history of the germ cells of the Largemouth Black Bass, *Micropterus salmoides salmoides* (Lacepède). *J. Morph.*, **88**, 471–542.

Kotani, M. (1957) On the formation of primordial germ cells from the presumptive ectoderm of *Triturus* gastrulae. *J. Inst. Polytech.*, *Osaka*, **8**, 145–59.

Kotani, M. (1958) The formation of germ cells after extirpation of the presumptive lateral plate mesoderm of *Triturus* gastrulae. *J. Inst. Polytech.*, *Osaka*, **9**, 195–209.

Mikamo, M. & Witschi, E. (1963) Functional sex-reversal in genetic females of *Xenopus laevis*, induced by implanted testes. *Genetics*, **48**, 1411–21.

Monroy, A. (1939) Sulla localizzazione delle cellule genitali primordiali in fasi precoci di sviluppo. Richerche sperimentali in Anfibi Anuri. *Arch. ital. Anat. Embryol.*, **41**, 368–89.

Nieuwkoop, P. D. (1947) Experimental investigations on the origin and determination of the germ cells and on the development of the lateral plate and germ ridges in Urodeles. *Arch. néerl. Zool.*, **8**, 1–205.

Nieuwkoop, P. D. (1949) The present state of the problem of the 'Keimbahn' in the Vertebrates. *Experientia*, **5**, 308–12.

Nieuwkoop, P. D. (1956a) Are there direct relationships between the cortical layer of the fertilized egg and the development of the future axial system in *Xenopus laevis* embryos ? *Publ. Staz. zool. Napoli*, **28**, 241–9.

Nieuwkoop, P. D. (1956b) The early development up to stage 15. In *Normal Table of Xenopus laevis* (Daudin), ed. P. D. Nieuwkoop & J. Faber. North Holland Publ. Co., Amsterdam.

Nieuwkoop, P. D. & Suminski, E. H. (1959) Does the so-called 'germinal cytoplasm' play an important role in the development of the primordial germ cells ? *Arch. Anat. micr. Morphol. exp.*, **48**, 189–98.

Padoa, E. (1963) Le gonadi di girini di *Rana esculenta* da uova irradiate con ultravioletto. *Monit. zool. ital.*, **71**, 238–49.

Padoa, E. (1964) Qualche precisazione sulla possibilita' di distruggere con l'ultravioletto il plasma germinale delle uova di *Rana esculenta*. *Boll. Soc. ital. Biol. sper.*, **40**, 272–5.

Schectmann, A. M. (1934) Unipolar ingression in *Triturus torosus*: a hitherto undescribed movement in the pregastrular stages of a Urodele. *Univ. Calif. Publ. Zool.*, **39**, 303–10.

Smith, D. L. (1964) A test of the capacity of presumptive somatic cells to transform into primordial germ cells in the Mexican axolotl. *J. exp. Zool.*, **156**, 229–42.

Takamoto, K. (1953) The development of entoderm-free embryo. *J. Inst. Polytech., Osaka*, **4**, 53–60.

Witschi, E. (1929) Studies on sex differentiation and sex determination in amphibians. I: Development and sexual differentiation of the gonads of *Rana sylvatica*. *J. exp. Zool.*, **52**, 235–53.

2

INTERSEXUALITY IN DOMESTIC MAMMALS

J. D. BIGGERS AND R. A. McFEELY

School of Veterinary Medicine, University of Pennsylvania, Philadelphia, U.S.A.

A. INTRODUCTION

The discovery of sexual dimorphism in somatic nuclei (Barr and Bertram, 1949) led to extensive studies of intersexuality in man. These studies were intensified as a result of the development of a method for displaying the chromosomes in cultures of peripheral blood (Moorhead, Nowell, Mellman, Battips and Hungerford, 1960). Comparable studies of intersexuality in domestic mammals have been slow in developing, but during the past three years sufficient information has been collected to warrant a general survey of the current position. In the present review we will confine ourselves to intersexuality in the cow, sheep, goat, horse, pig, dog and cat. Many reports of intersexuality in domestic mammals have been published over the years, most of them prior to the availability of cytogenetical methods. We will not attempt to review all this literature since precise information on the genetical sex of many of the cases is lacking, and therefore the interpretation is often equivocal. A sufficient number of references are included to provide an entrée into the older literature. Other references, particularly to the European literature, are given by Koch (1963). General accounts of fundamental aspects of intersexuality have been written by Gowen (1961), Sohval (1963) and Beatty (1964), all of whom have adopted somewhat different points of view.

Intersexuality can be analysed from two standpoints: (1) by striving for a causal explanation in terms of the theory of sexual differentiation as currently accepted, and (2) by attempting to establish a clinical classification which can be used to facilitate differential diagnosis. Both approaches have been successfully employed to discuss human conditions. The situation in all domestic mammals is affected by the paucity of adequately described cases. Thus at present it seems useful to discuss the various conditions only from a causal point of view. A clinical analysis must await the thorough investigation of many more cases.

Sex is determined at three levels: genetic, gonadal and by the nature of the accessory genital organs. Normal individuals only exist if all three levels are of the same sex. If the sex of at least one level differs from the rest, an intersex results. Thus, cases of intersexuality may arise in three primary ways:

(a) Aberrations of known genetic and chromosomal origin,

(b) Aberrations of gonadogenesis,

(c) Reversal of the sex of the accessory genital organs.

In the present review these causes are used to classify the types of intersexuality in domestic mammals. It is important to realize, however, that these causes may not be mutually exclusive, and the accumulation of new data on a particular syndrome may cause its reclassification.

The following definitions are used:

An *intersex* is an individual with congenital anatomical variations such that the diagnosis of sex is confused. The individual may have some of the reproductive organs of both sexes, or be genetically one sex and phenotypically the other.

A *true hermaphrodite* has the gonads of both sexes, either as a separate ovary and testis, or combined into an ovotestis.

A *pseudohermaphrodite* has the gonads of one sex only, but possesses reproductive organs with some of the characteristics of the opposite sex. Such an individual is classed as a male or female on the type of gonad present. Therefore, a male pseudohermaphrodite has largely female external genitalia, but the gonadal tissue is testicular.

B. MAJOR FEATURES OF NORMAL DEVELOPMENT OF THE GENITAL TRACT

All the domestic mammals are dioecious, that is, each individual produces either male or female gametes. In the animals under discussion in this review each gamete contains n chromosomes, comprising $(n-1)$ autosomes and one sex chromosome. This constitutes the haploid set. In normal animals the gametes produced by the female all possess similar sex chromosomes. In the male, however, two types of gamete are produced in equal numbers. These gametes differ in their sex chromosomes, which are denoted X and Y respectively. Furthermore, one of these types, conventionally designated the X chromosome, is identical with that found in the female gamete. When a new individual is formed by the fusion of male and female gametes, two types of zygote may therefore arise, one containing two identical sex chromosomes which is a genetic female, and one containing an X and a Y chromosome which is a genetic male. We thus distinguish the homogametic sex (XX) and the heterogametic sex (XY). The number of chromosomes in the new individual is $2n$ and is termed the diploid set. This distinction between the genetic make-up of the sexes is important since during development the gonad associated with the heterogametic sex plays a dominant role.

A list of the diploid numbers and a description of the chromosomes of each species is given in Table I. The chromosome complement for a particular species is relatively constant, and when the metaphase chromosomes are displayed for analysis it is termed the karyotype. The shape of an individual metaphase chromosome is described in terms of the position of the centromere and the relative lengths of the long and short arms. When the centromere is located in the middle, the chromosome is called a metacentric chromosome. If the centromere is located terminally, the chromosome is a telocentric chromosome. Included in this category are those chromosomes in which there are short arms so minute that they cannot be measured. When the centromere appears in an intermediate position the ratio of

TABLE I

CHROMOSOMES OF DOMESTIC MAMMALS

(Only recently published key references are quoted)

Species	No.	Autosomes	Sex Chromosomes	References
Cow	60	29 pairs of telocentric chromosomes which progressively decrease in length	X–large submetacentric Y–very small metacentric	Melander (1959) Crossley and Clarke (1962) Nichols, Levan and Lawrence (1962) Sasaki and Makino (1962)
Horse	64	Not definitely known 13–14 metacentrics and submetacentrics 16–17 telocentric and subtelocentric	X–large submetacentric Y–small telocentric	Benirschke, Brownhill and Beath (1962) Trujillo, Stenius, Christian and Ohno (1962)
Pig	38	1 pair very large subtelocentrics 3 pairs large telocentrics 4 pairs medium subtelocentrics 5 pairs medium submetacentrics 2 pairs small metacentrics 3 pairs small telocentrics	X–not definitively demonstrated, probably medium submetacentric Y–smallest metacentric	Giminez-Martin, Lopez-Saez and Monge (1962) McConnell, Fechheimer and Gilmore (1963)
Goat	60	29 pairs of telocentric chromosomes which progressively decrease in length	X–not definitively demonstrated, probably large telocentric Y–smallest telocentric	Unpublished data
Sheep	54	3 pairs of large metacentrics 23 pairs of telocentric chromosomes which progressively decrease in length	X–not definitively demonstrated Y–smallest telocentric	Borland (1964) McFee, Banner and Murphree (1965)
Dog	78	38 pairs of telocentric chromosomes which progressively decrease in length	X–large submetacentric Y–small submetacentric	Moore and Lambert (1963) Gustavsson (1964)
Cat	38	3 pairs large submetacentric 4 pairs large subtelocentric 2 pairs large metacentric 4 pairs medium submetacentric 3 pairs small metacentric 2 pairs small telocentric	X–large submetacentric Y–small metacentric	Cranmore and Alpen (1964)

the length of the long arms to the short arms is important. A sub-metacentric chromosome has a ratio in the range of 1.1–1.9 to 1. When the ratio is 2 to 1 or greater the chromosome is termed a subtelocentric chromosome. These types of chromosome are shown in Fig. 1.

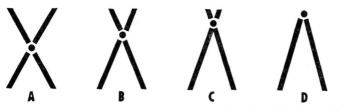

Fig. 1. Classification of types of chromosomes based on the ratio of the long and short arms. A. Metacentric. B. Submetacentric. C. Subtelocentric. D. Telocentric.

The ultimate sexual development of an individual is thought to be dependent upon the type and quantity of sex-determining genes present in the chromosomes (Sohval, 1963). Genes for both sexes have been presumed to be present in each embryo (Goldschmidt, 1952). The female-determining genes are thought to be positioned mostly, if not entirely, within the X chromosomes, while the male determiners are situated in the Y chromosome and perhaps also in the autosomes. A female develops as a result of the unequal balance of female determiners on the two X chromosomes, while the male determiners on the Y chromosome and autosomes outweigh the single X in a male (Sohval, 1963). In further development one of the X chromosomes in the female becomes tightly coiled and inactivated during interphase.

The occurrence of sexual dimorphism of interphase nuclei from certain tissues of many mammalian species has been of great import-ance in the study of intersexes. A simple cytological examination can provide an estimate of the number of X chromosomes in a cell. This estimate is based upon the presence of a dark-staining chromatin mass or masses located within the nucleus of many cells. There is good evidence that the number of these sex chromatin bodies is equal to the number of X chromosomes less one. The most commonly accepted theory as to the nature of the sex chromatin is that it consists of the heterochromatic portion of the inactivated X chromosome (see Sohval, 1963, for a review of the literature). This hypothesis explains why it is rarely seen in males which possess only one X chromosome. The sex chromatin mass also appears as a 'drumstick' appendage on the nucleus of some polymorphonuclear leukocytes in

TABLE II

SEXUAL DIMORPHISM IN SOMATIC CELLS OF DOMESTIC MAMMALS

(Selected references)

Species	Nerve Cells	Buccal Epithelium	Neutrophil 'Drumstick'	Other Tissue	References
Cow	Present	Not present	Not practical	Liver, adrenal, pancreas with special technique	Moore, Graham and Barr (1957a) Struck (1961) Lang and Hansel (1959) Colby and Calhoun (1963)
Horse		Present	Present	Leydig cell	Struck (1961) Franz and Widmaier (1960) Rangel (1959) Colby and Calhoun (1963)
Pig	Present	Present	Present but in small numbers		Cantwell, Johnston and Zeller (1958) Struck (1961) Rangel (1959) Colby and Calhoun (1963)
Goat	Present	Not present	Present		Moore and Barr (1953) Struck (1961) Rangel (1959) Colby and Calhoun (1963)
Sheep	Present	Not present	Present		Struck (1961) Rangel (1959) Bohme (1962)
Dog	Present	Present	Present	Most tissues	Moore and Barr (1953) Struck (1961) Rangel (1959) Colby and Calhoun (1963)
Cat	Present	Present	Present	Most tissues	Barr and Bertram (1949) Graham and Barr (1952) Struck (1961) Colby and Calhoun (1963)

some species. A list of species and tissues from which sex chromatin has been demonstrated is given in Table II.

The second phase of sex development is gonadogenesis. The genital ridges, in which the gonads and reproductive ducts develop, are formed early in organogenesis. At first the gonad is histologically identical in both sexes and is said to be at the ambisexual or indifferent stage of development. It consists of two parts: the cortex, and the medulla. Gradually one of these parts predominates while the other regresses and eventually disappears. If the cortex predominates, an ovary is formed, and if the medulla predominates, a testis results.

The development of the gonad is closely linked with the development of the mesonephros and its associated ducts. Two systems of ducts arise in both sexes: the Wolffian or mesonephric ducts and the Müllerian or paramesonephric ducts. If the gonads are normal testes, the Wolffian ducts persist and develop into the male ductal system and seminal vesicles, while the Müllerian ducts regress. Conversely, if the animal possesses normal ovaries, the Müllerian ducts persist as the oviducts, uterus, cervix and anterior vagina, while the Wolffian ducts regress. The lower end of the reproductive tract is formed from the urogenital sinus. The external genitalia develop from the genital tubercle.

The basic pattern of the genital tract is established very early in development. During the relatively long period before the onset of adult sexual function, the genital tract is highly susceptible to external influences which may produce alterations in structure or function.

From this brief survey of the normal development of the gonads and genital tract the three main aspects of sexual development are readily recognized: (i) the genetic determination of sex, (ii) gonadogenesis, (iii) the genesis and maturation of the accessory genital organs. In normal development each of these stages is dependent upon events occurring in antecedent stages. Yet there is the remarkable fact that during the indifferent stage of gonadogenesis all individuals are potentially capable of developing partially and sometimes completely into phenotypic males or females independently of their genetic sex. As a result of this plasticity, any disturbance of normal development may result in sexual development away from that initially determined by hereditary factors, thus giving rise to various forms of intersexuality and other abnormalities of the genitalia.

C. ABERRATIONS OF GENETIC AND CHROMOSOMAL ORIGIN

Three conditions will be discussed in this section. The first is male pseudohermaphroditism in the goat. This condition is caused by a recessive gene and is the only intersexual condition in domestic mammals which has been studied intensively from a genetic point of view. The second is intersexuality in the pig. There is strong evidence that this condition is also genetically determined, but the studies which have been made so far are very incomplete compared with those on the goat. Both species are of particular interest cytogenetically, since the majority of intersexual cases studied so far have testicular tissue and an XX chromosome constitution. The third condition is the male tortoiseshell (tricolour) cat which has now been shown to have an XXY chromosome constitution, and is therefore analogous to the Klinefelter syndrome in man. Other types of intersex are, of course, also found in all three species: for example, true hermaphroditism is known in all three, but little is known of its genetical and cytogenetical basis.

1. Pseudohermaphroditism in the goat

Pseudohermaphroditism is widespread in goats and has a very high incidence in some areas (Table III). A genetic basis for the condition was suspected many years ago, and in 1939 Eaton and Simmons suggested that it was caused by a single recessive gene. Asdell (1944) pointed out that most, if not all, of the intersexes are polled. He therefore postulated that the condition is determined by a recessive gene linked to the already known dominant autosomal gene (P) which causes polledness. Later it was shown that the very high incidence of intersexuality among goats in Japan was created by the selection of polled animals for breeding (Kondo, 1955).

A detailed study of the anatomy of the genitalia in pseudohermaphrodite goats was made by Crew (1924) and Eaton (1943). The observations of Eaton are particularly valuable since they were made on the U.S. Department of Agriculture herds at Beltsville, Maryland, where the genetical basis of the intersexual condition was later definitely established (Eaton, 1945). Affected animals show a wide range of abnormality, from phenotypically almost normal males through many intermediate gradations to almost normal females. Despite the variability in the morphology of the external genitalia and the accessory reproductive organs, the intersexes possess only testicular tissue. Thus the condition is conventionally described as male pseudohermaphroditism. Many sporadic cases of this condition have been described, showing that the gene is widely distributed in the goat population (Somervail, 1937; Hill, 1941; Halley and Baxter, 1953).

The genetic sex of male goat pseudohermaphrodites has been discussed since the condition was first recognized. For example Crew (1924), on the basis of anatomical findings and influenced by contemporary studies on freemartinism, suggested that these intersexes are all genetic males. This hypothesis is now considered wrong, since strong arguments can be evinced to show that male goat pseudohermaphrodites are probably genetic females. Asdell (1944) was the first to make this suggestion in a discussion of Eaton and Simmon's (1939) data on the Saanen breed; he pointed out that if the intersexes are counted as females, an approximately normal sex ratio is obtained. Other data confirmed this (Table III). However,

TABLE III

INCIDENCE OF PSEUDOHERMAPHRODITISM IN GOATS

Country	Breed	Percentage			Sex ratio*	Reference
		Males	Females	Intersexes		
U.S.A.	Saanen	49.3	39.6	11.0	50.6	Eaton and Simmons (1939)
U.S.A.	Taggenburg	46.3	47.6	6.0	53.6	Eaton and Simmons (1939)
United Kingdom	?	55.1	30.0	14.9	44.9	Paget (1943)
Germany	?	57.7	36.1	6.2	42.3	Brandsch (1959)
Israel	Saanen	51.8	42.4	5.8	48.2	Laor, Barnea, Angel and Soller (1962)

*Calculated as % (females and intersexes).

recent more detailed studies on the Saanen breed in Germany have shown that there are insufficient females and intersexes to give a normal 50% sex ratio (Buechi, 1957; Brandsch, 1959). The problem has been studied further in the Saanen breed by Soller and Angel (1964) working in Israel (Table IV). The results show that intersexes only appear in the two mating types which give rise to homozygous polled offspring (PP). If, within these categories, the intersexes are counted as females, the sex ratio is low. In the group expected to give 50% homozygous offspring (1) the sex ratio is very low. Consequently the type of data shown in Table III may provide underestimates of the true sex ratio. Soller and Angel (1964) propose two

TABLE IV

THE RELATION OF THE SEX RATIO AND THE INCIDENCE OF
INTERSEXES IN VARIOUS MATING TYPES IN GOATS (MODIFIED
FROM SOLLER AND ANGEL, 1964).

Mating type	Genotype Sire Dam		Expected % horned	% Males	% Females	% Intersexes	Sex ratio*
1	PP	Pp	0	61.4	20	18.6	38.6
2	Pp	Pp	25	52.1	40	7.9	47.9
3	pp	Pp	50	50.8	49.2	0	49.2
4	PP	pp	0	48.6	51.4	0	51.4
5	Pp	pp	50	47.5	52.5	0	52.5
6	pp	pp	100	46.4	53.6	0	53.6
TOTAL	—	—	—	51.8	42.4	5.8	48.2

*Calculated as % (females and intersexes).

theories to account for the deficiency of females, particularly in
$PP \times Pp$ matings: (1) the 'sex-reversal' theory, according to which
homozygous females are completely transformed into phenotypic
males, and (2) the 'lethal' theory, which postulates that homozygous
females are subject to a high degree of embryonic mortality. Further
work is required to show which of these theories is correct.

The results just described emphasize the difficulty of analysing
the statistical data on sex ratios, and hence reduce the value of this
type of evidence in determining the genetic sex of the pseudohermaphrodite goat. Obviously more direct cytogenetic techniques are
required, and some preliminary results have been published. Lüers
and Struck (1959) and Bielanska-Osuchowska (1960) have reported
the presence of sex chromatin in three and nine cases of male goat
pseudohermaphroditism respectively. In our laboratory the karyotypes of three cases of male pseudohermaphroditism have been
studied and all have XX sex chromosomes (McFeely, Hare and

Biggers, unpublished). One of these is shown in Plate 1. There is one published case of pseudohermaphroditism in the male goat which is apparently in conflict with these preliminary cytogenetic observations. This was an animal described by Makino (1952) as having XY chromosomes.

The genetic mechanism involved in the aetiology of male pseudohermaphroditism in the goat is still unknown. Two mechanisms have been postulated: (1) pleiotropic action of the gene P for polledness (Eaton, 1945), and (2) a recessive gene closely linked with P (Asdell, 1944; Kondo, 1955). The rarity of horned pseudohermaphrodites led Eaton (1945) to postulate the complex pleiotropic effects of the single gene P, and so far no case of a horned pseudohermaphrodite has demolished this view. The distinction between the two genetic mechanisms is of no consequence in calculating the frequencies shown in Tables III and IV.

The evidence that male goat pseudohermaphrodites were genetic females was consistent with the action of a recessive gene affecting only female (XX) zygotes. Gowen (1961) therefore suggested that the Hr gene in Drosophila was superficially similar to that causing pseudohermaphroditism in goats, since the Hr gene also influences the female zygote only. Recently, however, Soller, Laor, Barnea, Weiss and Ayalon (1963) have shown that the gene causing pseudohermaphroditism in females also causes infertility in male goats. Thus the analogy with the Hr gene in Drosophila should be disregarded.

In 1959 Welshons and Russell made the important observation that the Y chromosome of mice plays a crucial role in determining the development of testes. Other evidence from the study of human intersexes (see the article by Jacobs, page 61, — Ed.) supports the hypothesis that the Y chromosome in mammals is essential if the male gonad is to develop, but the strong evidence that male goat pseudohermaphrodites are genetic females conflicts with this view. The frequent suggestion that male goat pseudohermaphrodites could be mosaics in which XY cells can be found only in the testes seems unlikely, since it would imply that some 10% of all goats were mosaics, and it is difficult to envisage a mechanism at meiosis or first cleavage which would result in such a high incidence of mosaicism.

2. Intersexes in pigs

Intersexes are common in pigs, but not to the same degree as in goats. For example, Freudenberg (1957) has reported an incidence in Germany of 0.2%. There is strong evidence that intersexuality in pigs is a genetically determined condition (Koch, Fischer and Schumand, 1957). According to Baker (1925), this appears to have been known to the natives of the New Hebrides who use hermaphrodite pigs in religious ceremonies. They purposely bred from animals already known to have had intersexual young. Presumably the incidence of intersexuality in pigs has not reached the high level found in some goat populations because the genetic factors involved are not linked with a character selectively favoured by breeders.

Anatomical studies of intersexual pigs have shown that male and female pseudohermaphrodites and true hermaphrodites occur (Koch, 1963). The male pseudohermaphrodite is the most common (Holz, Petersen and Freudenberg, cited by Koch (1963)). As in the goat the anatomical features range from female to male types.

There have been insufficient studies on the sex ratio to indicate the genetic sex of the intersexes. However, cytogenetical studies have been made on a few animals. Cantwell, Johnston and Zeller (1958) studied the sex chromatin in the neurones of six cases of intersexual pigs. Four of these were male pseudohermaphrodites, and one was a case of ovarian agenesis; they all exhibited sex chromatin and presumably were genetic females. (The remaining case was a true hermaphrodite and is discussed on page 52). Lüers and Struck (1959) also found sex chromatin in an intersexual pig. Makino, Sasaki, Sofuni and Ishikawa (1962) examined the karyotype of a male pseudohermaphrodite pig and found a normal 36+XX female constitution. McFeely, Hare and Biggers (unpublished) have examined the karyotypes of two male pseudohermaphrodite pigs and found a normal 36+XX female constitution in both. Although Johnston, Zeller and Cantwell (1958) suggested the possibility that some cases of intersexual pigs are analogous to Klinefelter's syndrome in humans, no example of an XXY chromosome constitution has yet been described in the pig.

Pedigree studies by Freudenberg (1957) and Johnston et al. (1958) indicate that many cases of intersexuality in pigs are caused primarily by a recessive gene, whose final expression is influenced by other modifier genes. The occurrence of cryptorchidism in herds producing intersexes has also raised the possibility that the same genes may produce sexual aberrations in both males and females.

The demonstration in the pig of male pseudohermaphrodites with an XX chromosome constitution is of interest in view of the currently accepted theory that testes only develop in mammals when a Y

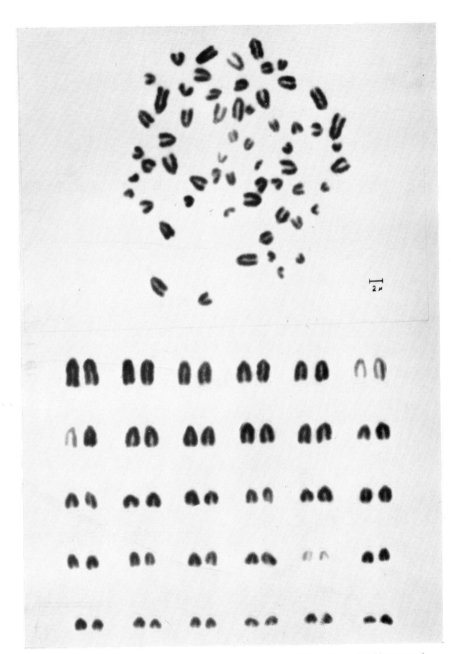

Plate 1. Karyotype of a case of male goat pseudohermaphroditism. The animal is assumed to be a genetic female since there are 30 identical pairs of chromosomes and no Y chromosome.

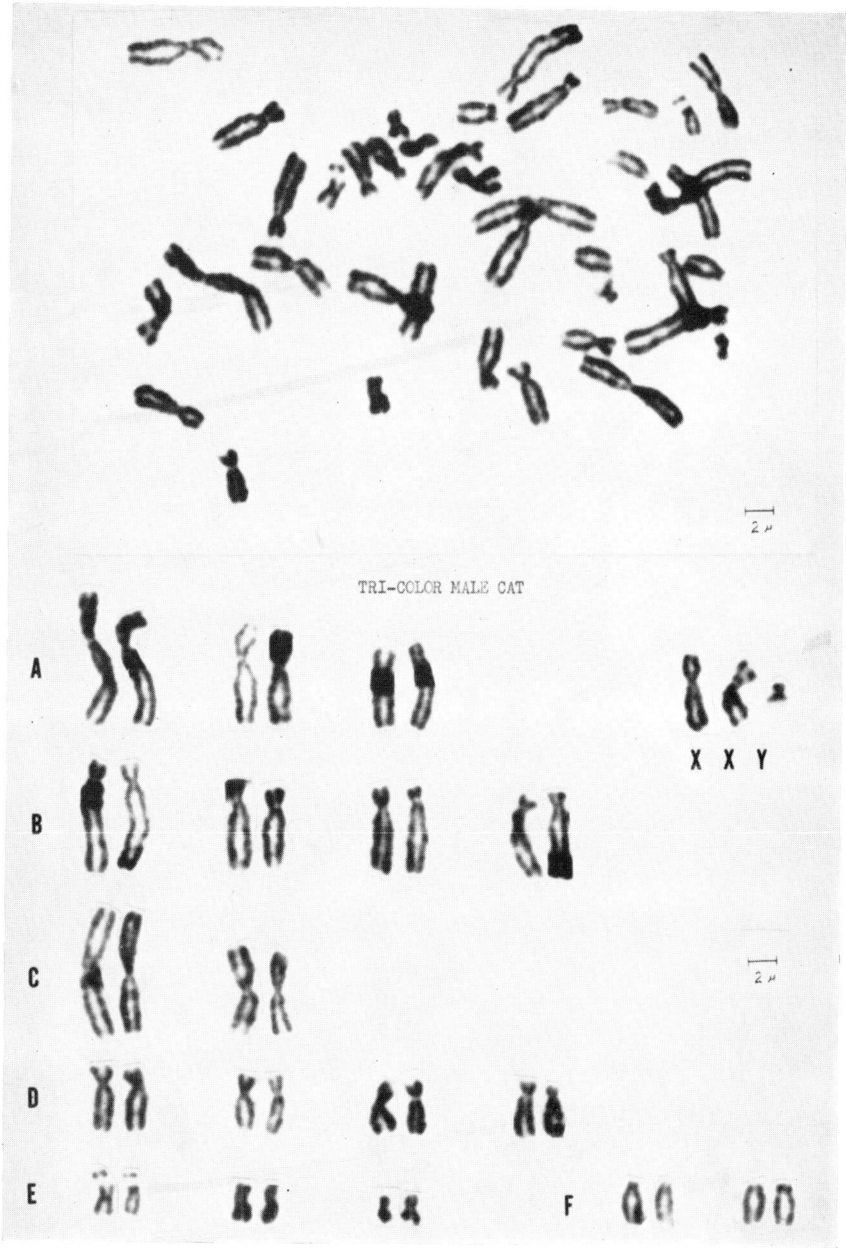
2 μ
TRI-COLOR MALE CAT
A
X X Y
B
C
2 μ
D
E
F

Plate 2a.

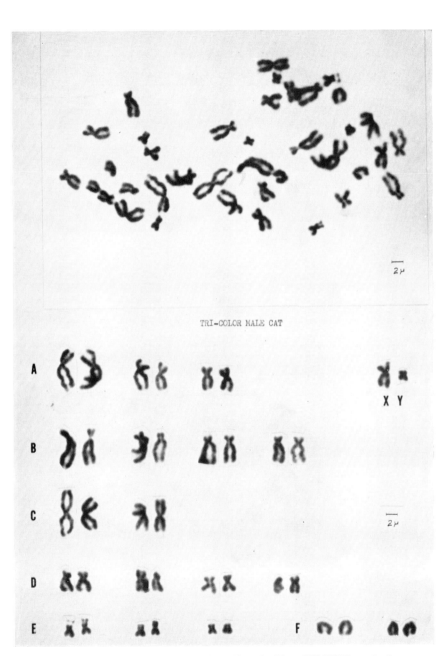

Plate 2b. Karyotype of a male tortoiseshell cat. The animal is an XY/XXY mosaic, the two cell lines having 38 (2b) and 39 (2a) chromosomes respectively.

chromosome is present. The problem has already been discussed, in connection with male pseudohermaphroditism in the goat.

3. Male tortoiseshell (tricolour) cat

In the cat the gene which determines the yellow coat colour (y) is carried on the X chromosome, and is epistatic to autosomal genes which control the coat colours black and tabby. Its allele, non-yellow (y $^+$), allows the expression of black and tabby (Robinson, 1959).

TABLE V

THE INHERITANCE OF X^y AND X^{y+} GENES IN THE CAT, INCLUDING THE ABNORMAL TORTOISESHELL MALE

Phenotype	Genotype	
	Female	Male
Yellow	$X^y X^y$	$X^y X$
Tortoiseshell	$X^y X^{y+}$	$(X^y X^y Y)$
Non-yellow (black, tabby) ..	$X^{y+} X^{y+}$	$X^{y+} Y$

The results of mating yellow with black or tabby phenotypes are shown in Table V. The table demonstrates that a normal genetic male tortoiseshell cat cannot exist. It is for this reason that geneticists have been intrigued by the rare occurrence of these animals, the majority of which are sterile. A variety of theories have been suggested to explain the origin of the male tortoiseshell cat (Robinson, 1959).

The suggestion that male tortoiseshell cats are aneuploids was first made by Little (1919), who postulated that the condition arose by non-disjunction. However, at that time knowledge of the genetics of sex determination was based on Drosophila experiments, and Little therefore predicted that male tortoiseshell cats should be XO. The recent discovery that maleness in mammals is determined chiefly by the Y chromosome requires that the male tortoiseshell cat be XXY.

The suggestion that male tortoiseshell cats were very similar to cases of Klinefelter syndrome in man was made by Lenz, Nowakowski, Prader and Schirren (1959). In 1961 Thuline and Norby described a male tortoiseshell cat which had positive sex chromatin and 39 chromosomes, and which was therefore presumed to be XXY. A similar conclusion was reached independently by Frota-Pessoa (1962). Recently a male tortoiseshell cat with 39 chromosomes and a proved XXY constitution has been found (Jones, 1963, quoted by Chu, Thuline and Norby, 1964).

The commonest way in which an XXY constitution can occur is by non-disjunction of an X chromosome at the second meiotic division in the ovum, followed by fertilization of the XX ovum by a Y sperm. The converse of this is the fertilization of an ovum having no X chromosome, because of non-disjunction at the second meiotic division, by an X sperm, giving an XO constitution. The existence of cats of this type has been predicted by Frota-Pessoa (1962), but so far none has been reported.

Sterile male tortoiseshell cats may also be associated with more complex chromosome disturbances. Plate 2 shows the karyotypes of a sterile male tortoiseshell cat which was an XY/XXY mosaic (McFeely, Hare and Biggers, unpublished). The XY cells contained the diploid (38) number of chromosomes, while the XXY cells contained 39 chromosomes. What is probably a more unusual case is provided by Chu et al. (1964), who found a triploid-diploid chimaera. The diploid cells were XX ($n=38$) and the triploid cells were XXY ($n=57$). The second case demonstrates that the Y chromosome can produce a male phenotype even in the presence of an excess number of autosomes. This suggests that in the cat the autosomes play little part in determining the external characteristics of the male.

The XXY chromosome constitution has not so far been found in cats other than tortoiseshells. This is presumably because the genetics of tortoiseshell enables it to act as a genetic marker for the condition. Tortoiseshell females contain two types of hair (Table V). These types may be intimately mingled to give a brindled effect, or they may be segregated into distinct areas of yellow and non-yellow hair, as is seen in the true tortoiseshell cat. The occurrence of two hair colours in cats with $X^y X^{y+}$ genotypes is expected on Lyon's hypothesis (Lyon, 1961, 1962). This hypothesis has recently been reviewed by Davidson (1964). The inactivation of one X chromosome, which results in the appearance of sex chromatin in somatic cells, must occur early in development in the cat, since sex chromatin appears at about the blastocyst stage (Austin and Amoroso, 1957). Lyon postulated that in a cat with an $X^y X^{y+}$ chromosome constitution, the X^y chromosome may be inactivated in some cells and the X^{y+} chromosome in others. The animal will be a genetic mosaic, which will result in mixed hair colours if both types of cell occur in the skin. Thus in a cat with an $X^yX^{y+}Y$ constitution, the tortoiseshell coat will be determined by the inactivation of the X^y and X^{y+} chromosomes, and the maleness by the Y chromosome.

The tortoiseshell coat only occurs in the heterozygous X^yX^{y+} condition, not in the two homozygous conditions, X^yX^y and $X^{y+}X^{y+}$. Yet there is no reason to suppose that X^yX^yY and $X^{y+}X^{y+}Y$ karyotypes do not occur. In fact, the second case described by Thuline and Norby (1961) may be an example of an $X^{y+}X^{y+}Y$ constitution. Animals with an X^yO and $X^{y+}O$ chromosome constitution will of course not have tortoiseshell coats either. The situation with respect to coat colour in mosaics is even more complex. For example, in the diploid-triploid chimaera of Chu et al. (1964) the animal could have had any of the following constitutions: $X^yX^y/X^yX^{y+}Y$, $X^{y+}X^{y+}/X^yX^{y+}Y$, X^yX^{y+}/X^yX^yY, $X^yX^{y+}/X^{y+}X^{y+}Y$ or $X^yX^{y+}/X^yX^{y+}Y$. Obviously the coat colour would depend on the relative contribution to the skin of the two types of clone. These considerations emphasize the fact that the XXY constitution is almost certainly not unique to male tortoiseshell cats: chromosome aberrations may be common in all types of cat, but will not be detected unless the affected animals are distinguished by a genetic marker, or are recognized as infertile and then analysed cytogenetically. More subtle evidence may be required for the detection of these cases. For example, Little (1957) mated a yellow male (X^yY) with a tortoiseshell female (X^yX^{y+}) and obtained, contrary to expectation, a black female. This could have been due to non-disjunction in the male, giving rise to a zygote of $X^{y+}O$ karyotype, but unfortunately the animal is no longer available for further investigation.

So far we have been concerned only with sterile male tortoiseshell cats. However, there is no doubt that on rare occasions fully fertile male tortoiseshell cats occur (Bamber and Herdman, 1932; Komai and Ishihara, 1956; Ishihara, 1956; Matano, 1963). Ishihara (1956) has made an extensive cytogenetic analysis of two fertile male cats, and has shown a diploid number of 38 with XY constitution. These observations have caused at least one author (Gowen, 1961) to reject the hypothesis that many male tortoiseshell cats are XXY. However, the fertile male tortoiseshell cats could well be chimaeras, with for instance an $X^yY/X^{y+}Y$ constitution. A more complex alternative is an XY/XXY constitution, that can exist in several combinations with respect to the y and y $^+$ genes, and in which the spermatogonia are all XY.

D. ABERRATIONS OF GONADOGENESIS

Two conditions will be discussed in this section. The first is free-martinism, which is caused by an intermingling of the blood of male and female siblings early in intra-uterine life. This phenomenon results in a modification of gonadogenesis in genetic females. The second is true hermaphroditism, where an individual develops both male and female gonadal tissue.

1. Freemartinism

Freemartins occur commonly in cattle, when a heifer shares a common uterine environment with a male. As a result the heifer takes on male characteristics and is sterile. A bovine freemartin has normal external genitalia, its gonads may resemble testes to a greater or lesser degree, and the development of its Müllerian ducts is suppressed while the derivatives of the Wolffian ducts may be highly developed.

The classical account of the aetiology of freemartinism in births of twin cattle was published by Lillie (1916, 1917), and the histological structure of the gonads was described by Chapin (1917). These papers are of great historical importance in embryology and reproductive physiology, since from them stems the vast amount of work which has now been done on the hormonal control of sexual development. The fundamental facts concerning freemartins upon which Lillie based his theory had also been discovered independently and somewhat earlier by Tandler and Keller (1911). These facts are:

(a) The twins are dizygotic, as shown by the presence of two corpora lutea,

(b) All twin pairs consist of one normal male and one abnormal intersex,

(c) The freemartins have to be classified as genetic females in order to satisfy the expected 1:1 sex ratio in a population of twins,

(d) The chorions of the twins nearly always fuse early in development, and invariably a vascular connection is established between their circulations.

Before 1916 there was considerable debate as to the genetic sex of freemartins. Lillie, however, takes precedence for pointing out that the first three of the above facts are sufficient to establish that a freemartin is a genetic female. As a result he proposed his celebrated theory that a humoral substance produced in the testes of the male foetus gains access to the female foetus, and diverts development of the still ambisexual gonad in the male direction. In historical perspective this theory was a natural consequence of the times, since the physiological world was in a ferment over the recent discovery of hormones. Lillie's ideas played a crucial role in the establishment of the discipline of endocrinology. Nowadays, some half a century later, some reservations about Lillie's theory must be made. These doubts have arisen for three main reasons:

(a) The discovery that almost all cattle twins, including heterosexual ones, are erythrocyte mosaics, which implies that blood cells must have been exchanged between the male and female foetuses *in utero*.

(b) The discovery that almost all cattle twins, including heterosexual ones, will accept skin grafts from their twin partners when they are adult, implying again that cells were exchanged between the pairs in foetal life.

(c) The demonstration of male and female cells in both the male and female members of dissimilar twins.

Thus a chemical influence of the male foetus on the female can no longer be regarded as the only mechanism: the exchange of cells is also possible. We appear to be at a crossroads—should we accept a humoral or a cellular explanation of freemartinism? Further, if one or the other is accepted, does this also involve choosing between a humoral and a cellular explanation of gonadal differentiation? In order critically to evaluate our knowledge of freemartinism, we shall deal first with cattle, since the condition is mainly confined to this species. Secondly, we shall review the evidence for freemartinism in other species; and thirdly we shall discuss species where freemartinism might be expected to occur but does not.

(a) CATTLE

(i) *Genetic sex of the freemartin:* The establishment of the fact that freemartins are genetic females, which was crucial to Lillie's theory, had at that time to be based on statistical considerations of the sex ratio. Today, cytogenetic studies have provided more direct evidence that freemartins are female. The first such study was that of Moore, Graham and Barr (1957b), who found sex chromatin in the neurones of two free-martins. More recently Makino, Sasaki and Sofuni (1962) have studied the chromosomes of freemartins in cultures of lung fibroblasts (two animals) and white blood cells (one animal). All three cultures showed a $58+XX$ chromosome constitution, and no chromosomal abnormalities were found. Thus the cytogenetic evidence supports the belief that freemartins are genetic females.

(ii) *Multiple births and freemartinism:* Although Lillie's theory of freemartinism, namely that the intersex is a genetic female, was based on the analysis of twins in order to simplify the sex ratio expectation, there is ample evidence that the condition occurs also in multiple births of higher order. Table VI lists reports of freemartins in cattle triplets, quadruplets and quintuplets.

TABLE VI

NATURAL CASES OF MULTIPLE BIRTHS (>2) IN COWS IN WHICH FREEMARTINISM WAS REPORTED

Type	No. Females	No. Males	Reference
Triplets ..	1	2	Buyse (1936)
	2	1	Pearl (1912)
	2	1	Bissonnette (1928)
	1	2	Bissonnette (1928)
Quadruplets	3	1	Hutt (1930)
Quintuplets	1	4	Owen, Davis and Morgan (1946)
	4	1	Rendel, Gahne and Maijala (1962) Rajakoski and Hafez (1963)

(iii) *Intermingling of the foetal circulations:* Studies on the foetal membranes of all types of cattle twins show that the chorions nearly always fuse. Even when one chorionic sac develops in each uterine horn, they eventually meet and fuse in the body of the uterus. The fusion of the chorions is so intimate that extensive arterial and venous anastomoses occur, so that blood can be exchanged between foetuses. The earliest that freemartinism has been detected *in utero* is about four weeks (Swett, Mathews and Graves, 1940). Thus the fusion of the circulations occurs very early in pregnancy.

In the last twenty years other evidence has been obtained which provides direct evidence that blood cells, and perhaps other cells, are exchanged between cattle foetuses *in utero*.

First Owen (1945) and Owen, Davis and Morgan (1946) demonstrated that the blood groups of cattle twins, including dizygotic twins of different sex, are very often identical. Further, in a particularly interesting case of quintuplets, four males and one female, all had identical blood groups. Essentially the same phenomenon has been described recently in another case of quintuplets, consisting of one male and four females (Rendel, Gahne and Maijala, 1962). The probability of these observations arising by chance is extremely small, since cattle have approximately forty blood groups; it seems that the only tenable explanation for the uniformity of blood groups between siblings is to postulate an exchange of cells in foetal life. After the foetal blood cells enter the recipient foetus, some of them apparently settle in the bone marrow, and their descendants remain in the circulation for the rest of the animal's life. Thus most members of a multiple birth in cattle are red cell chimaeras (erythrocyte mosaics). In 1952 Stone, Stormont and Irwin examined 74 cases of heterosexual twins, and found that 66 (89.2%) were erythrocyte mosaics. Twelve of these females were killed, and all had abnormal genital tracts. The eight heifers from twins which were not erythrocyte mosaics all matured and bore offspring. This evidence demonstrates the high correlation which exists between the occurrence of erythrocyte mosaicism and sterility.

Secondly Anderson, Billingham, Lampkin and Medawar (1951) and Billingham, Lampkin, Medawar and Williams (1952) showed that skin grafts exchanged between dizygotic cattle twins survived indefinitely. Normally homografts are only expected to survive if the donor and recipient are of identical genotype, e.g. monozygotic twins, or members of a highly inbred line. In recent years it has been discovered that if embryos or newborn animals are injected with various foreign tissues they acquire a tolerance to these tissues which lasts throughout life (see Billingham, 1958, for a review of the literature). An obvious interpretation of the skin grafting experiments on cattle twins is that the twin partners acquire a tolerance to each other's antigens *in utero*, through the exchange of cells between their circulations. Of 42 pairs of twins, 86% proved to be tolerant of each other's skin, a figure which agrees remarkably well with the fact that freemartins occur in 91% of twins of unlike sex (Swett *et al.*, 1940), and that 89.2% of twins are red cell chimaeras (Stone *et al.*, 1952). These figures suggest that fusion of the foetal circulations fails to occur in about 10% of the cases. Recently Williams, Gordon and Edwards (1963) have shown that if both foetuses occupy one uterine horn, vascular anastomoses occur in 100% of cases, whereas when there is only one foetus in each horn vascular anastomoses occur in only 67% of cases.

Further evidence for an exchange of cells between the foetuses was obtained by Fechheimer, Herschler and Gilmore (1963). They examined blood cultures from seven females (presumed freemartins) and four males from eleven sets of unlike cattle twins, and, unlike Makino *et al.* (1962), found both XX and XY cells in all cases. If such exchanges occur regularly, we should expect the males and females of 90% of all sets of unlike-sexed cattle twins to be XX/XY mosaics.

Since there is strong evidence that migratory blood cells pass between early cattle embryos *in utero*, Ohno, Trujillo, Stenius, Christian and Teplitz (1962) studied the possibility that migratory primordial germ cells also pass between the embryos. They found that the testes of one male twin to a freemartin contained 20% of cells with a $58+XX$ chromosome constitution. This suggests that primordial germ cells may pass from one foetus to another in early pregnancy. Unfortunately, it was impossible to demonstrate cells with a $58+XY$ constitution in the gonads of freemartins.

There is thus a considerable amount of evidence that cells can be exchanged between cattle foetuses sharing a common uterine environment. Whether these directly influence gonadal differentiation is still unknown, but the possibility that freemartinism is basically caused by mosaicism rather than by hormonal influences must now be taken seriously. Quantitative considerations will necessarily play an important role in the analysis of this condition, particularly the degree of cellular interchange between the foetuses. Present evidence indicates that this may be very variable. Thus, Irwin (1955) showed that twin cattle resemble one another in the proportions of the various blood groups which they show, e.g. twin A and twin B may both have 60% type A and 40% type B blood. This suggests that the exchange may be almost complete. In contrast, Ohno *et al.* (1962) found that the exchange of erythrocytes was far from complete. The complexity of the problem is illustrated by the study of Rendel *et al.* (1962) on a case of bovine quintuplets each derived from fertilization of a single egg. The quintuplets consisted of a bull and four freemartins. Two of the freemartins were extreme cases, and had blood groups very similar to the bull. The two other freemartins were only mildly afflicted and had only exchanged a relatively small amount of blood with the bull. This indicates that the degree of gonadal disturbance is possibly correlated with the number of cells transmitted from the male to the female.

(b) FREEMARTINISM IN SPECIES OTHER THAN CATTLE

There are many reports in the literature of so-called 'freemartinism' in species other than the cow (see Lillie, 1917; Swett *et al.*, 1940). It is often very difficult, however, to be sure that these cases are analogous to the bovine freemartin, since other types of intersex often have similar pathology. If we reserve the term freemartin for a modified female which has exchanged whole blood with a male sibling during a shared period of intra-uterine life, we find that in all species other than the cow the evidence for the occurrence of freemartinism is incomplete. The sheep, pig and goat are the only three species which merit further discussion.

(*i*) *Sheep:* Although Lillie (1917) found several reports of the occurrence of freemartinism in sheep, he was unable to ascertain the evidence on which these reports were based. Subsequently several cases of intersex in sheep have been described where the pathological changes in the genital tract were very similar to those found in the bovine freemartin. The first was described by Fraser Roberts and Greenwood (1928) but unfortunately the co-twin was not observed, and therefore its sex is unknown. The second and more completely described case is that of Ewen and Hummason (1947). Another case of freemartinism, in an Astrakhan ewe, was described by Iurchenko (1962).

It has been known for many years that although the chorions of twin sheep commonly fuse, the anastomosis of blood vessels is very rare. Nevertheless, there are sporadic reports that vascular anastomoses can occur (Rotermund (quoted by Stormont, Weir and Lane, 1953); Petskoi, 1953). Recent experimental evidence has shown that vascular anastomoses are more frequent if three or more young are present in the uterus (Slee, 1963). More recently Alexander and Williams (1964) have described a case of freemartinism in sheep with major anastomoses between the foetal circulations. Further, in recent years immunological evidence has accumulated which demonstrates that whole blood can be exchanged between sheep foetuses *in utero*. Stormont *et al.* (1953) have described a case of red cell chimaerism in heterosexual lamb twins where the female had abnormal genitalia. Hraba, Hasek and Cumlivsky (1956) have described a case of triplets in sheep (one male, two females); skin grafts were exchanged between the lambs, and subsequently the male lamb and one of the female lambs were found to be tolerant of each other's skin. Unfortunately, no information was collected on the genitalia of the tolerant female lamb (personal communication). Moore and Rowson (1958) have described an example of heterosexual twin lambs which were tolerant of each other's skin, the female having abnormal genitalia. Thus it appears from all this evidence that freemartinism in the sheep can occur on rare occasions. However, the evidence is equivocal in one aspect, since the diagnosis of the sex of the intersexual sib is based in all cases on the appearance of the modified genitalia. In the cow the evidence as to the sex of freemartins is independent of such potentially ambiguous evidence, since it is based on a statistical argument concerning the sex ratio of a population of twins, as well as the determination of somatic sex and the direct examination of sex chromosomes. It is unlikely that in the sheep sufficient cases will arise to warrant a statistical analysis. However, in all future cases every effort should be made to examine the chromosomes.

(*ii*) *Pigs:* Fusion of the adjacent chorions is fairly common in the pig, but vascular anastomoses are rare. Nevertheless, seven cases of freemartinism in pigs have been described by Hughes (1927, 1929), and another case by Hoadley (1928). The evidence that these examples were cases of freemartinism was based on anatomical demonstrations of the fusion of blood vessels from different foetuses, and the presence of abnormalities of the gonads and genitalia of the the presumptive females. The male foetuses were all normal.

(*iii*) *Goats:* The evidence that freemartinism is found in the goat is extremely scanty, though various authors have asserted that cases do occur (Keller, 1920). In the goat adjacent chorions fuse, but vascular anastomoses are rare. However, anastomoses have been reported by Petskoi (1953).

(c) EXCHANGE OF BLOOD IN SPECIES WHICH DO NOT EXHIBIT FREE-MARTINISM

An important question is whether the exchange of blood between heterosexual embryos is a sufficient condition for freemartinism to occur. In general the answer is no, since exchange of blood between embryos occurs frequently in marmosets, and similar cases are also known in man. Yet in neither of these species has freemartinism ever been seen.

The marmoset is unique among Primates in that it invariably produces two young at a time. The phenomenon has been studied in two species: the common marmoset (*Hapale jacchus* L.) (Hill, 1926) and Geoffroy's tamarin (*Oedipomidas geoffroyi*) (Wislocki, 1932, 1939). The twins are dizygotic, and very early on in development their chorions fuse and vascular anastomoses develop between the two foetal circulations. Thus, on average, 50% of pregnancies will consist of heterosexual pairs. Wislocki (1939) was able to identify and examine three heterosexual pairs and in these specimens no sign of genital abnormality was found in the females. Furthermore, the examination of several dozen female genital tracts revealed no significant abnormalities.

Recently Benirschke, Anderson and Brownhill (1962) demonstrated the existence of bone marrow chimaerism in two adult male common marmosets and one adult female lionheaded marmoset (*Leontocebus rosalia*). In a subsequent paper, bone marrow chimaerism was described in three other species, the cottontop (*Oedipomidas oedipas*), *Tamarinus nigricollis* and the pygmy marmoset (*Cebuella pygmea*) (Benirschke and Brownhill, 1962). Thus the exchange of cells between twins in several members of the marmoset family has been fully confirmed. The fact that primordial germ cells can also pass between foetuses has also been shown in three species: *Callithrix jacchus*, *Cebuella pygmaea* and *Tamarinus mystax* (Benirschke and Brownhill, 1963). Thus in this group of mammals exchange of cells and blood occurs between siblings, yet this does not prejudice sexual development.

The occurrence of vascular anastomoses in the marmoset, and no genital abnormalities, is of particular interest in view of several cases of human blood chimaerism (Dunsford, Bowley, Hutchison, Thompson, Sanger and Race, 1953; Booth, Plaut, James, Ikin, Moores, Sanger and Race, 1957; Nicholas, Jenkins and Marsh, 1957; Ueno, Suzuki and Yamazawa, 1959; Woodruff, Fox, Buckton and Jacobs,

1962). Although there have been legends that freemartins occur in humans, there is no evidence that authentic cases have been observed (Lillie, 1917; Swett *et al.*, 1940).

At present we have no adequate explanation as to why freemartinism occurs in the cow, sheep and pig, but not in the marmoset and man. An attempt has been made to explain this in terms of the enzymatic properties of the placenta (Ryan, Benirschke and Smith, 1961). These authors have shown that the marmoset placenta can convert androstenedione-4-C^{14} to oestrone, whereas preliminary experiments with bovine placenta have failed to demonstrate this conversion. Consequently, the theory has been promulgated that in marmosets and man a female foetus is protected from male foetal androgens by their destruction in the placenta.

2. True Hermaphrodites

True hermaphroditism, in which both ovarian and testicular tissue are present either as separate organs or combined in ovotestes, has been seen in all species of domestic mammal. It has been described frequently in the pig (Baker, 1926), but rather infrequently in other species. The anatomical features, which are very variable, have been well described in numerous case reports. Only four cases, whose sex chromatin or chromosomes have been examined, will be considered in this review. Much more work on the cytogenetics of this condition in domestic mammals is required.

Thuline and Norby (personal communication) have described a true hermaphrodite cat, with a left scrotal testis and a right intraabdominal juvenile ovary. Phenotypically the animal was male. Sex chromatin was present in buccal smear cells. Studies of the chromosomes showed a diploid number of 38, with male and female cells both present. Thus the animal was an XX/XY mosaic.

A case of true hermaphroditism in the dog has been examined in this laboratory (McFeely, Hare and Biggers, unpublished). The animal was a phenotypic female with an hypertrophied clitoris. Internally, bilateral ovotestes were found with a normal female genital tract. Cultures of peripheral blood showed a diploid number of 78 with XX chromosomes. Unfortunately, no other tissues were available for study so it has been impossible to demonstrate that this animal is a mosaic.

Cantwell *et al.* (1958) found sex chromatin in a case of true hermaphroditism in the pig.

Franz and Widmaier (1960) described a case of true hermaphroditism in the horse, which had ovotestes. Sex chromatin was demonstrated in the Leydig cells and drumsticks on the neutrophils. Thus, as in human cases of true hermaphroditism, XX cells are usually present. Nevertheless, it is likely that many of these cases will be complex mosaics.

E. REVERSAL OF THE SEX OF THE ACCESSORY GENITAL ORGANS

A deviation of the accessory sex structures away from the sex of the gonads is probably the most common finding in intersexual animals. As has been alluded to in the earlier sections on genetic sex determination and gonadogenesis, this is not an exclusive category, but rather, a frequent observation in all kinds of intersex conditions. No attempt will be made to describe the multitude of anatomical findings which have been reported in the literature in cases of male and female pseudohermaphroditism. However, a brief account will be given of possible mechanisms of phenotypic sex reversal. In 1903 Bouin and Ancel first proposed that hormones controlled the differentiation of genital structures in the embryo. The first circumstantial evidence in support of this idea was provided by Lillie's analysis of freemartinism. In considering the accessory genital structures, it is assumed that hormones elaborated by the foetal testes are responsible for the development of the male accessory genital organs. The experiments of Jost (1947) showed that castration of a male rabbit foetus at the proper stage of development would result in persistence of the Müllerian duct system and development of the urogenital sinus and external genitalia into approximately normal female structures.

At present two main categories of abnormality can be recognized: male and female pseudohermaphrodites.

1. Male pseudohermaphroditism

These animals phenotypically resemble females but possess testes. The anatomical findings are so varied that they cannot be adequately covered in a review of this type. Practically any degree of feminization can occur. The foetal testis presumably fails in varying degrees to elaborate sufficient hormones to produce full differentiation of the male accessory genital structures.

An example of this is a case of a two-and-a-half year-old Santa Gertrudis cow examined in our laboratory (McFeely, Hare and Biggers, unpublished). The animal was a phenotypic female, although somewhat masculine in general conformation. The genetic sex was male as determined by chromosome analysis. The gonads were testes which had descended through the inguinal canal and were embedded in the supramammary fat. The ductal system was of Wolffian origin and normal for a male. The urogenital sinus had developed into a vagina and the external genitalia were female with a slightly enlarged clitoris. The foetal testes had presumably failed to exert sufficient influence on the development of the urogenital sinus and external genitalia.

Many, if not all, male pseudohermaphrodites can be explained in a similar manner.

2. *Female pseudohermaphroditism*

These animals possess female gonads, but are phenotypic males as a result of the exertion of androgenic influences upon the developing genital tract of a female. The degree of external masculinization ranges from a hypertrophic clitoris to the formation of a penis located within its normal anatomical location. The variation is apparently a function of the time and duration of exposure to androgens. Androgenic substances can originate from several sources but produce similar deviations. The adreno-genital syndrome seen in humans results from a biochemical lesion in the pathways of steroidogenesis, resulting in excessive production of adrenal androgens which alter the development of the accessory sex organs in a male direction. Well documented cases of this syndrome are not found among domestic animals. The presence of a functional tumour producing androgens within the dam can also produce masculinization. Apparently these tumours are rare in domestic animals. Pseudohermaphroditism can also be drug-induced. There are many cases of human female pseudohermaphroditism induced by androgenic-like drugs given to the mother. Curtis and Grant (1964) have reported on masculinization of a litter of puppies whose dam received a synthetic progestin with androgenic properties.

A case of female pseudohermaphroditism in a dog has been studied in this laboratory. The chromosomal and gonadal sex were both female, while the external genitalia were completely masculine (McFeely and Biggers, 1965).

The anatomical features described in cases in this category are far too numerous to mention. It is sufficient to say that the degree of external masculinization ranges from a hypertrophic clitoris to the formation of a penis located within its normal anatomical location. The variation is apparently a function of the time and duration of exposure to androgens.

REFERENCES

Alexander, G. and Williams, D. (1964) Ovine freemartins. *Nature*, **201**, 1296–8.
Anderson, D., Billingham, R. E., Lampkin, G. H. and Medawar, P. B. (1951) The use of skin grafting to distinguish between monozygotic and dizygotic twins in cattle. *Heredity*, **5**, 379–97.
Asdell, A. S. (1944) The genetic sex of intersexual goats and a probable linkage with the gene for hornlessness. *Science*, **99**, 124.
Austin, C. R. and Amoroso, E. C. (1957) Sex chromatin in early cat embryos. *Exp. Cell Res.*, **13**, 419–21.
Baker, J. R. (1925) On sex-integrade pigs: their anatomy, genetics and developmental physiology. *Brit. J. exp. Biol.*, **2**, 247–63.
Baker, J. R. (1926) Asymmetry in hermaphrodite pigs. *J. Anat.*, **60**, 374–81.
Bamber, R. C. and Herdman, E. C. (1932) A report on the progeny of a tortoiseshell male cat, together with a discussion of his gametic constitution. *J. Genet.*, **26**, 115–28.
Barr, M. L. and Bertram, E. G. (1949) A morphological distinction between neurones of the male and female, and the behaviour of the nucleolar satellite during accelerated nucleoprotein synthesis. *Nature, London*, **163**, 676–7.
Beatty, R. A. (1964) Chromosome deviations and sex in vertebrates. In *Intersexuality in Vertebrates Including Man*, ed. C. N. Armstrong and A. J. Marshall, Academic Press, London and New York.
Benirschke, K., Anderson, J. M. and Brownhill, L. E. (1962) Marrow chimerism in marmosets. *Science*, **138**, 513–5.
Benirschke, K. and Brownhill, L. E. (1962) Further observations on marrow chimerism in marmosets. *Cytogenetics*, **1**, 245–57.
Benirschke, K. and Brownhill, L. E. (1963) Heterosexual cells in testes of chimeric marmoset monkeys. *Cytogenetics*, **2**, 331–41.
Benirschke, K., Brownhill, L. E. and Beath, M. M. (1962) Chromosomes of the horse, the donkey and their hybrids, the mule and the hinny. *J. Reprod. Fertil.*, **4**, 319–26.
Bielanska-Osuchowska, Z. (1960) Hermaphroditism in goats. III. Cytogenetic sex diagnosis in hermaphrodite goats. *Med. vet.*, *Varsovie*, **16**, 658–62. (In Polish).
Billingham, R. E. (1958) Actively acquired tolerance and its role in development. In *The Chemical Basis of Development*, ed. W. D. McElroy and B. Glass. Johns Hopkins Press, Baltimore.
Billingham, R. E., Lampkin, G. H., Medawar, P. B. and Williams, H. L. (1952,) Tolerance to homografts, twin diagnosis, and the freemartin condition in cattle. *Heredity*, **6**, 201–12.
Bissonnette, T. H. (1928) Notes on multiple pregnancies in cattle, with special reference to three cases of prenatal triplets and the freemartins involved. *Amer. J. Anat.*, **42**, 29–73.
Böhme, G. (1962) Kritische Betrachtungen über die Geschlechtsdiagnose aus dem Blutbild bei den Haussäugetieren am Beispiel des Schafes. *Berl. Munch. tieranztl. Woschr.*, **75**, 289–95.

Booth, P. B., Plaut, G., James, J. D., Ikin, E. W., Moores, P., Sanger, R. and Race, R. R. (1957) Blood chimaerism in a pair of twins. *Brit. Med.J.*, 1, 1456–8.

Borland, R. (1964) Chromosomes of domestic sheep. *J. Hered.*, **55**, 61–4.

Bouin, P. and Ancel, P. (1903) Sur la signification de la glande interstitielle du testicule embryonnaire. *Compt. rend. Soc. Biol.*, *Paris*, **55**, 1682–4.

Brandsch, H. (1959) Die Vererbung geschlechtlicher Missbildung und des Hornebei der Hausziege in ihrer gegenseitigen Beziehung. *Arch. Geflugelz. Kleins tierk.*, **8**, 310–63.

Buechi, H. F. (1957) Untersuchungen uber das verschobene Geschlechtsverhaltnis, die Intersexualitat und die Fruchtbarkeit bei der Milchziege. Dissertation, Zurich. Quoted by W. Koch in Oversier (1963).

Buyse, A. (1936) A case of extreme sex-modification in an adult bovine freemartin. *Anat. Rec.*, **66**, 43–58.

Cantwell, G. E., Johnston, E. F. and Zeller, J. H. (1958) The sex chromatin of swine intersexes. *J. Hered.*, **49**, 199–201.

Chapin, C. L. (1917) A microscopic study of the reproductive system of foetal freemartins. *J. exp. Zool.*, **23**, 453–82.

Chu, E. H. Y., Thuline, H. C. and Norby, D. E. (1964) Triploid-diploid chimerism in a male tortoiseshell cat. *Cytogenetics*, **3**, 1–18.

Colby, E. B. and Calhoun, L. (1963) Accessory nuclear lobule on the polymorphonuclear neutrophil leukocyte of domestic animals. *Acta Cytol.*, **7**, 346–50.

Cranmore, D. and Alpen, E. L. (1964) Chromosomes of the domestic cat. *Nature*, **204**, 99–100.

Crew, F. A. E. (1924) Studies in intersexuality. I. A peculiar type of developmental intersexuality in the male of the domestic mammals. *Proc. Roy. Soc. B.*, **95**, 90–109.

Crossley, R. and Clarke, G. (1962) The application of tissue culture techniques to the chromosome analysis of *Bos taurus*. *Genet. Res.* (Camb.), **3**, 167–8.

Curtis, E. M. and Grant, R. P. (1964) Masculinization of female pups by progestogens. *J.A.M.A.*, **144**, 395–8.

Davidson, R. G. (1964) The Lyon hypothesis. *J. Pediat.*, **65**, 765–75.

Dunsford, I., Bowley, C. C., Hutchison, A. M., Thompson, J. S., Sanger, R. and Race, R. R. (1953) A human blood-group chimaera. *Brit. Med. J.*, **2**, 81.

Eaton, O. N. (1943) An anatomical study of hermaphroditism in goats. *Amer. J. Vet. Res.*, **4**, 333–43.

Eaton, O. N. (1945) The relation between polled and hermaphroditic characters in dairy goats. *Genetics*, **30**, 51–61.

Eaton, O. N. and Simmons, V. L. (1939) Hermaphroditism in milk goats. *J. Hered.*, **30**, 261–6.

Ewen, A. H. and Hummason, F. A. (1947) An ovine freemartin. *J. Hered.*, **38**, 149–52.

Fechheimer, N. S., Herschler, M. S. and Gilmore, L. O. (1963) Sex chromosome mosaicism in unlike cattle twins. In *Genetics Today*, ed. S. J. Geerts, MacMillan and Company, New York.

Franz, W. and Widmaier, R. (1960) Ein intersexuelles, Kernmorphologisch wiebliches Pferd. *Berl. Munch. tieranzfl. Woschr.*, **73**, 341–60.

Fraser Roberts, J. A. and Greenwood, A. W. (1928) An extreme freemartin and a freemartin-like condition in the sheep. *J. Anat.*, **63**, 87–94.

Freudenberg, F. (1957) Die Bedeutung der Intersexualität beim Schweiz als erbliche Geschlechtsorgan missbildung. *Monatschefte für Veterwärmedizin*, **12**, 608–13.

Frota-Pessoa, O. (1962) XO and XXY karyotypes in cats? *Lancet*, 1304.

Giminez-Martin, G., Lopez-Saez, J. F. and Monge, E. G. (1962) Somatic chromosomes of the pig. *J. Hered.*, **53**, 281 and 290.

Goldschmidt, R. (1952) *Understanding Heredity. An Introduction to Genetics.* John Wiley & Sons, Inc., New York.

Gowen, J. W. (1961) Cytologic and Genetic basis of sex. In *Sex and Internal Secretions*, 3rd edition, ed. W. C. Young, Williams & Wilkins Company, Baltimore, Maryland.

Graham, M. A. and Barr, M. L. (1952) Sex differences in morphology of metabolic nuclei in somatic cells of cat. *Anat. Rec.*, **112**, 709–23.

Gustavsson, I. (1964) The chromosomes of the dog. *Hereditas*, **51**, 187–9.

Halley, G. and Baxter, J. S. (1953) Leucocyte invasion of the genital tract of an intersexual goat. *J. Comp. Path. Therap.*, **63**, 179–83.

Hill, J. P. (1926) Demonstration of the Embryologia varia (development of *Hapale jacchus*). *J. Anat.*, **60**, 486–7.

Hill, R. T. (1941) Abnormal sex anatomy of a goat. *Endocrinol.*, **29**, 1003–7.

Hoadley, L. (1928) Twin heterosexual pig embryos (32 mm.) found within fused membranes. *Anat. Rec.*, **38**, 177–88.

Hraba, T., Hasek, M. and Cumlivsky, B. (1956) Immunological approximation of sheep triplets, natural embryonic parabionts. *Folia Biologica*, **2**, 282–3.

Hughes, W. (1927) Sex-intergrades in foetal pigs. *Biol. Bull.*, **52**, 121–37.

Hughes, W. (1929) The freemartin condition in swine. *Anat. Rec.*, **41**, 213–45.

Hutt, F. B. (1930) Bovine quadruplets including twins apparently monozygotic. *J. Hered.*, **21**, 339–48.

Irwin, M. R. (1955) In *Biological Specificity and Growth*, ed. E. G. Butler. Princeton Univ. Press.

Ishihara, T. (1956) Cytological studies of tortoiseshell male cats. *Cytologia*, **21**, 391–8.

Iurchenko, V. T. (1962) A case of freemartinism in Astrakhan ewes resulting from vascular parabiosis in a pair of twins of different sex. *Dokl. Akad. Nauk.*, **146**, 254–6.

Johnston, E. F., Zeller, J. H. and Cantwell, G. (1958) Sex anomalies in swine. *J. Hered.*, **49**, 255–61.

Jost, A. (1947) Recherches sur la différenciation de l'embryon de lapin. III. Role des gonades foetales dans la différenciation seruelle somatique. *Arch. Anat. micr. Morph. exp.*, **36**, 271–315.

Keller, K. (1920) Zur Fruge der sterilen Zwillingskälber. Wien. tierärztl. Monat. Bd. 7 (Quoted by Crew, 1923).

Koch, P., Fischer, H. and Schumann, H. (1957) *Erbpathologie der Landwirtschaftichen Haustiere.* Paul Parey, Berlin and Hamburg.

Koch, W. (1963) Intersexuality in Mammals. In *Intersexuality*, ed. C. Overzier, Academic Press, London and New York.

Komai, T. and Ishihara, T. (1956) On the origin of the male tortoise-shell cat. *J. Hered.*, **47**, 287–91.

Kondo, K. (1955) The frequency of occurrence of intersexes in milk goats. *Jap. J. Genet.*, **30**, 139–46.

Lang, D. R. and Hansel, W. (1959) A sexual dimorphism in three somatic tissues of cattle. *J. Dairy Sci.*, **42**, 1330–7.

Laor, M., Barnea, R., Angel, H. and Soller, M. (1962) Polledness and hermaphroditism in Saanen goats. *Israel J. Agric. Res.*, **12**, 83–8.

Lenz, W., Nowakowski, H., Prader, A. and Schirren, C. (1959) Die Aetiologie des Kleinefelter-Syndroms. *Schweiz. med. Wschr.*, **89**, 727–31.

Lillie, F. R. (1916) The theory of the free-martin. *Science*, **43**, 611–3.

Lillie, F. R. (1917) The freemartin; a study of the action of sex hormones in the foetal life of cattle. *J. exp. Zool.*, **23**, 371–452.

Little, C. C. (1919) Colour inheritance in cats, with special reference to the colours black, yellow and tortoise-shell. *J. Genet.*, **8**, 279–90.

Little, C. C. (1957) The yellow Siamese cat. *J. Hered.*, **48**, 57–8.

Lüers, T. and Struck, E. (1959) Untersuchungen zur geschlechtsspezifischen Struktur der Neutrophilenkerne bei einigen Haustieren (Ziege, Schaf, Schwein, unter Berucksichtigung der Zwitter). *Zool. Anz.*, **164**, 89–103.

Lyon, M. F. (1961) Gene action in the X-chromosome of the mouse (*Mus musculus* L.) *Nature*, **190**, 372–3.

Lyon, M. F. (1962) Sex chromatin and gene action in the mammalian X-chromosome. *Human Genet.*, **14**, 135–48.

McConnell, J., Fechheimer, N. S. and Gilmore, L. O. (1963) Somatic chromosomes of the domestic pig. *J. Anim. Sci.*, **22**, 374–9.

McFee, A. F., Banner, M. W. and Murphree, R. L. (1965) Chromosome analysis of peripheral leucocytes of the sheep. *J. Anim. Sci.*, **24**, 551–4.

McFeely, R. A. and Biggers, J. D. (1965) A rare case of female pseudohermaphroditism in the dog. *Vet. Rec.*, **77**, 696–8.

Makino, S. (1952) Constitution of the sex chromosome in an intersex goat. *Jap. Sci. Rev. Biol.*, No. 1.

Makino, S., Sasaki, M. S. and Sofuni, T. (1962) Notes on the chromosomes of bovine freemartins. *Proc. Jap. Acad.*, **38**, 541–4.

Makino, S., Sasaki, M. S., Sofuni, T. and Ishikawa, T. (1962) Chromosome condition of an intersex swine. *Proc. Japan Acad.*, **38**, 686–9.

Matano (1963) A study of the chromosomes in the cat. *Jap. J. Genet.*, **38**, 147–56. (In Japanese.)

Melander, Y. (1959) The mitotic chromosomes of some Cavicorn mammals. *Hereditas*, **45**, 649–64.

Moore, K. L. and Barr, M. L. (1953) Morphology of the nerve cell nucleus in mammals, with special reference to the sex chromatin. *J. comp. Neurol.*, **98**, 213–27.

Moore, K. L., Graham, M. A. and Barr, M. L. (1957a) Sex chromatin. *J. exp. Zool.*, **135**, 101–25.

Moore, K. L., Graham, M. A. and Barr, M. L. (1957b) Sex chromatin in the Freemartin. *Anat. Rec.*, **108**, 402.

Moore, N. W. and Rowson, L. E. A. (1958) Freemartins in sheep. *Nature, Lond.*, **182**, 1754–5.

Moore, W. and Lambert, P. D. (1963) The chromosomes of the beagle dog. *J. Hered.*, **54**, 273–6.

Moorhead, P. S., Nowell, P. C., Mellman, W. J., Battips, D. M. and Hungerford D. A. (1960) Chromosome preparations of leucocytes cultured from human peripheral blood. *Exp. Cell Res.*, **20**, 613–16.

Nicholas, J. W., Jenkins, W. J. and Marsh, W. L. (1957) Human blood chimaeras. A study of surviving twins. *Brit. Med. J.*, i, 1458–60.

Nichols, W. W., Levan, A., and Lawrence, W. C. (1962) Bovine chromosomes by the peripheral blood method. *Hereditas*, **48**, 536–8.

Ohno, S., Trujillo, J. M., Stenius, C., Christian, L. C. and Teplitz, R. L. (1962) Possible germ cell chimaeras among newborn dizygotic twin calves (*Bostaurus*). *Cytogenetics*, **1**, 258–65.

Owen, R. D. (1945) Immunogenetic consequences of vascular anastomoses between bovine twins. *Science*, **102**, 400–1.

Owen, R. D., Davis, H. P. and Morgan, R. F. (1946) Quintuplet calves and erythrocyte mosaicism. *J. Hered.*, **37**, 291–7.

Paget, R. F. (1943) Hermaphrodites. *British Goat Soc. Monthly J.*, **36**, 57–60.

Pearl (1912) A case of triplet calves, with some general considerations regarding multiple gestation in normally uniparous animals. *Ann. Rep. Maine Agr. Exp. Stat.*, pp. 259–282.

Petskoi, P. G. (1953) Conditions of intrauterine development of *Bos taurus* which lead to freemartinism. *Dokladi of the U.S.S.R. Academy of Sciences*, **90**, 693.

Rajakoski, E. and Hafez, E.S.E. (1963) Derivatives of cortical cords in adult freemartin gonads of bovine quintuplets. *Anat. Rec.*, **147**, 457–67.

Rangel, N. M. (1959) Sex chromatin and other nuclear appendages in heterophil leucocytes of mammals and birds. *Arq. Esc. Super Dr. Veter.*, **12**, 365–98.

Rendel, J., Gahne, B. and Maijala, K. (1962) A set of five-egg cattle quintuplets with complicated chimerism. *Hereditas.*, **48**, 201–14.

Robinson, R. (1959) Genetics of the domestic cat. *Bibliogr. genet.*, **18**, 273–362.

Ryan, K. J., Benirschke, K. and Smith, O. W. (1961) Conversion of androstenedione-4-C^{14} to estrone by the marmoset placenta. *Endocrinology*, **69**, 613–8.

Sasaki, M. S. and Makino, S. (1962) A revised study of the chromosomes of somatic cells *in vitro* of *Bos taurus* and *Equus caballus*. *J. Hered.*, **53**, 157–62.

Slee, J. (1963) Immunological tolerance between littermates in sheep. *Nature*, **200**, 654–6.

Sohval, A. R. (1963) Chromosomes and sex chromatin in normal and anomalous sexual development. *Physiol. Rev.*, **43**, 306–56.

Soller, M. and Angel, H. (1964) Polledness and abnormal sex ratios in Saanen goats. *J. Hered.*, **55**, 139–42.

Soller, M., Laor, M., Barnea, R., Weiss, Y. and Ayalon, N. (1963) Polledness and infertility in male Saanen goats. *J. Hered.*, **54**, 237–40.

Somervail, M. L. (1937) Intersexual development in the goat. *Vet. J.*, **93**, 60–1.

Stone, W., Stormont, C. and Irwin, M. R. (1952) Blood typing as a means of differentiating the potentially fertile from the non-fertile heifer born twin with a bull. *J. Anim. Sci.*, **11**, 744.

Stormont, C., Weir, W. C. and Lane, L. L. (1953) Erythrocyte mosaicism in a pair of sheep twins. *Science*, **118**, 695–6.

Struck, E. (1961) Vergleichende untersuchungen über das „Geschlechtschromatin" bei einigen Haustieren mit hilfe des Buccaltests. *Z. Zellforsch.*, **55**, 662–72.

Swett, W. W., Mathews, C. A. and Graves, R. R. (1940) Early recognition of the freemartin condition in heifers twinborn with bulls. *J. agr. Res.*, **61**, 587–623.

Tandler, J. and Keller, K. (1911) Ueber das Verhalten des Chorions bei verschiedengeschlechtlicher Zwillingsgravidität des hindes und über die Morphologie des Genitales der weiblichen Tiere, welche einer solchen Gravidität entstammen. *Deut. Tierärztl. Wchnschr.*, **19**, 148–9.

Thuline, H. C. and Norby, D. E. (1961) Spontaneous occurrence of chromosome abnormality in cats. *Science*, **134**, 554–5.

Trujillo, J. M., Stenius, C., Christian, L. C. and Ohno, S. (1962) Chromosomes of the horse, the donkey, and the mule. *Chromosoma (Berl..)*, **13**, 243–8.

Ueno, S., Suzuki, K. and Yamazawa, K. (1959) Human chimerism in one of a pair of twins. *Acta Genetica et Statistica Medica*, **9**, 47–63.

Welshons, W. J. and Russell, L. B. (1959) The Y chromosome as the bearer of male determining factors of the mouse. *Proc. Natl. Acad. Sci., U.S.*, **45**, 560–6.

Williams, G., Gordon, I. and Edwards, J. (1963) Observations on the frequency of fused foetal circulations in twin bearing cattle. *Brit. Vet. J.*, **119**, 467–72.

Wislocki, G. B. (1932) Placentation in the marmoset (*Oedipomidas geoffroyi*) with remarks on twinning in monkeys. *Anat. Rec.*, **52**, 381–99.

Wislocki, G. B. (1939) Observations on twinning in marmosets. *Amer. J. Anat.*, **64**, 445–83.

Woodruff, M. F. A., Fox, M., Buckton, K. A. and Jacobs, P. A. (1962) The recognition of human blood chimaeras. *Lancet*, **iii**, 192–4.

3

ABNORMALITIES OF THE SEX CHROMOSOMES IN MAN

Patricia A. Jacobs

Medical Research Council Clinical Effects of Radiation Research Unit,
Edinburgh 4, Scotland

A. INTRODUCTION

Until 1959 it was believed that sex determination in man operated in much the same way as in Drosophila. It was known that the female was the homogametic and the male the heterogametic sex. Femaleness was considered to be determined by the presence of two X chromosomes together with 22 pairs of autosomes, while maleness was determined by the presence of one X and one Y chromosome, together with 22 pairs of autosomes. If abnormalities of the numbers of sex chromosomes in man were compatible with life it was considered that they would have the same general phenotypic effect as in the fruit fly, in that the presence or absence of the Y chromosome would have little effect on the phenotype, and sex would be determined by a balance between female-determining genes on the X chromosomes and male-determining genes on the autosomes. Against this background Barr and Bertram (1949) showed that in many female mammals including man, there was, in a proportion of interphase nuclei, a small dark-staining Feulgen-positive body which was absent in males. This was considered to be the heterochromatic portions of the two X chromosomes, and this interpretation of the so-called Barr body or sex chromatin body remained in vogue for about ten years. Shortly after Barr's discovery it was found that phenotypic males with the features of Klinefelter's syndrome often had a sex chromatin body, while in two groups of phenotypic females, many of those with the features of Turner's syndrome and all of those with testicular feminization, the cells were chromatin-negative. Individuals in these three groups were considered to be examples of sex-reversal.

In 1959, however, it was shown that a number of chromatin-positive males with Klinefelter's syndrome had an XXY sex chromosome complement and therefore could not be sex-reversed females (Jacobs and Strong, 1959; Ford, Jones et al., 1959). Later in the same year it was shown that chromatin-negative females with Turner's syndrome were not sex-reversed males, but had only 45 chromosomes and a single X sex chromosome (Ford, Polani et al., 1959). It was apparent, therefore, even in the early days of human cytogenetics, that man, unlike Drosophila, had a strongly male-determining Y chromosome. Soon afterwards it was found that man was not alone in the masculinizing effect of his Y chromosome. Recent work has shown that the mouse has a similar, though not identical, sex-determining mechanism (Table I).

TABLE I

| Species | XX | XY | Sex Chromosome Constitution | | XXX |
			XO	XXY	
Drosophila	Normal Female	Normal Male	Phenotypically Normal Male Sterile	Phenotypically Normal Female Fertile	Phenotypically Abnormal Female Sterile
Mouse	Normal Female	Normal Male	Phenotypically Normal Female Fertile	Phenotypically Normal Male Sterile	
Man	Normal Female	Normal Male	Phenotypically Abnormal Female Sterile	Phenotypically Normal Male Sterile	Phenotypically Normal Female Fertile

Since the early days of human cytogenetics great use has been made of the many different examples of individuals with abnormal sex chromosome complements to enquire more closely into the mechanisms of sex determination and sex differentiation in man.

B. THE HUMAN SEX CHROMOSOMES

The X chromosome is a medium-sized submetacentric chromosome indistinguishable on morphological grounds from the autosomes of pairs 6–12, sometimes known as the C group of chromosomes. Normal females, therefore, have 16 chromosomes in this group, while normal males have only 15 (Plate 1).

The Y chromosome is a small acrocentric chromosome with features akin to those of the members of pairs 21–22, sometimes known as the G group of chromosomes (Plate 2). It can usually be distinguished on morphological grounds from these autosomes because at metaphase, the stage of division at which somatic chromosomes are usually examined, the chromatids of the Y chromosome tend to lie in close proximity to one another, and the chromatic material of the Y chromosome may show a characteristically fuzzy appearance. Another distinction is that satellites are often seen on the short arms of autosome pairs 21–22 but never on the Y chromosome. It can show considerable size variation from person to person, varying from about the same length as the autosomes of group 13–15 to half the length or less of the autosomes in group 21–22. Unusually large or small Y chromosomes have been shown to be inherited from father to son and are apparently without any phenotypic effect. The size of the Y is the same in all cells in any one individual.

C. SEXUAL DIMORPHISM IN INTERPHASE CELLS

1. *Sex chromatin*

The sex chromatin body, first described by Barr and Bertram (1949), is present in the nuclei of a proportion of the cells of the female members of many species including man. It is a plano-convex mass, about 1μ in diameter, which often appears attached to the nuclear membrane. In diploid cells the maximum number of sex chromatin bodies is one less than the number of X chromosomes.

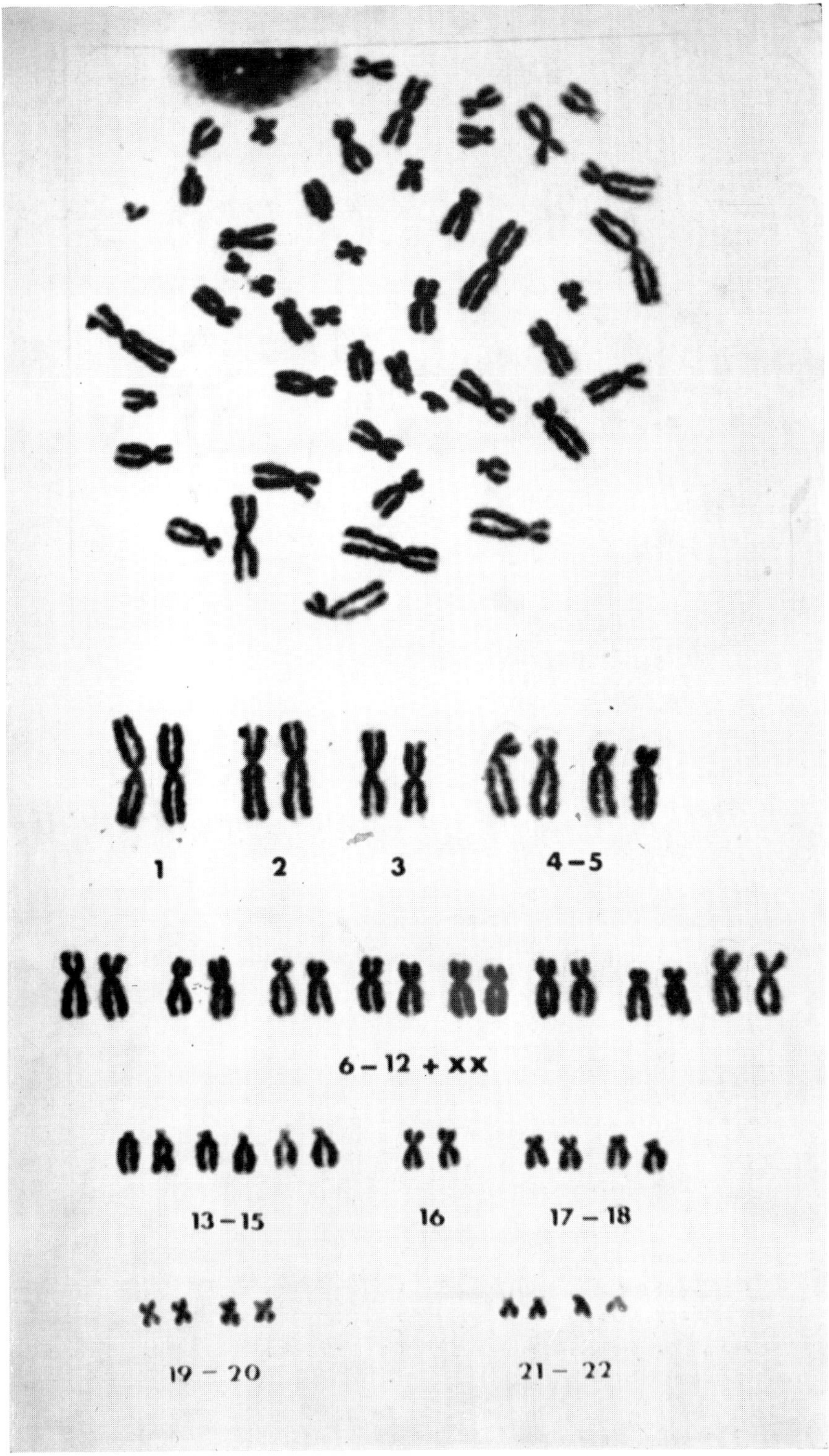

Plate 1. Cell and karyotype from a normal female.

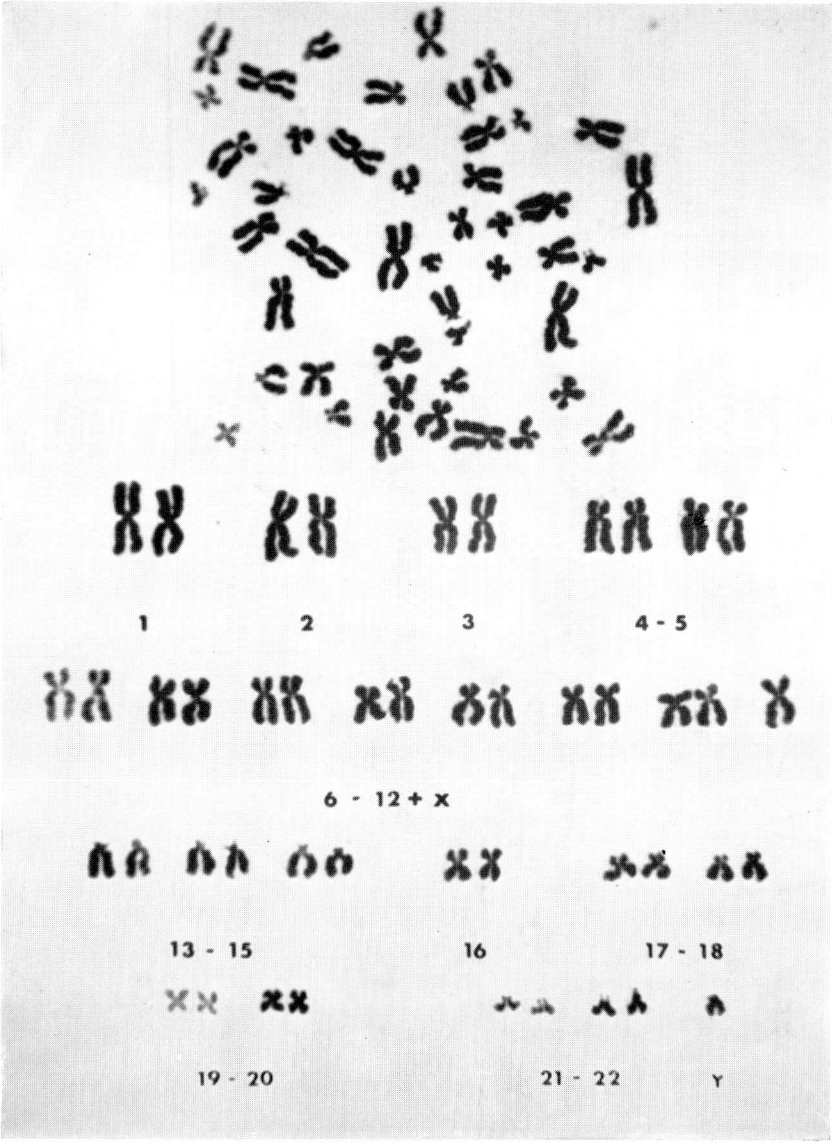

Plate 2. Cell and karyotype from a normal male.

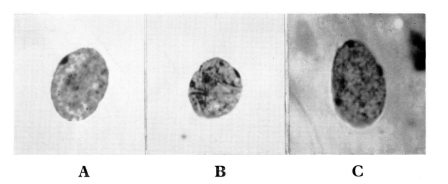

A   B   C

Plate 3. Sex chromatin:
   (A) A single sex chromatin body in a cell from an XX female.
   (B) Two sex chromatin bodies in a cell from an XXX female.
   (C) Three sex chromatin bodies in a cell from an XXXXY male.

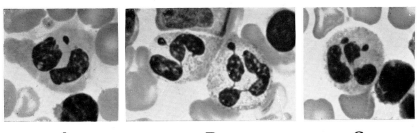

A   B   C

Plate 4. Drumsticks:
   (A) A single drumstick in a cell from an XX female.
   (B) Two cells showing a single abnormally large drumstick from a female with an X
       isochromosome for the long arm of the X constitution.
   (C) Two drumsticks in a cell from an XXX female.

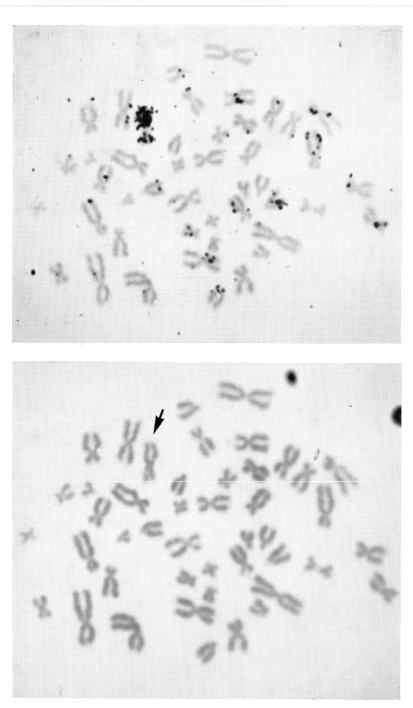

Plate 5. A cell from a normal female which has been treated with tritium-labelled thymidine at the end of the synthetic period. Above is a photograph of the cell showing the auto-radiographic grains and the heavily labelled medium-sized chromosome, and below is the same cell with the grains removed.

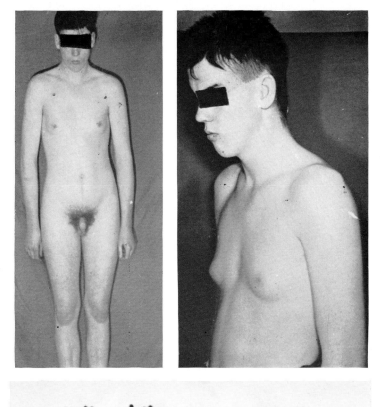

Plate 6. A typical example of Klinefelter's syndrome in a young adult, together with the karyotype of an XXY cell.

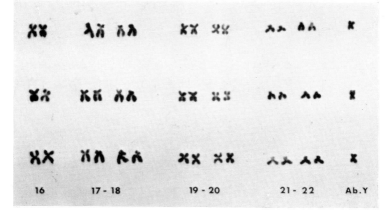

Plate 7. The small chromosomes from three cells of a male with an abnormal Y chromosome, presumed to be due to a pericentric inversion.

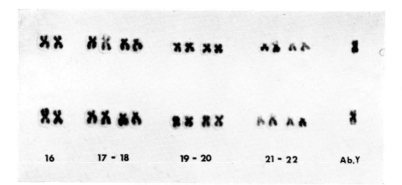

Plate 8. The small chromosomes from two cells of a female with an abnormal chromosome presumed to be an isochromosome for the long arm of the Y.

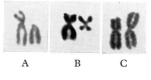

Plate 9. Structurally abnormal X chromosomes:

(A) X + deletion of short arm of X.

(B) X + deletion of most of long arm of X.

(C) X + isochromosome for long arm of the X.

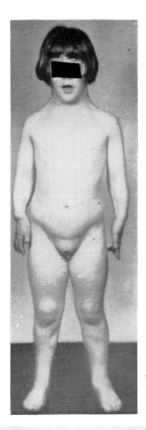

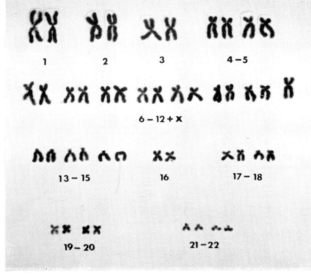

Plate 10. A typical child with Turner's syndrome, together with the karyotype of an XO cell.

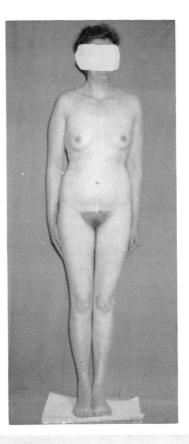

Plate 11. An XXX female and karyotype.

Any gross alteration in the size of the X chromosome is reflected in an alteration in size of the sex chromatin body, so that an individual with an abnormally small X chromosome will have small sex chromatin bodies, and an individual with an abnormally large X chromosome will have sex chromatin bodies which appear larger than normal (Plate 3). Sex chromatin is seen in a great variety of different tissues and its demonstration is a very simple procedure. Suitably stained smears of squamous cells, obtained by scraping the buccal mucosa, have been widely used to determine the frequency of individuals with X chromosome abnormalities in various sub-groups of the human population.

2. Drumsticks

Davidson and Robertson Smith (1954) showed that a small proportion of polymorphonuclear leucocytes from normal females had a characteristic club-shaped appendage, or 'drumstick', which was not present in the cells of normal males. It is now known that this represents one X chromosome and that, as in the case of the sex chromatin body, the maximum number present in any one cell is one less than the number of X chromosomes present. Alterations in morphology of the X chromosome may also be reflected by alteration in the morphology of the drumstick (Plate 4). As drumsticks are only present in a small proportion of polymorphonuclear leucocytes, and as their recognition is time-consuming, they are not commonly used as a tool for screening large populations to detect abnormalities of the X chromosome.

D. CURRENT VIEWS ON THE FORMATION OF THE SEX CHROMATIN BODY

It has been realized since 1960 that the number of sex chromatin bodies is one less than the number of X chromosomes in diploid or near diploid cells (Harnden, 1961), and also that sex chromatin is composed of heterochromatic material which, by analogy with regions of chromosomes in other species which are heterochromatic in interphase, is relatively genetically inactive. Ohno, Kaplan and Kinosita (1959) first suggested that the sex chromatin body was formed by a single X chromosome. They found a single, positively heteropyknotic chromosome in the prophase nuclei of the females of several mammalian species including man, but not in the cells of

5

males. Labelling experiments using tritiated thymidine have shown that the time of synthesis of DNA is not the same in all chromosomes. In particular a number of medium-sized chromosomes, equal to the number of sex chromatin bodies in the cell, replicate their DNA later than the other chromosomes (German, 1964). This has been demonstrated for human cells in culture, and has also been shown to be true for the cells of a number of other mammals both *in vitro* and *in vivo* (Gartler and Burt, 1964; Galton and Holt, 1965). In normal males there is no sex chromatin body, and no late-synthesizing medium-sized chromosome. In normal females there is one sex chromatin body and one late-labelling medium-sized chromosome (Plate 5); in individuals with three X chromosomes there are two sex chromatin bodies and two late-labelling medium-sized chromosomes, and so on up to cells with five X chromosomes, the greatest number so far found. In other words, the number of sex chromatin bodies seen in interphase cells is one less than the number of X chromosomes present in the cell, and equal to the number of late-labelling medium-sized chromosomes. Consequently these latter are presumed to be X chromosomes which are in whole, or in part, relatively inactive genetically. Lyon (1961) suggested an interesting hypothesis to explain the single X constitution of the sex chromatin in mammals, and also the behaviour of X-linked genes. She postulated that for a period in embryogenesis both the X chromosomes in females were isopyknotic and genetically active, but that at a relatively early stage a change supervened, with one X chromosome becoming heteropyknotic, forming a sex chromatin body in interphase, and ceasing to be active genetically. It was presumed to be a matter of chance whether the inactivated X chromosome was of maternal or paternal origin, but once one or the other chromosome had become heterochromatic in a cell, then that same chromosome would remain inactive in all the progeny of that cell. This hypothesis has been largely borne out by experiment and observation, and normal females have been shown to be effective mosaics for a number of X-linked genes, thus conforming to the theoretical predictions of the hypothesis (Davidson, Nitowsky and Childs, 1963).

There are, however, two aspects in which observation apparently fails to confirm the Lyon hypothesis. First, the prediction of mosaicism fails to hold true for the Xg blood group which is X-linked. Possibly the Xg locus is in a small region of the X chromosome which does not become heteropyknotic in interphase and is therefore not inactivated. The second aspect relates to individuals possessing one normal and one structurally abnormal X chromosome. It does not appear to be a matter of chance which chromosome is inactivated: so far it has been found that it is always the abnormal X chromosome which is the late-synthesizer of DNA and forms the sex chromatin body (Muldal, Gilbert et al., 1963). There are two possible explanations for this. There may be a mechanism operating during embryogenesis which ensures that the abnormal X chromosome is inactivated in every cell. Alternatively the normal and abnormal X chromosomes may be inactivated randomly but only those cells with a functionally normal X chromosome are viable and become included in the embryo.

E. INCIDENCE OF INDIVIDUALS WITH AN ABNORMAL SEX CHROMOSOME CONSTITUTION

The study of buccal smears is, as already explained, a valuable method for estimating the frequency of individuals in various subgroups of the population who have an abnormal sex chromosome complement. But the technique has short-comings, and will inevitably lead to an underestimate of the incidence of abnormalities. For example, XYY males cannot be identified in this way.

1. Newborn baby population

Pooled data from a number of surveys totalling more than 25,000 live-born children have shown that the frequency of live-born male children with an abnormal sex chromosome pattern is about 2 per thousand, while amongst females about 0.4 per thousand are chromatin-negative, and 1.2 per thousand are sex chromatin double-positive (MacLean, Harnden et al., 1964; Moore, 1959; Bergemann, 1961).

2. 'Normal' adult population

Two surveys have been done on more or less normal adult male populations. One was based on a survey of hospital outpatients in which about 1,000 males were screened, while another was based on recruits to the American Armed Services. In a series of 1,000 men personally examined by Kaplan and Norfleet (1961), 2 were found to be chromatin-postive. However, only 17 men were found to be chromatin-positive in a series of about 74,000 men examined by medical corpsmen (Paulsen, de Souza et al., 1964). These results suggest that the incidence of chromatin-positive males in the adult population may be somewhat lower than in the newborn baby survey.

3. Patients in mental defective institutions

A large number of surveys have been made of mental defective institutions (Miller, 1964), and the frequency of chromatin-positive males has been found to be about 10 per thousand, a five-fold increase over that in the newborn population. By contrast the number of chromatin-negative females found, 0.3 per thousand, is no greater than that in the general population. However, the number of chromatin double-positive females is about 4.3 per thousand, a four-fold increase over the number found in the newborn population. A considerable proportion of the chromatin-positive males in mental defective institutions have a past history of anti-social behaviour and many of them had been admitted to mental defective institutions through the courts. Forssman and Hambert (1963) and Casey (personal communication) both surveyed institutes for criminal or hard-to-manage patients of sub-normal intelligence, in Sweden and England respectively. In the Swedish institution 15 chromatin-positive males were found in a total of 760, 20 per thousand, while Casey found 16 chromatin-positive males amongst a total of 682, 24 per thousand. Both these surveys suggest that sex chromosome abnormalities in males predispose to criminal behaviour. In the 320 females surveyed by Casey from the same institution 2 were found to be chromatin-double-positive; this incidence, 6 per thousand, is not significantly different from that found in other surveys of mentally sub-normal females.

F. INDIVIDUALS IN WHOM ALL THE CELLS HAVE THE SAME ABNORMAL COMPLEMENT OF SEX CHROMOSOMES

1. Phenotypic males with an additional X chromosome

Phenotypic males with an additional X chromosome show clinically the features of seminiferous tubule dysgenesis or Klinefelter's syndrome (Plate 6). These features are somewhat variable but testicular changes are always present. Before puberty the testes are only distinguishable from those of normal prepubertal males by a reduction in the numbers of spermatogonial cells. After puberty, however, regressive changes take place, characterized by marked degeneration and hyalinization of the seminiferous tubules, unusual numbers of Leydig cells, and only very rarely any evidence of spermatogenesis. Obviously the testes do not undergo normal development so that hypogonadism is a constant clinical feature.

The case of a typical **XXY** male is given below:

J.B., a 33-year-old clerk, was identified during a sex chromatin survey of males attending a sub-fertility clinic. He had been married for six years, practised contraception for the first two years of marriage, but during the last four years his wife had not become pregnant.

FAMILY HISTORY: J.B. is the youngest of a sibship of six. His mother was 42 years old and his father 41 years old at the time of his birth. His oldest brother died at the age of 3 weeks of diphtheria, but his remaining three sisters and one brother are all alive and well. His eldest sister is not married, but the other two sisters and his remaining brother are all married and have children.

EXTERNAL EXAMINATION: A tall well-built man of normal appearance.

Weight—89.1 kg.; Height—185.5 cm.; Arm Span—181.5 cm.; Crown to Pubis—89 cm.; Pubis to Sole—96.5 cm.

SEXUAL DEVELOPMENT: The penis and scrotum were normally developed but both testes were small, measuring between 1 and 2 cm. in length. His axillary and pubic hair were normal in amount, but the latter was of feminine distribution. Chest hair was absent and there was a reduced growth of facial hair necessitating shaving about twice a week. His head hair receded at the temples, and there was no evidence of breast development.

OTHER FEATURES: Colour vision was normal. I.Q. (Wechsler-Bellevue scale) was 90.

HISTOLOGY OF TESTIS: A biopsy of left testis showed generalized atrophy and hyalinization of the seminiferous tubules, and no evidence of spermatogenesis.

LABORATORY INVESTIGATIONS:

Nuclear Sex:

Buccal mucosa—chromatin positive (52% single bodies).
Drumsticks—8 drumsticks in 500 polymorphs.

Chromosomes:

	<45	45	46	47	48	>48	Total
Blood		1	1	28			30
Skin	1	1	1	27			30

All the cells with 47 chromosomes had an additional chromosome in the medium size-range and the patient therefore appears to have an XXY sex chromosome constitution in both blood and skin.

This case of a typical XXY male illustrates many of the features which are associated with this condition. First, the mothers of such patients are often elderly when the patient is born. This has been shown to be true for many conditions which are associated with an additional chromosome (Penrose, 1964). Secondly, the patients are often rather tall with somewhat eunuchoid proportions, their leg length being long in relation to their height. The external genitalia are usually normally developed, although a few cases have been reported which have had various degrees of hypospadias, while in many instances the pattern of body hair distribution is more female than male. In a proportion of these subjects breast development is present and there is some evidence that the risk of developing breast cancer is appreciably greater than in normal males.

On average the I.Q. of males with an extra X chromosome is lower than that of the normal population, and such males are significantly more often found in mental defective institutions than in the general population, the greatest number being found among high grade mental defectives. As they are all sterile, many males who have an additional X chromosome ultimately find their way to male subfertility clinics: Ferguson-Smith, Lennox, Mack and Stewart (1957) found that 3% of all males attending such a clinic were chromatin-positive, while if they considered only males with severe oligospermia or azoospermia the proportion was as high as 11%.

2. Phenotypic males with more than one additional X chromosome

Phenotypic males have been described with two or three additional X chromosomes (Barr, Carr et al., 1962; Barr, Carr et al., 1964). There is some correlation between the severity of the associated abnormal development and the number of X chromosomes present. Individuals with an XXXY constitution usually only differ from typical XXY males in that the testicular changes are more gross and the I.Q. lower, whereas XXXXY males can show a number of malformations not seen in the less abnormal subjects, for example radio-ulnar synostosis.

The case report of a typical XXXXY male is given below:

T.J. was 43 years old when he was identified during a nuclear-sexing survey of an institution for mental defectives.

FAMILY HISTORY: T.J. is the younger of two sibs. His mother was 43 years old and his father 51 years old at the time of his birth. His sister is 14 years older than the patient and is thought to be alive and well. She is married and is said to have children.

EXTERNAL EXAMINATION: The patient was tall and thin with a very narrow shoulder girdle, long limbs and a marked scoliosis. His hands were very small and both 5th fingers incurved. A notable feature was gross prognathism.

Weight—63.5 kg.; Height—180 cm.; Arm Span—203 cm.; Crown to Pubis —82.5 cm.; Pelvis to Sole—95 cm.

SEXUAL DEVELOPMENT: The penis and scrotum were underdeveloped. The testes were not definable but tissue, possibly testicular in nature, was palpable at the end of each vas deferens. The axillary, facial and pubic hair were normally developed, but there was slight gynaecomastia, each breast measuring about 2 cm. in diameter.

OTHER FEATURES: The patient had left-sided radio-ulnar synostosis. He was of severely sub-normal intelligence, his I.Q. being 45 (Wechsler-Bellevue scale).

LABORATORY INVESTIGATIONS:

Nuclear Sex:

Buccal mucosa—chromatin positive (42% single bodies, 44% double bodies, 12% triple bodies).

Drumsticks—12 single drumsticks and 3 double drumsticks in 5,000 polymorphs.

Chromosomes:

	<47	47	48	49	50	>50	Total
Blood		1	2	46	1		50
Skin			1	29			30

All cells with 49 chromosomes had the additional chromosomes in the medium size-range and the patient is therefore considered to have an XXXXY sex chromosome constitution in both blood and skin.

This case report illustrates a number of salient features which are found in males with two or more additional X chromosomes. First, such individuals are usually severely mentally retarded. In fact no such individual has been described of normal intelligence. Secondly, the degree of underdevelopment of the primary and secondary sex characters is usually very marked. The testes are extremely small and cannot be defined clinically, while some underdevelopment of the penis or scrotum is the rule, sometimes linked with hypospadias. Thirdly, there are usually skeletal abnormalities present, and the great majority of cases described with more than three X chromosomes have shown some degree of fusion of the radius and ulna in one or both forearms (Barr *et al.*, 1962).

Males with more than one additional X chromosome are rare in the general population. None have been found in surveys of newborn babies or normal adults; all who have so far been described have been identified either as babies or young children with congenital malformations of their genitalia, or as adults recognised in surveys of mental defective institutions.

3. Males with an XXYY sex chromosome complement

Males with both an extra X and an extra Y chromosome are clinically similar to the XXY male. They have small testes and show a similar range of failure of development of the secondary sex characteristics. Not many individuals with this chromosome abnormality have been studied as yet, and it is not known whether they have features in common which distinguish them from XXY males. There is a suggestion that they are rather tall and have more eunuchoid proportions than the latter, and may be unusually prone to the development of acromegaly. In older XXYY males varicose veins and varicose ulceration of the lower limbs have often been reported (Barr et al., 1964).

Casey (personal communication) found in his survey of institutes for criminal and hard-to-manage patients with sub-normal intelligence, that 7 of the 21 chromatin-positive males had an XXYY constitution in all or the great majority of their cells. This is a significantly higher proportion than that found in similar studies of mental defective institutions, and suggests that this particular constitution may be a predisposing factor to criminal behaviour.

4. Males with an XYY sex chromosome complement

There are several reports in the literature of males who have 47 chromosomes, the additional chromosome being a Y (Sandberg, Koepf et al., 1961; Fraccaro, Bott et al., 1962; Ricci and Malacarne, 1964). In practice the recognition of such individuals is difficult, because there is no simple procedure such as nuclear sex screening for their identification in the population. The reports of such individuals are, therefore, few in number, but this may well be a reflection of the difficulty of identifying them rather than of their rarity. No clear phenotypic picture emerges from the published data. The first XYY male described was a normal fertile adult who was examined because he had several abnormal children, amongst them a mongol (Sandberg et al., 1961). However, the great majority of cases which have been described subsequently have been mentally defective, and the adult cases have had some degree of hypogonadism. How much this reflects a true picture of the XYY male is doubtful, as most published examples were ascertained either because of hypogonadism or because of mental retardation, or both.

5. Males with structural abnormalities of the Y chromosome

Apart from the reports of numerous individuals who have unusually long or short Y chromosomes, three males have been described who have a structurally abnormal Y chromosome in all their cells. In all three men the Y chromosome appeared metacentric and similar to pairs 19/20 (Plate 7). The first individual described with a structural abnormality of the Y chromosome was a normal elderly male (Jacobs, Brunton and Court Brown, 1964). He had no children, but as his wife died a few years after their marriage, his lack of offspring may not be a reflection of his abnormal chromosome. A second individual who had a similar structurally abnormal Y chromosome was a Klinefelter with an XXY sex chromosome constitution (Jacobs, unpublished). In neither of these individuals was it possible to study the chromosomes of any male relatives. However, the third man described with a structurally abnormal Y chromosome was a normal fertile male (Soloman, Hamm and Green, 1964). He was the father of a son who showed the features of Klinefelter's syndrome, and who inherited the abnormal Y chromosome of his father.

The most reasonable explanation for the structurally abnormal Y chromosomes of these three individuals is that a pericentric inversion has occurred. There may have been little or no loss of genetic material and the Y chromosome therefore functions normally. We do not know whether the association of additional X-chromosome material with the abnormal Y in two instances is fortuitous or not.

6. Females with a single-X sex chromosome constitution

There have been many reports of chromatin-negative women who have 45 chromosomes and an XO constitution (Jones, Ferguson-Smith and Heller, 1963; Lindsten, 1963). Such women usually have a number of congenital abnormalities characteristic of gonadal dysgenesis or Turner's syndrome. The features which are most commonly present are shortness of stature and rudimentary streak gonads, associated with primary amenorrhoea and failure of development of the secondary sex characteristics (Plate 10).

A typical case is described below:

Miss A.D. is a 22-year-old primary school teacher. She was referred to a hospital when she was 17 years old for investigation of retardation of growth and primary amenorrhoea.

FAMILY HISTORY: Miss A.D. is the second member of a sibship of three. The mother was 24 and her father 29 years old at the time of her birth. Her elder sister and younger brother are both alive and well and are both of normal height.

EXTERNAL EXAMINATION: The patient is a short stockily built girl who looks much younger than her 22 years. She has a very low hair line at the base of her neck and her neck is short with slight bilateral webbing. Her eyes are wide set and she has a right internal stabismus and many pigmental naevi on her face, trunk and limbs. She has a slightly increased carrying angle and her hands are short and broad with very short 4th metacarpals.

SEXUAL DEVELOPMENT: The external genitalia are small and under-developed and the vagina is also small. At operation an infantile uterus and streak gonads were found. The patient had no axillary hair and scanty pelvic hair. There was no breast development and the nipples were wide set and infantile.

OTHER FEATURES: Colour vision was normal and her intelligence was above average. Intravenous pyelography showed a fusion of the lower poles of the kidneys.

HISTOLOGY: Biopsies of both right and left gonads showed tissue which resembled ovarian stroma but no primordial follicles were present.

LABORATORY INVESTIGATIONS:

Nuclear Sex:

Buccal mucosa—Chromatin-negative.

Blood—No division in 750 polymorphs.

Chromosomes:

	<44	44	45	46	>46	Total
Blood			30			30
Skin		1	24			25
Left gonad	1	1	23			25
Right gonad	1	—	24			25

All cells with 45 chromosomes have only 15 medium-sized chromosomes, and no Y chromosome is present. The patient therefore appears to have an XO sex-chromosome constitution.

The above case report illustrates many of the salient features associated with an XO sex-chromosome constitution. First, the age of the mother at the birth of such individuals is not increased (Boyer, Ferguson-Smith and Grumbach, 1961). Secondly, females with a single X chromosome are very short in stature and frequently have a number of other abnormalities such as a short and often webbed neck, a low hair nuchial line, numerous pigmented naevi, an increased carrying angle at the elbow, short 4th metacarpals or metatarsals and developmental abnormalities of the kidneys. An XO sex chromosome constitution is also often associated with congenital abnormalities of the heart, especially coarctation of the aorta. Thirdly, unless there has been treatment with sex hormones, sexual development is usually retarded at the infantile stage. Breast development is absent and both the pubic and axillary hair are either very scanty or not developed at all. Surgical examination of the internal genitalia shows streaks of gonadal tissue in which there are few, if any, germinal elements. Finally the intelligence of females with an XO constitution does not appear to differ from that of women in the general population.

Several reported cases of XO females have menstruated spontaneously, and one case is known who has had a child (Monardo, 1965; Bahner, Schwarz et al., 1960). While this latter woman has had chromosome studies done on numerous tissues, including the ovary, the possibility that she may have an XX cell line in the germinal cells of the ovary cannot be ruled out. Unlike the other common sex chromosome abnormalities, females with an XO constitution are often recognizable at birth by their anatomical features, for instance congenital heart abnormalities, webbing of the neck, and lymphoedema of the extremities. These females may also present as children with retarded growth or as young women with primary amenorrhoea. Nakagome, Hibi et al. (1963) showed in a survey of Japanese schoolgirls that amongst those who fell short of the mean height by more than two standard deviations, 1.49% were chromatin-negative. When he considered only girls more than three standard deviations below normal in height, as many as 7.32% were chromatin-negative. No less than 40% of women presenting at a gynaecological clinic with unexplained primary amenorrhoea had a sex chromosome abnormality (Jacobs, Harnden et al., 1961).

7. Females with structurally abnormal X chromosomes

A number of females have been described who have one normal and one structurally abnormal X chromosome. The structurally abnormal chromosomes are of three main types: deletion of all or most of the short arm of an X; deletion of all or most of the long arm of an X; or an isochromosome for the long arm of an X (Plate 9). In addition to these, numerous individuals have been described with a single X chromosome together with a minute chromosome. This is usually assumed to be the centric region of the missing sex chromosome, but it is impossible in many instances to know whether it represents an X or a Y chromosome.

(i) DELETION OF THE SHORT ARM OF AN X

The few individuals who have been described with a deletion of the short arm of the X chromosome are clinically indistinguishable from XO females, in that they are of short stature and have streak gonads together with sexual infantilism (Jacobs *et al.*, 1961). They are, however, sex chromatin positive, though their sex chromatin bodies and drumsticks are smaller than normal.

(ii) DELETION OF MOST OF THE LONG ARM OF AN X

Three individuals have been described who have a deletion of most of the long arm of an X chromosome (Becker, Paris and Albert, 1963; de Grouchy, Lamy *et al.*, 1961; Jacobs, Harnden *et al.*, 1960). They all showed primary amenorrhoea and failure of development of the secondary sex characters. However, unlike the XO females they have all been of normal stature. They were sex chromatin positive, but few sex chromatin bodies were seen and their size was very much reduced.

(iii) ISOCHROMOSOME FOR THE LONG ARM OF THE X

An isochromosome for the long arm of the X is the most common structural abnormality of the X chromosome which has been described. It arises by misdivision of the centromere, probably during meiosis; this results in an X chromosome composed of two long arms and no short arms, which appears very similar to the chromosomes of pair three (Fraccaro, Ikkos *et al.*, 1960). Clinically, individuals with an isochromosome for the long arm of the X are similar to those with an XO sex chromosome constitution, though they may have less severe somatic abnormalities. They are sex chromatin positive, and both their sex chromatin bodies and their drumsticks are larger than normal.

8. *Females with an XXX complement of sex chromosomes*

Females with an XXX sex chromosome complement are one of the least well understood groups of individuals with a sex chromosome abnormality. The majority have been identified during surveys of mental defective institutions because of the presence of two sex chromatin bodies in a proportion of their cells. However the first XXX female described was both phenotypically and intellectually normal, and was examined because she had menstruated very irregularly for a few years and menstruation had ceased completely at the age of 19 (Plate 11) (Jacobs, Baikie *et al.*, 1959). Several other XXX women have been described who have a history of irregular menstruation, secondary amenorrhoea or an abnormally early menopause. Where it has been possible to examine such individuals at operation the ovaries have contained rather few follicles, and have been comparable to those of women at or near the menopause (Johnston, Ferguson-Smith *et al.*, 1961). However, most XXX females menstruate normally and many are known to have had children (Stewart and Sanderson, 1960).

A typical case is described below:

The patient, Miss C.M., is a 34-year-old female who was identified during a nuclear sexing survey of a mental defective institution.

FAMILY HISTORY: Miss C.M. is the youngest of a sibship of four. Her mother was 36 and her father 35 years old at the time of her birth. Her three sisters are all alive and well and there is no history of mental defect in the family. She has had two illegitimate children, a boy and a girl.

EXTERNAL EXAMINATION: The patient is an apparently normal female.

Weight—63.7 kg.; Height—172 cm.; Arm Span—168 cm.; Crown to Pubis —89 cm.; Pubis to Sole—84 cm.

SEXUAL DEVELOPMENT: The external genitalia and breasts are normally developed. Menarche occurred at 12 years of age and menstruation is regular, 4/28 days. Both axillary and pubic hair are normally developed.

OTHER FEATURES: The patient is a high grade mental defective. I.Q. 75 (Wechsler-Bellevue). Her two children show no abnormal features; the male is chromatin-negative, and the female normally chromatin-positive.

LABORATORY INVESTIGATIONS:

Nuclear Sex:

Buccal mucosa—chromatin-positive (55% single bodies, 26% double bodies).

Drumsticks—6 drumsticks and 1 double drumstick in 1,000 polymorphs.

Chromosomes:

	<46	46	47	48	>48	Total
Blood	—	—	30	—		30
Skin	1	1	28			30

All cells with 47 chromosomes had an additional medium-sized chromosome so the patient is considered to have an XXX sex chromosome constitution.

The above case report illustrates some of the features associated with the XXX genotype. First, there is the increased maternal age, secondly there is the apparently normal phenotypic and sexual development and thirdly there is the finding that the children born to XXX females are both clinically and cytogenetically normal. A large number of such children are now known, and in all cases where sex chromatin or chromosome studies have been done, the children have been found to be normal. The fact that XXX women do not produce XXX or XXY children suggests that there is some selection mechanism operating against an XX ovum produced by an XXX woman. Finally there is the low intelligence which is associated with the XXX genotype. Such women are four times as frequent among populations of the mentally sub-normal as among newborn babies.

9. Females with more than one extra X chromosome

Rare individuals have been described with an XXXX or an XXXXX sex chromosome constitution (Carr, Barr and Plunkett, 1961; Kesaree and Woolley, 1963). All such individuals have been grossly mentally defective. Where the XXXX sex chromosome constitution has been described in adults, the menstrual history and development of the sex characteristics have been normal.

10. Females with an X chromosome and a structurally abnormal Y chromosome

Two females have been described with negative sex chromatin and 46 chromosomes, having one normal X chromosome and an abnormal metacentric chromosome approximately the size of a chromosome No. 16 (Plate 8) (Court Brown, Harnden et al., 1964; Jacobs, unpublished). The abnormal chromosome does not synthesize DNA late in the synthetic period and this, together with the fact that its chromatids often lie very close together and have the characteristic fuzzy appearance of Y chromosome material, strongly suggests that this chromosome is a structurally abnormal Y chromosome, probably an isochromosome for the long arms of the Y. Both patients are of normal stature, have primary amenorrhoea and failure of development of the secondary sex characters, and, apart from a rather deep voice in one, neither shows any evidence of masculinization. Examination of the internal genitalia of one showed an infantile uterus and streak gonads. Histologically the gonads showed only connective tissue with no evidence of any ovarian elements. As there is no evidence of any other cell line being present in either patient, it appears that this particular structural abnormality of a Y chromosome is associated with the development of a poorly developed phenotypic female.

G. MOSAICS

In the section above, the abnormal sex chromosome complements described have been presumed to be present in all, or certainly the great majority, of the cells of the affected subjects. Many individuals have now been reported, however, in whom there are two or more cell lines which differ from one another in their sex chromosome constitutions. In such people one cell line may be normal, and one or more abnormal, or every line may be abnormal. Two or more cell lines may be present in any one tissue, or one tissue may consist largely or wholly of cells with one sex chromosome constitution, while another tissue contains cells with a different complement. All such individuals are referred to as sex chromosome mosaics. The cell lines differ most commonly in the number of sex chromosomes, but the difference can be purely structural, or both number and structure may be involved (Blank, 1964).

Before considering mosaicism in further detail, it must be emphasized that the sex chromosome complement of humans is usually studied in lymphocytes from cultures of the peripheral blood, or in fibroblasts grown most commonly from samples of skin. Occasionally chromosomes are examined from primitive haemopoetic cells obtained from preparations of bone marrow. In all instances, therefore, the cells studied are either haemopoetic cells or fibroblasts, so the spectrum of tissues studied is very limited. Therefore, while one can say that a particular individual is a sex chromosome mosaic, one can never be sure that an individual showing evidence for only one cell line is not a mosaic. The phenotypic appearance of individuals known to be mosaics depends mainly on two factors, the sex chromosome constitutions of the constituent cell lines and the distribution of these lines within the body. In this context the constitution of gonadal cells may be particularly important. Such a variety of mosaics have now been described that it is not possible to deal with all of them. However, the main features of mosaicism and their biological implications can be illustrated by dealing with two of the commoner types, namely XY/XXY and XO/XY mosaicism.

1. XY/XXY Mosaics

The phenotype of individuals who are XY/XXY mosaics ranges from that of a normal male to that of a typical XXY male with Klinefelter's syndrome. Such individuals can be chromatin-positive or chromatin-negative depending on the composition of cells in the tissues studied, or they may have a lower proportion of chromatin-positive cells than is normally found in people with two X chromosomes in every cell.

From Table II it can be seen that the proportion of chromatin-positive males who are XY/XXY mosaics differs in different populations, and while some of the figures may be biased because of the method of ascertainment there is little doubt that the highest proportion of XY/XXY mosaics is found in surveys of the general population. It therefore seems reasonable to suppose that at least some XY/XXY mosaics will develop into fertile individuals. A few individuals recognised as having XY/XXY mosaicism have been proven to be fertile (Court Brown, Mantle et al., 1964). It may be that the greater the proportion of XY cells in the testes, the more likely is the subject to be fertile and the less evident will be the features of Klinefelter's syndrome. Conversely if the representation of XY cells in the gonadal tissue is low, then the subject will perhaps tend to have all the features of the XXY male including sterility.

2. XO/XY Mosaics

In some ways the most interesting form of sex chromosome mosaicism is that in which the cell lines have XO and XY complements. One might predict that the range of phenotype could run from normal male to female with the features of Turner's syndrome, depending on the relative proportions of the cell lines in the gonads. Recognition of those subjects which had a normal male phenotype would, in ordinary circumstances, be a purely chance event. However two XO/XY males have been found because they each had a twin who was clinically abnormal; in both cases the twin was of the opposite phenotypic sex, although there was good evidence that both twin pairs were monozygotic (Dent and Edwards, 1964; Jacobs,

TABLE II

Source of chromatin-positive males	Total chromatin-positive males analysed	No. who were XY/XXY	Proportion XY/XXY
Survey of newborn and school population	22	7	31.8%
Survey of institutions for mentally diseased and defective	64	6	9.4%
Hospital patients	99	8	8.0%

6

unpublished). The female member of each pair was studied because she showed the features of Turner's syndrome, and in each instance an XO/XY complement was found. In the male twin of one pair no XY cell has been found, but the twin is normally developed as a male and married, and it must be presumed that XY cells are present at least in his gonads. In the case of the other male twin, XO/XY mosaicism was demonstrated both in blood cells and in fibroblasts from the testes. Examples of XO/XY mosaicism have also been found among adult females with the features of gonadal dysgenesis, who have been studied because of a primary failure to menstruate; examination of the internal genitalia has shown streak gonads typical of females with an XO complement. A phenotypic female has even been found with XO/XYY mosaicism; she showed the features of Turner's syndrome (Jacobs et al., 1961).

Yet another outcome could be predicted if the XO cells were to be confined mainly to one gonad and the XY cells to the other. This might be expected to result in a form of hermaphroditism, in which one gonad was a testis, associated with a vas deferens, and the other a streak gonad, associated with a Fallopian tube and possibly a uterus. Such individuals have been found, with XO/XY mosaicism in somatic cells (Turner, Greenblatt and Dominguez, 1963; Court Brown et al., 1964). It may be that the gonad developing as a testis is composed wholly or largely of XY cells, and that appearing as a streak is composed of XO cells. Studies of cases of this nature raise the interesting question of the extent to which the development of the gonads and their related structures are dependent on the chromosome constitution of the constituent cells rather than on the hormonal environment. It is perhaps surprising that in the XO/XY hermaphrodite the presence of male hormones produced by apparently normal testicular tissue does little to influence the development of the presumptive XO gonad and its associated structures in a male direction, or to prevent the development of the associated female structures.

H. TRUE HERMAPHRODITES

The chromosome constitutions of several true hermaphrodites have been investigated and most have been either XX or XX/XY (Sasaki and Makino, 1960; Rosenberg, Clayton and Hsu, 1963; Gartler, Waxman and Giblett, 1962). Hermaphrodites with an

XO/XY constitution, such as the case described above, are not considered by the purists to be true hermaphrodites as they lack fully developed ovarian tissue. There have been several reports of true hermaphrodites who possess both ovarian and testicular tissue, yet in whom only XX cells have been found. Several chromatin-positive males who have the features of Klinefelter's syndrome have also been shown to have an XX sex chromosome constitution (Court Brown et al., 1964). Either such individuals must have a second cell line with a Y chromosome which accounts for the development of the testicular tissue, or testicular tissue must be able to develop in the absence of a Y chromosome.

It is only possible to obtain the XX/XY type of mosaicism either by an extremely complicated series of divisional errors occurring after fertilization, or by an error such as the single or double fertilization of a binucleate egg, or the fusion of two embryos of different sex to form a single foetus. Gartler and his colleagues (1962) have described an XX/XY true hermaphrodite who had two populations of red cells with many antigenic differences. They concluded from studies of the relevant antigens of the parents that the mosaicism arose through fertilization of two egg nuclei by different sperms, although it was impossible to say how the two egg nuclei had arisen.

Other XX/XY true hermaphrodites with two populations of antigenically different red cells have been reported. For example, Zuelzer, Beattie and Reisman (1964) have described a male with slight breast development, whose mosaic constitution was recognized during routine red-cell typing of blood donors. From their studies of the antigens of the patient and his parents it was evident that both the mother and the father of the patient had contributed two sets of genetic material. The authors concluded that the XX/XY constitution had arisen by fertilization of the egg by one sperm and the polar body by another. Several XX/XY true hermaphrodites have been found in whom blood group mosaicism has not been detected (Race and Sanger, personal communication). This could either be because the blood-forming tissue was composed of a single cell line, or because the XX/XY mosaicism had arisen by a series of post-zygotic divisional errors, occurring either in a normal male zygote or more probably in one with an XXY sex chromosome constitution.

I. AETIOLOGY OF SEX CHROMOSOME ABNORMALITIES

Abnormal numbers of sex chromosomes arise in several ways, but all involve a misdivision of the sex chromosomes at one or more cell divisions. If this occurs during the formation of the germ cells in one or other parent the resulting individual will show the abnormality in all his cells. If, however, the misdivision occurs during embryogenesis the resultant individual may be a mosaic.

If divisional errors, such as non-disjunction or anaphase lagging, occur during the first meiotic division in one or other parent, the result will be gametes with XX, XY or O sex chromosome complements, whereas divisional errors at the second meiotic division will result in gametes with XX, YY or O complements. If successive divisional errors involving the sex chromosome were to occur in the formation of a single gamete, a more bizarre chromosome constitution might result. Fertilization of a normal egg by an XY, O or YY sperm would result in an XXY, XO or XYY zygote, whereas fertilization by a normal sperm of an XX or O ovum would result in an XXX, XXY, XO or YO zygote. Individuals with all these genotypes have been described with the exception of the YO, which is considered to be inviable. The relative frequency at birth of XXY, XXX and XO individuals is known from nuclear sex surveys of newborn babies, but the frequency of XYY males is unknown as they cannot be detected by nuclear sexing. On theoretical grounds we should expect the XXX and XXY genotypes to occur with about the same frequency, and the XO genotype to occur with a frequency at least equal to the sum of the XXX and XXY. In fact the frequency of chromatin-negative females is only 0.4 per thousand at birth, whereas that of chromatin-positive males is about 2.1 and of chromatin-double-positive females about 1.3 per thousand (MacLean *et al.*, 1964). Therefore it would appear that there is a strong selection factor operating against the XO female. This genotype is often associated with severe congenital abnormalities, particularly of the cardio-vascular system, and it may be that these lesions are a cause of foetal death. Carr (1963 and personal communication), in a study of the chromosome constitution of 200 consecutive spontaneous abortions, found that 44 had an abnormal chromosome constitution, and no fewer than 11 of these had an XO constitution. As approximately 10% of all pregnancies terminate in an abortion, the finding that about 5% of these had an XO sex complement more than compensates for the missing XO individuals.

It has been shown that the frequency of conception of XXX and XXY individuals is associated with increasing maternal age, as are all the autosomal trisomies which have been described in man. In contrast XO individuals show no such association. At least three explanations have been put forward to account for this. First, while increasing maternal age undoubtedly increases the risk of non-disjunction of both the sex chromosomes and the autosomes, it may be that an ovum with no sex chromosome is inviable, and that all XO individuals result from post-zygotic errors. There is some evidence to support this, in that a higher proportion of individuals with Turner's syndrome are mosaics than of those with Klinefelter's syndrome or than of XXX females. Further, it is known that XO mice can result from X-irradiation of eggs subsequent to their fertilization (Russell and Saylors, 1960). Secondly, it may be that the great majority of XO females arise as a result of divisional errors occurring during spermatogenesis. Some evidence to support this suggestion comes from the finding that the X in an XO individual is much more often of maternal than of paternal origin (see below). Thirdly, we know that the intra-uterine mortality of XO embryos is high, and it may be that those carried by young mothers have a greater chance of survival than the great majority which are carried by older mothers. There is, as yet, insufficient information available regarding the age of mothers of XO abortions to make the necessary comparison with the age of mothers of XO live births.

Whatever the mechanism for producing the mistakes, it is often possible to tell which parental chromosomes were involved by a study of the inheritance of X-linked genes. The most frequently used ones are those for red/green colour blindness and the Xg blood-group genes, as these are both common in the population. Thus Stewart (1960) showed in an XO individual that the single X must have been inherited from the mother: the patient was red/green colour blind, while the father's colour vision was normal, and the mother was known to be heterozygous for red/green colour blindness. This suggests that non-disjunction had taken place during the formation of the sperm, and an X ovum had been fertilized by a sperm having no sex chromosome. However, post-zygotic loss of the paternal sex chromosome is not ruled out. Nowakowski, Lenz and Parada (1959) described three XXY males who were all red/green colour blind, yet who all had fathers with normal colour vision. All three must therefore have inherited both their X chromosomes from their mothers. More recently the sex-linked blood group Xg has been used to demonstrate the origin of the X chromosome in a variety of individuals with abnormal sex chromosome constitutions. Out of 56 XO females where the propositus and both parents were tested for the Xg^a gene, the X was paternal in origin in one instance, maternal in origin in 20, while the remaining 35 investigations were uninformative (Lindsten, Bowen et al., 1963). Two individuals with an XXXXY sex chromosome constitution were Xg(a–) negative, while their fathers were Xg(a+), showing that all four X's were of maternal origin; the abnormal constitution probably arose by non-disjunctions in both first and second maternal meiotic divisions (Lewis, Froland et al., 1964). An XXYY male has been described who is Xg(a+) and who has been shown to have an Xg(a+) father and an Xg(a–) mother, suggesting that non-disjunction of the sex chromosome occurred in the first and second meiotic division in the course of spermatogenesis (Chapelle, Hortling et al., 1964).

J. CONCLUSIONS

1. The X chromosome

The X chromosome is a medium-sized submetacentric chromosome which, when there is only one present in the cell, behaves in a fashion indistinguishable from that of the autosomes. When there is more than one present in the cell, the additional X chromosomes behave in a different way. They remain wholly or partially condensed during interphase, when they are visible as the sex chromatin bodies, and it is assumed that this heterochromatic appearance is a reflection of their relative genetic inactivity. While this is true of a great many tissues it is not true of all, and a noteworthy exception are the cells constituting the female germ line. The inactive X starts its synthesis of DNA late in the S period and is the last chromosome to complete DNA synthesis. The behaviour of most, but not all, of the genes on the X chromosome is compatible with the Lyon hypothesis, which postulates that in the very early stages of embryogenesis all the X chromosomes in a cell are active, and that there is then a sudden inactivation of all X chromosomes present in excess of one. The hypothesis further suggests that this process happens at random, and that once a certain X has become inactivated, be it paternally or maternally derived, the same X is always inactivated in that cell and its progeny, so that all females are really mosaics for X-linked genes.

An individual with a single X chromosome is an underdeveloped female. The genetically 'neutral' type in man would therefore seem to be an underdeveloped female with non-differentiated streak gonads, and an additional X chromosome is required for the development of a differentiated ovary. We also know that such XO females are short in stature, as are females with one normal X and one isochromosome for the long arm of the X, and females with one normal X and one abnormal X which has the short arms deleted. However, a female with one normal X and one X which has a long arm deletion is of normal stature. It follows that there must be a gene or genes on the short arm of the X which are necessary in double dose in the female for development of normal stature.

We know that the addition of an X chromosome or chromosomes to a normal female lowers the intelligence, but appears to have no other consistent effect on the phenotype. In some instances however it adversely affects the development and function of the ovaries, and they appear to have a reduced number of follicles in association with a precocious menopause. When XXX women are fertile they produce children with normal sex chromosomes, so there must be a strong selecting factor operating against XX ova, at least in XXX females.

The addition of an X chromosome to a normal male lowers the intelligence and also causes the abnormal development of the testes, the seminiferous tubules of which become hyalinized. Spermatogenesis is virtually absent. Secondary sexual characteristics are also undeveloped to a greater or lesser degree. If a phenotypic male has as many as three or four additional X chromosomes the testes are very reduced in size and the external genitalia are often malformed. In general the greater the number of X chromosomes the lower the intelligence and the more marked the abnormalities, but even four X chromosomes do not overcome the masculizing effect of one Y.

2. The Y chromosome

The Y chromosome is a small acrocentric chromosome which can be distinguished from the small acrocentric autosomes by the absence of satellites, the fuzzy appearance of the chromatids, and their propensity for being in close apposition to one another. Its size is rather variable from individual to individual, but in any one individual or family the size is constant. The variation in size affects only the long arms and appears to be without phenotypic effect. The Y chromosome is normally necessary for the development of the undifferentiated gonad into a testis and the subsequent development of the male phenotype. The Y chromosome in man is very strongly male-determining, as it can overcome the feminizing effects of as many as four X chromosomes to produce a phenotypic male, albeit an imperfect one.

The effects of the addition of a Y chromosome to a male phenotype is little understood, but it would appear at least in some instances to be associated with failure of the correct development of the testes and secondary sex characteristics, and possibly also with a lowering of the intelligence.

Alterations of the morphology of the Y chromosomes have been described. Where these do not involve a loss of material from the short arm they do not appear to be associated with any phenotypic effect. However, two individuals have been described who are apparently lacking the material of the short arm of the Y, having instead the material of the long arm in duplicate. Both have been poorly developed *females* of normal height and intelligence. If these observations are confirmed they suggest that the masculinizing genes of the Y chromosome are located on the short arms, and that without these genes the embryo develops, even in the presence of the major part of the Y chromosome, in a female direction. Such individuals are of normal height, in contrast to XO and X isochromosome-long arm-X females, suggesting that there are one or more genes on the long arm of the Y which control stature. Further, the X isochromosome-long-arm-Y women are both of normal intelligence, whereas the majority of the XYY males so far reported have been mentally defective. This suggests that if there are genes on the Y chromosome which effect a lowering of the intelligence when present in double dose, they must be situated on the short arm of the Y chromosome.

REFERENCES

Bahner, F., Schwarz, G., Hienz, H. A. and Walter, K. (1960) Turner-Syndrom mit voll Ausgebildeten Sekundaren Geschlechtsmerkmalen und Fertilität. *Acta endocrin.*, **35**, 397.

Barr, M. L. and Bertram, E. G. (1949) A morphological distinction between neurones of the male and female, and the behaviour of the nucleolar satellite during accelerated nucleoprotein synthesis. *Nature (Lond.)*, **163**, 676.

Barr, M. L., Carr, D. H., Pozsony, J., Wilson, R. A., Dunn, H. G., Jacobson, T. S. and Miller, J. R. (1962) The XXXXY sex chromosome abnormality. *Canad. med. Ass. J.*, **87**, 891.

Barr, M. L., Carr, D. H., Soltan, H. C., Weins, R. G., and Plunkett, E. R. (1964) The XXYY variant of Klinefelter's syndrome. *Canad. med. Ass. J.*, **90**, 575.

Becker, K. L., Paris, J. and Albert, A. (1963) Gonadal dysgenesis and hypopituitarism (deletion-induced hemizygosity). Proc. Staff Meet. Mayo Clinic, 38, 467.

Bergemann, E. (1961) Geschlechtschromatintiestimmungen am Neugeborenen. Schweiz. med. Wschr., 10, 292.

Blank, C. E. (1964) Some aspects of chromosome mosaicism in clinical medicine. Lancet, ii, 903.

Boyer, S. H., Ferguson-Smith, M. A. and Grumbach, M. M. (1961) The lack of influence of parental age and birth order in the aetiology of nuclear sex chromatin-negative Turner's syndrome. Ann. hum. Genet., 25, 215.

Carr, D. H. (1963) Chromosome studies in abortuses and stillborn infants. Lancet, ii, 603.

Carr, D. H., Barr, M. L. and Plunkett, E. R. (1961) An XXXX sex chromosome complement in two mentally defective females. J. Canad. Med. Assoc., 84, 131.

Chapelle, A., Hortling, H., Sanger, R. and Race, R. R. (1964) Successive nondisjunction at first and second meiotic division of spermatogenesis. Evidence of chromosomes and Xg. Cytogenetics, 3, 334.

Court Brown, W. M., Harnden, D. G., Jacobs, P. A., MacLean, N. and Mantle, D. J. (1964) Abnormalities of the sex chromosome complement in man. Medical Research Council Special Report Series No. 305. H.M.S.O. (Lond.)

Court Brown, W. M., Mantle, D. J., Buckton, K. E. and Tough, I. M. (1964). Fertility in an XY/XXY male married to a translocation heterozygote. J. Med. Genet., 1, 35.

Davidson, R. G., Nitowsky, H. M. and Childs, B. (1963) Demonstration of two populations of cells in the human female heterozygous for glucose-6-phosphate dehydrogenase variants. Proc. nat. Acad. Sci., 50, 481.

Davidson, W. M. and Robertson Smith, D. (1954) A morphological sex difference in the polymorphonuclear neutrophil leucocytes. Brit. Med. J., 2, 6.

De Grouchy, J., Lamy, M., Yaneva, H., Salomon, Y. and Netter, A. (1961) Further abnormalities of the X chromosome in primary amenorrhoea or in severe oligomenorrhoea. Lancet, ii, 777.

Dent, T. and Edwards, J. H. (1964) Monozygotic twins of different sex. Genetics Today, 1, 304. Proceedings of the 11th International Congress of Genetics, The Hague, Holland.

Ferguson-Smith, M. A., Johnston, A. W. and Handmaker, S. D. (1960) Primary amentia and micro-orchidism associated with an XXXY sex-chromosome constitution. Lancet, ii, 184.

Ferguson-Smith, M. A., Lennox, B., Mack, W. S. and Stewart, J. S. S. (1957) Klinefelter's syndrome. Frequency and testicular morphology in relation to nuclear sex. Lancet, ii, 167.

Ford, C. E., Jones, K. W., Polani, P. E., de Almeida, J. C. and Briggs, J. H. (1959) A sex chromosome anomaly in a case of gonadal dysgenesis. Lancet, i, 711.

Ford, C. E., Polani, P. E., Briggs, J. H. and Bishop, P. M. F. (1959) A presumptive human XXY/XX mosaic. Nature (Lond.), 183, 1030.

Forssman, H. and Hambert, G. (1963) Incidence of Klinefelter's syndrome among mental patients. Lancet, i, 1327.

Fraccaro, M., Glenn Bott, M., Davies, P. and Schutt, W. (1962) Mental deficiency and undescended testis in two males with XYY sex chromosomes. Folia Hered. Path. (Milano), 11, 211.

Fraccaro, M., Ikkos, D., Lindsten, J., Luft, R. and Kaijser, K. (1960) A new type of chromosomal abnormality in gonadal dysgenesis. Lancet, ii, 1144.

Galton, M. and Holt, S. F. (1965) Asynchronous replication of the mouse sex chromosomes. Exp. Cell Res., 37, 111.

Gartler, S. M. and Burt, B. (1964) Replication patterns of bovine sex chromosomes in cell culture. *Cytogenetics*, **3**, 135.

Gartler, S. M., Waxman, S. H. and Giblett, E. (1962) An XX/XY human hermaphrodite resulting from double fertilization. *Proc. nat. Acad. Sci.*, **48**, 332.

German, J. (1964) The pattern of DNA synthesis in the chromosomes of human blood cells. *J. Cell Biol.*, **20**, 37.

Harnden, D. G. (1961) Nuclear sex in triploid XXY human cells. *Lancet, ii*, 488.

Jacobs, P. A., Baikie, A. G., Court Brown, W. M., MacGregor, T. N., MacLean, N. and Harnden, D. G. (1959) Evidence for the existence of the human 'super female'. *Lancet, ii*, 423.

Jacobs, P. A., Brunton, M. and Court Brown, W. M. (1964) Cytogenetic studies in leucocytes on the general population: subjects of ages 65 years and more. *Ann. hum. Genet.*, **27**, 353.

Jacobs, P. A., Harnden, D. G., Court Brown, W. M., Goldstein, J., Close, H. G., MacGregor, T. N., MacLean, N. and Strong, J. A. (1960) Abnormalities involving the X chromosome in women. *Lancet, i*, 1213.

Jacobs, P. A., Harnden, D. G., Buckton, K., Court Brown, W. M., King, J., McBride, J. A., MacGregor, T. N. and MacLean, N. (1961) Cytogenetic studies in primary amenorrhoea. *Lancet, i*, 1183.

Jacobs, P. A. and Strong, J. A. (1959) A case of human intersexuality having a possible XXY-sex determining mechanism. *Nature (Lond.)*, **183**, 302.

Johnston, A. W., Ferguson-Smith, M. A., Handmaker, S. D., Jones, H. W. and Jones, G. S. (1961) The triple-X syndrome. *Brit. med. J.*, **2**, 1046.

Jones, H. W., Ferguson-Smith, M. A., and Heller, R. H. (1963) The pathology and cytogenetics of gonadal agenesis. *Amer. J. Obstet. Gynec.*, **87**, 578.

Kaplan, N. M. and Norfleet, R. G. (1961) Hypogonadism in young men (with emphasis on Klinefelter's syndrome). *Ann. intern. Med.*, **54**, 461.

Kesaree, N. and Woolley, P. V. (1963) A phenotypic female with 49 chromosomes, presumably XXXXX. *J. Pediat.*, **63**, 1099.

Lewis, F. J. W., Froland, A., Sanger, R. and Race, R. R. (1964) Source of the X chromosomes in two XXXXY males. *Lancet, ii*, 589.

Lindsten, J. (1963) *The nature and origin of X chromosome aberrations in Turner's syndrome—a cytogenetical and clinical study of 57 patients.* Almquist & Wiksell, Stockholm.

Lindsten, J., Bowen, P., Lee, C. S. N., McKusick, V. A., Polani, P. E., Wingate, M., Edwards, J. H., Hamper, J., Tippett, P., Sanger, R. and Race, R. R. (1963) Source of the X in XO females: the evidence of Xg. *Lancet, i*, 558.

Lyon, M. F. (1961) Gene action in the X chromosome of the mouse (*Mus musculus L.*). *Nature (Lond.)*, **190**, 372.

MacLean, N., Harnden, D. G., Court Brown, W. M., Bond, J. and Mantle, D. J. (1964) Sex chromosome abnormalities in newborn babies. *Lancet, i*, 286.

Miller, O. J. (1964) The sex chromosome anomalies. *Amer. J. Obstet. Gynec.*, **90**, 1078.

Monardo, A. (1965) Gonadal dysgenesis in a woman after seventeen years of regular menses. *Amer. J. Obstet. Gynec.*, **91**, 106.

Moore, K. L. (1959) Sex reversal in newborn babies. *Lancet, i*, 217.

Muldal, S., Gilbert, C. W., Lajtha, L. G., Lindsten, J., Rowley, J. and Fraccaro, M. (1963) Tritiated thymidine incorporation in an isochromosome for the long arm of an X chromosome in man. *Lancet, i*, 861.

Nakagome, Y., Hibi, I., Konoshita, K., Nagao, T. and Aikawa, M. (1963) Incidence of Turner's syndrome in Japanese dwarfed girls. *Lancet, ii*, 412.

Nowakowski, H., Lenz, W. and Parada, J. (1959) Diskrepanz zwischen Chromatinbefund und genetischen Geschlecht beim Klinefelter-Syndrom. *Acta endocrin.*, **30**, 296.

Ohno, S., Kaplan, W. D. and Kinosita, R. (1959) Formation of the sex chromatin by a single X chromosome in liver cells of *Rattus norvegicus*. *Exp. Cell Res.*, **18**, 415.

Paulsen, C. A., de Souza, A., Yoshizuma, T. and Lewis, B. M. (1964) Results from a buccal smear survey in non-institutionalized adult males. *J. Clin. Endocrin.*, **24**, 1182.

Penrose, L. S. (1964) Review of 'Abnormalities of the sex chromosome complement in man'. *Ann. hum. Genet.*, **28**, 199.

Ricci, N. and Malacarne, P. (1964) An XYY human male. *Lancet*, *i*, 721.

Rosenberg, H. S., Clayton, G. W. and Hsu, T. C. (1963) Familial true hermaphrodism. *J. clin. Endocrin.*, **23**, 203.

Russell, L. B. and Saylors, C. L. (1960) Factors causing a high frequency of mice having the XO sex-chromosome constitution. *Science*, **131**, 1321.

Sandberg, A. A., Koepf, G. F., Ishihara, T. and Hauschka, T. S. (1961) An XYY human male. *Lancet*, *ii*, 488.

Sasaki, M. and Makino, S. (1960) The chromosomal constitution of a human hermaphrodite. *Texas Rep. Biol. Med.*, **18**, 493.

Soloman, I. L., Hamm, C. W. and Green, O. C. (1964) Chromosome studies on testicular tissue cultures and blood leucocytes of a male previously reported to have no Y chromosomes. *New Engl. J. Med.*, **271**, 586.

Stewart, J. S. S. (1960) Gonadal dysgenesis: the genetic significance of unusual variants. *Acta endocrin.*, **33**, 89.

Stewart, J. S. S. and Sanderson, A. R. (1960) Fertility and oligophrenia in an apparent triple-X female. *Lancet*, *ii*, 21.

Turner, H. H., Greenblatt, R. B. and Dominguez, H. (1963) Syndrome of gonadal dysgenesis and abdominal testis with an XO/XY chromosome mosaicism. *J. clin. Endocrin.*, **23**, 709.

Zuelzer, W. W., Beattie, K. M. and Reisman, L. E. (1964) Generalised unbalanced mosaicism attributable to dispermy and probable fertilization of a polar body. *Amer. J. hum. Genet.*, **16**, 38.

4

PHYSIOLOGY AND BIOCHEMISTRY OF POULTRY SEMEN

P. E. LAKE

Agricultural Research Council Poultry Research Centre,
King's Buildings, West Mains Road, Edinburgh 9, Scotland

A. INTRODUCTION

The anatomy of the reproductive tract of birds is quite different from that of mammals and it is therefore not surprising to find that avian semen exhibits several unique features of physiology and biochemistry. The impetus for research in this field was the great difficulty encountered in devising methods to store poultry semen *in vitro*. The criterion of successful storage is that the spermatozoa should retain the ability to survive and fertilize successive eggs in the oviduct for at least a week after insemination. The task is more difficult than with bull semen, where, though remarkably successful storage results have been achieved, no prolonged retention in the oviduct is required.

Interest in the physiology of avian semen has centred mainly around the common domestic fowl (*Gallus domesticus*) and the turkey (*Meleagris gallopavo*); a little practical work has begun recently on the artificial insemination of ducks, geese and quail, but nothing is known about the chemistry of their semen.

The semen of the fowl is the chief subject of this review because it has been the most extensively used for laboratory studies on the functions of avian spermatozoa. Observations made on fowl semen cannot, however, necessarily be applied directly to other avian species. A little information is available on the physiology of turkey semen, and will be discussed where it differs significantly from the fowl. Lorenz (1959, 1964) has reviewed work on avian reproductive physiology in general; the present review will therefore be concerned mainly with recent information on the biochemistry of poultry semen. It includes the parallel studies that have been made, in connection with artificial insemination, on the physical and chemical conditions that affect the survival of poultry spermatozoa *in vitro*.

Artificial insemination has assumed great practical importance as an adjunct in breeding certain types of turkey. For example, where geneticists have developed varieties and strains of turkeys which are heavy and have a broad breast, there is often difficulty in mating the heavy male and female; here artificial insemination is the only answer. The method has also been used to breed from fowl, turkeys and ducks kept in cages.

B. THE ORIGIN AND COMPOSITION OF FOWL SEMEN

1. *Accessory reproductive fluids*

The fowl does not possess the accessory reproductive organs found in common domestic mammals, e.g. seminal vesicles, prostate gland, Cowper's glands and the urethral glands of Littré. The extent of development of these accessory organs and the amount of secretion which they contribute to the ejaculate, varies among different species (Mann, 1964). Each type of mammalian organ produces specific chemical compounds in its secretion; these compounds are largely absent from fowl semen.

The fowl possesses a cloaca into which the rectum, ureters and vasa deferentia open. A *transparent fluid* can be obtained from certain erectile tissues in the proctodaeum of the cloaca (Fig. 1) by the

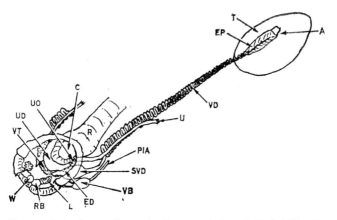

Fig. 1. Diagram of the cloaca and reproductive tract of the male fowl, *Gallus domesticus*. The right side of the reproductive tract is represented *in situ* and the dorsal part of the cloaca is removed. Adrenal gland, A; testis, T; epididymal region, EP; lower portion of the ureter, U; opening of ureter into cloaca, UO; rectum, R; coprodaeum, C; vas deferens, VD; sac-like ending of vas deferens, SVD; ejaculatory duct projecting into cloaca, ED; fold of vascular tissue forming border of urodaeum and proctodaeum, VT; urodaeum, UD; internal vascular body (gefässreichen Korper), VB; internal pudendal artery, PIA; erectile structures in the protodaeum, i.e. lymph fold, L, round fold, RB, and white body, W.

(Lake and El Jack(1964b), British Egg Marketing Board Symposium on Avian Physiology)

conventional massage method of semen collection. The interpretation of observations on the composition of fowl semen and the activity *in vitro* of fowl spermatozoa is complicated by the possibility that *transparent fluid* or urine is present in the semen. Thus, in the fowl, consideration of the significance of erectile cloacal tissues which, conjointly, have been termed the copulatory organ, is pertinent to a discussion of the semen. Nishiyama (1955) and Nishiyama and Ogawa (1961) described how during the erection of the copulatory organ in the fowl the internal vascular bodies (gefässreichen Körper, after Liebe, 1914) generated *transparent fluid,* from the blood plasma, which engorged the lymph folds in the proctodaeum and subsequently escaped through their surface epithelium during ejaculation. The amount of this fluid obtained during collection was extremely variable (Nishiyama, 1961), and was considered analogous to the accessory reproductive fluid of mammals. Lake (1956, 1957 a, b), on the other hand, did not wholly agree with this analogy. Semen can be collected without any contamination from *transparent fluid* when certain precautions are taken.

Nishiyama and Fujishima (1961) demonstrated that *transparent fluid* was ejected into semen collectors, attached over the cloaca of the male, during natural copulation. However, this observation does not prove conclusively that *transparent fluid* is part of the seminal plasma of the fowl, if, as in mammals, semen is defined as the mixture of spermatozoa and fluids that are expelled through the penis into the vagina during copulation. If a semen collector could be placed within the vagina of the hen, its contents after a natural copulation would constitute fowl semen.

Several conflicting observations must be taken into account in a consideration of the definition of fowl semen and of the significance of *transparent fluid* as accessory reproductive fluid. For example, semen can be collected from the males of some breeds of fowl without contamination with *transparent fluid* (Lake, 1957a). The contents of the vas deferens are forcibly ejaculated into the collecting vessel by the application of slight pressure to the engorged ejaculatory ducts, while the *transparent fluid* either forms spontaneously as a drop on the erected copulatory organ (and can be made to fall clear of the collector) or is obtained only by repeated massage and squeezing of the copulatory organ. Kamar (1958) and Tulloch (1962) developed techniques whereby massage of the abdomen caused erection and involuntary ejaculation. The resulting semen was markedly less contaminated with *transparent fluid*, faeces or urine. *Transparent fluid*, and other fluids from the cloaca, are inimical to the survival of spermatozoa *in vitro* (Lake, 1956), probably because they contain (*a*) blood-clotting agents which cause the agglutination of spermatozoa (Nishiyama, 1955) and (*b*) high levels of chloride and calcium derived from the blood plasma. Nishiyama (1952), in describing the characteristics of seminal plasma that contained much *transparent fluid*, drew attention to the presence of granules, blood corpuscles and desquamated cells. These are dubious components of true seminal plasma.

The limited available data on the composition of *transparent fluid* is given in Table I, together with information on male blood plasma from which it is derived. It is clear that in many respects *transparent fluid* is similar in composition to a dialysate of blood plasma. Nishiyama (1957) made an electrophoretic study of the proteins of the *transparent fluid* after a gelatinous mass (presumed to be fibrin) had been removed. There was much less protein in *transparent fluid* (0.4%) than in blood serum (5.1%). The protein fractions were the same in both fluids but there were slight quantitative differences, the most noticeable being a higher amount of albumin in *transparent fluid*.

A comment should be made about the acid phosphomonoesterase activity found in *transparent fluid*. The fluid was collected from normal cocks by further squeezing the copulatory organ after initial ejaculation had taken place in response to massage. Slight contamination by vas deferens fluid took place (Bell and Lake, 1962a); uncontaminated cloacal gland secretion might show a much lower phosphatase activity.

2. The physical and chemical properties of fowl seminal plasma

The composition of the seminal plasma of the fowl has been studied in an attempt to develop methods of prolonged storage of semen *in vitro*. Since spermatozoa survive in the vas deferens for a much longer time than they can be maintained *in vitro*, interest has been directed towards the composition of semen contaminated little if at all with *transparent fluid*. The vas deferens fluid is considered in general to be an isotonic, physiological medium for the spermatozoa, bearing the same relationship to them as the blood plasma does to the red blood corpuscles. But if the frequency of ejaculation is not optimal, increasing numbers of degenerating spermatozoa are found; under these conditions the chemical environment in the vas deferens is not likely to be ideal for the survival of spermatozoa.

In view of the uncertain and variable presence of *transparent fluid*, and sometimes urine, in the sampled semen of the fowl, the available data on the composition of fowl seminal plasma has been divided between Tables II and III. Table III refers to seminal plasma known to be contaminated minimally, if at all, with *transparent fluid*.

A knowledge of the chemical composition of the fluid of the vas deferens could provide, among other things, information on metabolic processes associated with the maturation and functions of the spermatozoa and the functions of the reproductive tract. Metabolic substrates, intermediary metabolites and end-products of metabolism of spermatozoa will all appear in the fluid. Although the vas deferens fluid might be considered as a favourable physiological medium for spermatozoa, it is unlikely that each of its components is intimately concerned with metabolic functions of the spermatozoa themselves (Lake and El Jack, 1964b). Seminal plasma in the vas deferens is not only a secretory product of intact cells, but also contains fragments of cells from the epithelium lining the reproductive tract (Lake, 1957b).

The chemical composition of fowl semen differs in several respects from that of the various mammals which have been studied (Mann, 1964), the differences being caused mainly by the absence both of

7

seminal vesicles and of the prostate gland, and by the shorter epididymis in the bird. In particular, freshly collected fowl semen is almost completely lacking in fructose, citric acid, ergothioneine, inositol, phosphorylcholine and glycerylphosphorylcholine (Tables II, III). All these compounds feature prominently in the semen of mammals.

Several points about the chemical composition and physical properties of the seminal fluids require comment. The freezing point depressions (Table II) of 0.81, 0.64 and 0.63 °C. for fowl semen, and 0.653 °C. for turkey seminal plasma, are large, even allowing for the inclusion of *transparent fluid* in the semen. Brown (1959) considered that his turkey semen samples were contaminated with urine and this may apply, possibly to a lesser extent, to the fowl semen samples. The freezing point depression of fowl vas deferens fluid (Table III) is only 0.593 °C., rather lower than that for blood plasma (Table I), but still greater than that found in mammals (Mann, 1964).

The concentration of uric acid reported in fowl semen in Table II is very high. Its source could be either the vas deferens or the ureters. The large variation between samples, and the relatively small amount of uric acid found in fresh vas deferens fluid (Table III), suggest that some samples of semen were contaminated with urine. The uric acid concentration in blood plasma is about 5.8 mg. per 100 ml. (Levine, Wolfson and Lenel, 1947); *transparent fluid* is derived from the blood, and is therefore unlikely to have been the source of all the uric acid found.

The pH of seminal plasma cited in Table II is higher than that reported for the fluid from the ejaculatory ducts (Table III); this could be partly attributable to the presence of *transparent fluid* (Table I). However, fowl seminal plasma and *transparent fluid* very rapidly become more alkaline *in vitro*, especially if separated from spermatozoa (Wilcox, 1958; Nishiyama and Fujishima, 1963); reported values for pH will therefore be dependent upon conditions of measurement. The great variation in reported values for the pH of fowl semen (6.5–8.5) cited by Wilcox and Shaffner (1957) could, among other things, be due to variable contamination with *transparent fluid* and urine.

Compared with the mammal, the amount of phosphorus in the seminal plasma of the fowl is small, perhaps because the epididymis in the bird is small. Most of the phosphorus in the seminal plasma of mammals is attributable to the large quantity of glycerylphosphorylcholine and phosphorylcholine produced in the extensive epididymis (White and MacLeod, 1963). About 66% of the phosphorus in the seminal plasma from the ejaculatory duct of the fowl is in the form of phospholipid (Table III).

Comparing Tables II and III it is obvious that the bulk of the free carbohydrate which has been reported in fowl seminal plasma consists of glucose, derived from the *transparent fluid*. Ejaculatory duct fluid may contain a small amount of fructose, but no glucose. It is not known whether any free carbohydrate is present in sperm-free vas deferens fluid; the dense concentration of spermatozoa would quickly utilise any free carbohydrate which may be secreted in the vas deferens. An interesting feature of fowl semen is the ability of the spermatozoa to convert glucose to fructose (Lorenz, 1958; Lake, Lorenz and Reiman, 1962; Scott, White and Annison, 1962b): some of the high levels of fructose reported from time to time in fowl semen may be due to this factor, especially if *transparent fluid* is present. The temperature during the collection of semen, and the length of time the semen was held before separation of spermatozoa and fluid, would influence the metabolic rate of the spermatozoa, and hence the conversion of glucose to fructose. Schindler and Scharf (1963) found that there was more fructose in fowl semen collected in the warm than in the cold. King, Isherwood and Mann (1958) found that the amount of sorbitol in seminal plasma of mammals was high when the fructose content was high. However, they reported a relatively high sorbitol concentration in fowl seminal plasma, with little or no fructose present. If the semen in this case contained much *transparent fluid*, sorbitol might have accumulated as a result of the spermatozoa being able to convert glucose to fructose via a pathway involving sorbitol as an intermediate (Lake *et al.*, 1962).

Fowl semen contains anthrone-reactive carbohydrate, other than glucose and fructose; this may be derived from mucoproteins secreted in the epididymal region of the male tract and in the cloaca (Lake, 1957b; Nishiyama and Ogawa, 1961). In view of the paucity of free monosaccharide in fowl seminal plasma, especially that from the vas deferens, future work on the bound carbohydrate might yield new information on the metabolic processes of fowl spermatozoa. Bound sialic acid has been found in the seminal plasma.

Comment should be made on the reporting of 'total reducing sugar' and 'total reducing substances' in semen and seminal plasma of the fowl (Tables II and III). It is possible that all reducing substances, e.g. glucose, fructose, ergothioneine, ascorbic acid, uric acid, glutathione and possibly sulphite were being estimated in each case by the methods used.

The bulk of the non-protein nitrogen of fowl and turkey seminal plasma is contained in free amino acids, chiefly glutamic acid, and in creatine (Lake and MacIndoe, 1959; Goldberg, Pence and Norman, 1961; Chubb and Cooper, 1962; Ahluwahlia, 1963; Graham, Johnson and Fahning, 1964). This contrasts greatly with the mammal. Fowl ejaculatory-duct seminal plasma (i.e. free from *transparent fluid*) contained about 175 mg. non-protein nitrogen per 100 ml.; about 67% was represented by free amino acids, of which nearly 90% was glutamic acid. This amino acid probably plays a large part in the maintenance of the osmotic pressure in fowl semen from the ejaculatory ducts (Lake and El Jack, 1964b). In the vas deferens fluid (Lake and MacIndoe, 1959) only small amounts of glycine, serine, alanine and aspartic acid were found in addition to the large amount of glutamic acid. Thus the bulk of the large variety of amino acids reported by Chubb and Cooper (1962), Ahluwahlia (1963) and Graham *et al.* (1964) may have originated in the *transparent fluid*. Lake (unpublished observations) observed chromatographically a wide range of free amino acids in the blood plasma of cocks, which paralleled those in *transparent fluid*. The relatively large amount of arginine found in seminal plasma (Table II) is interesting; the semen in this case was frozen and thawed prior to the separation of spermatozoa and seminal plasma and some of the arginine may have been derived from damaged spermatozoa. Daly, Mirsky and Ris (1951) found a high content of arginine in protamine-like material extracted from fowl spermatozoa, while Lake and MacIndoe (1959) did not observe any detectable amounts of arginine in freshly collected ejaculatory-duct fluid. The amount of urea reported to be present in fowl seminal plasma is high (Table II) and the significance of the finding obscure; corresponding information for vas deferens fluid is not yet available. The urea could have originated from urine, or, less probably, from spermatozoan breakdown during freezing and thawing. Coulson and Hughes (1930) reported 3.6 to 23 mg., and Davis (1927) 22 mg. urea per 100 ml., in fowl urine. Only about 1.7 mg. urea per 100 ml. was found in chicken blood and blood plasma (Pitts and Korr, 1938; Bell, 1957; Owen and Robinson, 1964), and *transparent fluid* is therefore unlikely to contain appreciable quantities of urea.

The large amount of lactic acid (77 mg. per 100 ml.) reported in seminal plasma (Table II) is probably abnormal as it refers to semen collected at 41 °C., when active glycolysis would occur in the spermatozoa. Schindler and Scharf (1963) reported levels of 27 mg. and 40 mg. lactic acid per 100 ml. of semen collected in the cold and warm respectively. Lake and El Jack (1964a) found 34 mg. per 100 ml. in ejaculatory-duct fluid obtained by collecting semen in the cold and centrifuging off the spermatozoa quickly at the same temperature.

Acid phosphomonoesterase activity in the seminal plasma is high (Wilcox, 1961; Bell and Lake, 1962a, b). In a comparative study including several mammals and the human, the cock was found to have the second highest activity to the human (Bell and Lake, 1962b). The enzyme(s) had different properties from that of the secretion of the prostate gland (Bell and Lake, 1962a), and was shown to be derived mainly from secretions of the vas deferens (Lake, 1962a).

General enzymological studies concerned with the functional metabolic processes of fowl spermatozoa are still lacking, although they would be of inestimable value for future work on the storage of fowl semen *in vitro* and the prolonged survival of spermatozoa in the oviduct. For example, an appreciable amount of 2-oxoglutaric acid has been found in vas deferens fluid, suggesting a possible association with the large quantity of glutamic acid present. Likewise, some of the reported ammonia might also be implicated in such a relationship. Bajpai and Brown (1963) commented on the high transaminase activity in turkey semen but its significance has not been investigated.

A general feature of mammalian seminal plasma is its high content of potassium (Mann, 1964). In poultry, the concentration of potassium is certainly higher in seminal than in blood plasma (Tables I, II and III; Lake and El Jack, 1964a), and is also very high in vas deferens fluid. Since fragments of the epithelial cells lining the vas deferens are discharged into the luminal fluid to become part of the seminal plasma, some of the potassium may have an intracellular source. Takeda (1959; Table III) reported 145 mg. potassium per 100 ml. of vas deferens fluid, which is remarkably high. However, Lake (unpublished observations) found 76 mg. potassium per 100 ml. in sperm-free vas deferens fluid collected by massage, and fluid from the entire vas deferens taken from killed males might contain an overall higher concentration. At present it is not known what effect the frequency of ejaculation (and thus the variation in the proportion of disintegrating spermatozoa in the vas deferens) has on the amount of free potassium in the seminal plasma of the bird. A large amount of potassium (113 mg. per 100 ml.) has been reported in turkey semen

(Brown, 1959; Table II), but some of this may have originated from urine.

The amount of calcium is low in seminal plasma and especially in the vas deferens fluid (Table III). The higher amount shown in Table II is most probably due to the inclusion of *transparent fluid* (Table I), derived from blood plasma. The sodium concentration of *transparent fluid*, vas deferens fluid and blood plasma is virtually the same and remains fairly constant (Tables I, II, III; Lake and El Jack, 1964a). The magnesium concentration in vas deferens fluid (Table III) is several times higher than in blood plasma and, again, some may be intracellular in origin. A most interesting feature of vas deferens fluid is the low chloride content; the role of chief anion is played by glutamate, and not by chloride as in blood plasma (Lake and El Jack, 1964b).

3. *The physical and chemical properties of the fowl spermatozoon*

The density of spermatozoa in fowl semen is high and values reported in the literature are extremely variable (Lake, 1962b), presumably because of the great variation in the amount of *transparent fluid* included in semen samples collected by massage.

Information on the general cytology of fowl spermatozoa has been reviewed by Lorenz (1959) and will not be dealt with here. Data on the chemical composition of spermatozoa themselves are meagre (Table III). However, in the author's laboratory, work is in progress on several aspects of the problem in connection with the development of techniques for storing semen *in vitro*. So far it has been shown that the intracellular concentration of potassium (238 mg. per 100 ml. cells) is high, in agreement with existing general knowledge on cells. A relatively large amount of magnesium (23.3 mg. per 100 ml. cells) is present and is presumably associated with mitochondria in the middlepiece of the spermatozoon. The intracellular calcium level is small but detectable; information about sodium and chloride is as yet incomplete.

Goldberg and Norman (1961) have shown that the fowl spermatozoon possesses the typical complement of cytochromes (a, a3, b and c).

Little information is available on the study of enzyme systems operating in spermatozoan function. Observations on the reduction of methylene blue or resazurin suggest that fowl spermatozoa possess dehydrogenase enzyme activity (Bogdonoff and Shaffner, 1954; Cooper and Rowell, 1958). Swyer (1947) was unable to demonstrate unequivocally the presence of hyaluronidase activity in fowl spermatozoa. In mammalian spermatozoa the enzyme activity is presumed to reside in the acrosome; the reported absence of hyaluronidase in the fowl may be due to technical difficulties in working with the minute acrosome of the fowl spermatozoon. Saeki and Morichi (1959) reported that fowl spermatozoa possessed an enzyme capable of initiating the rupture of the vitelline membrane of the hen's egg. Although it was thought possible that hyaluronidase was the causative agent, the authors emphasized that other unidentified enzymes or substances could have been responsible. It would be of interest to extend these investigations in the light of some recent work of Srivastava, Adams and Hartree (1965), who showed that lipoglycoprotein preparations from acrosomes of ram, rabbit and bull spermatozoa were capable of dispersing the corona radiata of rabbit eggs.

Studies on the incorporation of amino acids into the bull and goat spermatozoon suggested that the acrosome of the mature cell was capable of synthesizing proteins from amino acids (Abraham and Bhargava, 1963; Iype, Abraham and Bhargava, 1963). However, the same authors were unable to demonstrate any incorporation of amino acids in the fowl spermatozoon, which may be related to the fact that the acrosome in the bird is small. The failure of Hartree and Srivastava (1965) to find any sialomucoprotein in fowl spermatozoa, in spite of its presence in the acrosomes of ram, and possibly bull and rabbit, spermatozoa, may also be due to the technical difficulties of working with fowl spermatozoa.

Lake (1962c) reported a preliminary investigation of phosphorus compounds in fowl semen. In Table III the amounts present in the spermatozoa have been corrected for the trapped seminal plasma that would have been present under the particular conditions of centrifugation. The distribution of phosphorus compounds in the fowl spermatozoon is qualitatively similar to that found in the ram spermatozoon (Mann, 1964). However, in the fowl, phospholipid phosphorus accounts for the largest proportion of the total phosphorus next to deoxyribonucleoprotein-phosphorus. Perhaps the phospholipids are relatively more important to the economy of fowl spermatozoa. Unpublished observations have revealed that phospholipids constitute about 70% of the total lipids of fowl spermatozoa. Expressed as percentages of the total phospholipid, the following types have so far been found: phosphatidylinositol 7%, sphingolipid and lysolecithin 13.5%, lecithin 47%, phosphatidylserine 19%, phosphatidylethanolamine 12%, unidentified 1.5%. Plasmalogen forms of the phospholipids were indicated in the sphingolipid and lysolecithin, lecithin, phosphatidylserine and phosphatidylethanolamine fractions.

Ahluwahlia (1963) reported some inositol and erythritol in the spermatozoan fraction of fowl semen (Table II). However, owing to the method of collection of semen the spermatozoan fraction also contained precipitated material from the seminal plasma. Further work is necessary to identify absolutely the part of the semen in which the polyhydric alcohols are contained.

The volume of the fowl spermatozoon ($9.2\mu^3$) given in Table III is a preliminary determination made by Dr. Iversen, Beatty Memorial Hospital, Glasgow, using a Coulter counter. A value of about $11\mu^3$ was obtained mathematically in the author's laboratory, by measuring the length and breadth of a living spermatozoon from projections using a phase-contrast microscope. The thickness of different regions was obtained by interference microscopy (Iversen, 1964), and certain geometrical shapes were assumed for different parts of the spermatozoon. The acrosome was found to form about 2% of the volume of the spermatozoon. The fowl spermatozoon is on the whole smaller than that of domesticated mammals, and its shape is filiform rather than spheroidal. The volume of the bull spermatozoon was found to be $14-17\mu^3$ (Iversen, 1964). The amount of deoxyribonucleic acid per fowl spermatozoon (Mirsky and Ris, 1949; Vendrely, Knobloch and Vendrely, 1956) is about one-third of that in most mammalian spermatozoa (Mann, 1964).

C. STUDIES OF THE FOWL SPERMATOZOON *IN VITRO*

1. Metabolism of the fowl spermatozoon

Studies of the composition of fowl semen and the metabolism of the spermatozoa have revealed several differences from the mammal. Yet the problem of creating the correct conditions for the prolonged survival of fowl spermatozoa *in vitro* is still unsolved and may be complicated by the recent finding of breed differences, both in the metabolic rate of fowl spermatozoa (Goldberg and Norman, 1961), and in the storageability of diluted semen (Wilcox, Shaffner and Wilson, 1961). Discoveries of this nature recall the puzzling observations made by Kosin (1958), who found that the ambient temperature at which turkeys were kept, affected the oxygen uptake of their spermatozoa *in vitro*.

So far little attention has been given to a biochemical study of how the fowl spermatozoon is sustained naturally for such prolonged periods in the oviduct. Nevo (1965) showed that the respiration rate and motility of fowl spermatozoa are optimal in, and unaffected by, oxygen concentrations ranging from 0.6% (4 – 5 mm. Hg. partial pressure) to that of air. Below 0.6% oxygen concentration, there is a sharp reduction in the respiration rate. Aerobic conditions in the hen oviduct (35 mm. Hg. partial pressure of oxygen) would therefore be sufficient to support the maximum respiration and motility of spermatozoa (Nevo, 1965). Ogasawara and Lorenz (1964) showed that extracts of the magnum region of the oviduct stimulated respiration of fowl spermatozoa *in vitro*. Hamner and Williams (1963) suspended spermatozoa in the magnum *in vivo*, and found that afterwards *in vitro* the spermatozoa retained a twofold increase in oxygen uptake compared with controls that had not resided in the oviduct. Recent studies (Bobr, Lorenz and Ogasawara, 1964; Bobr, Ogasawara and Lorenz, 1964; Fujii, 1963; Fujii and Tamura, 1963) have shown that fowl spermatozoa reside for a time after insemination in glandular crypts in the proximal vagina. If the spermatozoa travel periodically from the vaginal region to the upper regions of the oviduct, where fertilization is known to occur, the stimulatory activity of the magnum secretions might well play an important role.

Lorenz (1959, 1964) has reviewed the earlier work on the metabolism of fowl spermatozoa *in vitro*. The spermatozoa are capable of deriving energy from aerobic and anaerobic glycolysis. Glucose, mannose and fructose can be used, and are more rapidly glycolysed under anaerobic conditions; glucose and mannose exert a sparing action on the utilization of fructose. Harris and Wilcox (1962) and Goldberg and Norman (1961) recently confirmed many of these observations, and the latter authors also confirmed the existence of a Pasteur effect in carbohydrate metabolism of fowl spermatozoa. They rightly pointed out the difficulties in appraising the results of different metabolic studies, because of alterations in the metabolism of spermatozoa caused by the composition and pH of suspending media and the act of washing the cells. The variable presence of *transparent fluid* (and thus glucose) in semen collected by massage has also to be borne in mind when assessing experimental results which report the stimulatory or inhibitory effect of various added substrates to fowl spermatozoa *in vitro*. An example of the uncertainty which can arise between working with whole semen or washed spermatozoa was given by Kosin (1944, 1958), who showed that added succinate increased the respiration rate of fowl but not of turkey spermatozoa. He suggested that, in the turkeys, there may have been a surplus of succinate in the semen itself.

De Muelenaere and Quicke (1960) and Wales and White (1961) recently confirmed that the respiration rate of spermatozoa *in vitro* increased, and retention of motility decreased, with increasing dilution of semen *per se*. A calcium-free Ringer-phosphate solution was used in the experiments of De Muelenaere and Quicke. Washing the spermatozoa also decreased their respiration rate.

Van Tienhoven (1960) and Ogasawara and Lorenz (1964) demonstrated that different physiological media and ions had variable effects on the respiration of spermatozoa. Van Tienhoven (1960) also showed that fowl spermatozoa could metabolize glycerol. Wales and Wallace (1964) later demonstrated certain differences from van Tienhoven (1960) in the effect of ions on the metabolism of fowl spermatozoa; potassium raised and magnesium lowered the oxygen uptake whilst phosphate had no effect. Wales and Wallace (1964) used a veronal buffer solution as a basic suspension medium, while van Tienhoven (1960) used various modifications of a phosphate buffer.

Scott, White and Annison (1962a) studied the oxidation of short-chained fatty acids $(C_1 - C_8)$ by the spermatozoa of the fowl and of a few common domestic mammals. Unlike the general trend in mammals, oxygen uptake was greatest in the presence not of acetate but of octanoate. Fowl spermatozoa, however, oxidized acetate, propionate and butyrate equally. These studies were made using a modified Krebs-Ringer phosphate medium which was free from fructose.

In terms of spermatozoan number, the overall metabolic rate of fowl spermatozoa in Krebs-Ringer phosphate was found to be lower than that of several mammals studied (Scott, White and Annison, 1962b). In veronal buffer, the spermatozoa of the cock were also found to have the lowest metabolic rate and lowest rate of fructolysis compared with those of the bull, dog and rabbit. Ogasawara (1957) obtained results which suggested that there was a difference between the metabolism of turkey and fowl spermatozoa under identical conditions; oxygen was consumed faster by turkey spermatozoa.

Oxygen uptake (measured in cubic millilitres of oxygen consumed by 10^8 cells per hour at 37° C.) was found to be 21 mm.[3] (Hamner and Williams, 1963) and 28 mm.[3] (Krenis and Strauss, 1961) for metabolizing rabbit and human leucocytes respectively. For spermatozoa it is considerably lower. For example, Scott et al. (1962b), in agreement with van Tienhoven (1960) and Goldberg and Norman (1961), all of whom used a similar suspending medium containing glucose, found an oxygen uptake of about 2.5 mm.[3] for fowl spermatozoa and between 4 and 8 for the spermatozoa of several mammals studied. Mammalian spermatozoa are larger than those of the fowl; this factor may be involved in the differences in oxygen uptake.

In a comparative study of the glycolytic activities of the spermatozoa of the ram, bull, dog and fowl, it was found that in contrast to the mammals, the oxygen uptake by fowl spermatozoa is only slightly increased in the presence of glucose and acetate, and that the effects of glucose and acetate are additive (Scott et al., 1962b). These workers and Goldberg and Norman (1961) found that oxygen uptake is stimulated slightly more by glucose than acetate.

Goldberg and Norman (1961) compared the respiratory activities of fowl and bull spermatozoa and found that although oxygen uptake for cock spermatozoa was much lower than for the bull, the former had a relatively higher metabolic efficiency than the latter. Metabolic efficiency was a measure of the hexose-sparing ability by efficient energy production and utilization aerobically.

Scott et al. (1962b) found that when washed fowl spermatozoa were incubated aerobically with labelled acetate and glucose there was evidence of a substantial utilization of unlabelled, tricarboxylic acid-cycle intermediates. This contrasts with the situation in several mammals studied, and Scott and his colleagues suggested that endogenous substrates contributed most to the total oxidative metabolism of the fowl spermatozoon. Goldberg and Norman (1961) found that the in vitro oxygen uptake and lactate accumulation by fowl spermatozoa under their conditions were more than sufficient to balance the glucose disappearance in metabolic studies. In view of this observation, these authors investigated the possibility of the utilisation of endogenous phospholipid. They concluded that phospholipid was not used as an energy source since the content of lipid-phosphorus was not reduced after 3 hours' incubation at 37 °C. with or without glucose. However, this does not necessarily imply that phospholipid is not used by fowl spermatozoa. Lake (1962b) obtained preliminary evidence suggesting that the acyl ester portion of phospholipids was removed from fowl spermatozoa during incubation in the presence or absence of sugar. The importance of endogenous lipid to the survival of fowl spermatozoa, both in vitro and in vivo, requires further investigation. From the results of metabolism studies involving the incubation of fowl and mammalian spermatozoa with a mixture of acetate and glucose, Scott *et al.* (1962b) showed that, unlike in several mammals, the oxidation of glucose and acetate is of a non-competitive nature. They suggested that coenzyme A, which is necessary for the oxidation of fatty acids, was possibly not limiting in fowl spermatozoa.

It has already been mentioned that fowl spermatozoa can convert glucose to fructose. Lake *et al.* (1962) suggested that a pathway involving sorbitol may be involved, rather than a process of glucose-6-phosphate isomerization, though the failure to demonstrate breakdown of fructose-6-phosphate by fowl spermatozoa could be explained by the inability of the compound to get into the cell. Scott *et al.* (1962b) suggested that the oxidative pentose-shunt pathway was not operating in the conversion of glucose to fructose.

Lake and MacIndoe (1959) found a large amount of free glutamic acid in fowl seminal plasma; this was confirmed by Chubb and Cooper (1962), Goldberg *et al.* (1961), Ahluwahlia (1963) and Graham *et al.* (1964). El Zayat and van Tienhoven (1961a) demonstrated that glutamate was catabolized by fowl spermatozoa; glycine was also used, but to a much smaller extent. When glutamate replaced chloride in a Tyrode's solution the respiration rate of spermatozoa was depressed; glutamate and glycine both depressed fructolysis. The fact that respiration was depressed does not necessarily imply that the spermatozoa lost their functional capacity; El Zayat and van Tienhoven (1961b) demonstrated that replacing chloride by glutamate or phosphate in a Tyrode solution reduced the formation of visually abnormal spermatozoa during *in vitro* storage.

Some interesting information, with possible far-reaching implications in work on the storage of semen, has recently been obtained concerning the effect of light on the metabolism of spermatozoa. Norman *et al.* (1962) showed that fowl spermatozoa could be made infertile by exposing them to 9,000 ft. c. of light for 4 hours. The presence of catalase or anaerobic conditions lessened the harmful effects of light, whilst oxygen enhanced them. Hamner and Williams (1961) and Williams and Hamner (1963) investigated the effect of light on the respiration of fowl spermatozoa *in vitro*, and demonstrated that light greatly increased their oxygen uptake. Cock spermatozoa doubled their respiration rate on exposure to light, but unlike mammals they had an appreciable oxygen uptake even in the dark. (This may, however, have been due to their immersion in Tyrode solution, whereas the spermatozoa of man and the rabbit were suspended in Krebs-Ringer phosphate solution.)

Goldberg and Norman (1961) were unable to state unequivocally that the cytochrome system served as a major terminal oxidative pathway in fowl spermatozoa or that it was functional in respiratory metabolism. Indirect evidence of the occurrence of oxidative phosphorylation, which is usually associated with cytochrome activity, was obtained after studying the effect of 2, 4-dinitrophenol on fowl spermatozoa (Norman *et al.*, 1960). Ubiquinones, especially ubiquinone-10, were effective in stimulating the respiration of cock spermatozoa (Williams and Hamner, 1963), possibly by affecting the electron transport system and uncoupling oxidative phosphorylation.

2. *Physical and chemical conditions affecting the functional survival of fowl spermatozoa in vitro*

Semen diluents, ideally, should provide optimal physical and chemical conditions for the indefinite *in vitro* maintenance of the fertilizing capacity of fowl spermatozoa. Many studies have been made in order to establish these conditions for the purposes of artificial insemination in poultry. Lorenz (1959, 1964) has described the earlier work, which showed the effect on the survival of spermatozoa of dilution *per se*, and of various physiological saline solutions. New work on the use of metabolic inhibitors (Blackwood and Harris, 1960; Harris, Wilcox and Shaffner, 1961) was also described.

Recently Wilcox and Clark (1962) and Harris and Hobbs (1964) have obtained evidence showing that four- to five-fold dilution of fowl semen is optimal for the survival of spermatozoa *in vitro*. This is a much lower dilution rate than that used for bull semen.

Various investigations have been made to determine whether fowl spermatozoa, like certain mammalian spermatozoa, are adversely affected by a rapid fall in temperature (cold-shock) when they are collected from the male. Wales and White (1959) showed that fowl spermatozoa could withstand rapid transfer to low temperatures (0 °C.) and high temperatures (55 °C.), as judged by their subsequent morphology. However, their fertilizing power and storage potential might have been impaired by such treatment. Recently Bajpai and Brown (1964), working with turkeys, collected semen normally and then held samples for ten minutes at different temperatures (0° to 25 °C.). Subsequent fertility tests suggested that spermatozoa suffered adverse effects at temperatures above and below 15 °C. There may be an optimum temperature under the conditions of storage, at which metabolic processes can just continue to provide sufficient energy to maintain the integrity of cell functions. Higher temperatures may result in the accumulation of metabolic by-products and the death of the cell.

In the previous section reference was made to work which showed that different ions had different effects on the metabolism of fowl spermatozoa *in vitro*. Several recent observations have been made on the effect of certain ions on the retention of motility of spermatozoa *in vitro*. Unlike the situation with the bull and ram, calcium ions were beneficial in maintaining motility of diluted fowl spermatozoa, but a concentration in excess of 1.2 mg. per 100 ml. caused agglutination of the spermatozoa (Wales and White, 1958a). This may explain the agglutinating effect on spermatozoa *in vitro* of *transparent fluid*, which has a much higher calcium content than vas deferens fluid. Since there is a possibility of contamination by urine during the collection of fowl semen, it is of interest that ammonium ions in excess of 8.5 mg. per 100 ml. decreased the motility of fowl spermatozoa, but did not affect those of certain mammals (Wales and White, 1958a). Potassium ions were beneficial to the survival of mammalian spermatozoa *in vitro*, in counteracting the deleterious effects of dilution *per se* (Wales and White, 1958a, 1961). The same authors demonstrated that potassium influenced the motility of fowl spermatozoa, and during the dilution of semen proved beneficial up to a concentration of about 45 mM. Potassium in excess of 180 mM. caused a decline in motility. These levels of potassium were far in excess of those investigated by van Tienhoven (1960) in respiration studies.

Fowl spermatozoa are more tolerant of hypertonic media than are those of mammals (Wales and White, 1958b), which is consistent with the natural body fluids of the bird having a greater freezing-point depression than in the mammal. It is difficult to assess the significance of pH and osmotic pressure in defining a suitable diluent for fowl spermatozoa. Wales and White (1958b) showed that fowl spermatozoa were motile between pH 5 and pH 10, with an optimum of pH 7. At high pH, sodium chloride became toxic to the cells; replacing it with glucose allayed the effect. Wilcox (1959a), using a phosphate medium, showed that varying the pH between 6.5 and 7.8 had little effect on fertility of semen; these observations were substantially in agreement with those of Wilcox and Shaffner (1957), who showed that fertility was maintained satisfactorily between pH 6.47 and 7.95, with an optimum between 7.03 and 7.27.

Hobbs and Harris (1963a), working with citrate buffers, found that at least for 24 hours' storage *in vitro*, solutions of pH 6 to 7 with a freezing point depression ($\triangle$) of 0.79 °C. were optimal for retaining the fertility of fowl spermatozoa. There appear to be differences between the survival requirements of turkey and fowl spermatozoa when stored in phosphate buffers, as Wilcox and Shaffner (1960) obtained poor results with turkey semen using methods previously found suitable for fowl semen (Wilcox and Shaffner, 1958; Wilcox, 1960). Harris *et al.* (1963) investigated citrate buffers and sodium bicarbonate, with and without gassing with carbon dioxide, for turkey semen storage; they achieved the best results in a medium with an osmotic pressure corresponding to $\triangle 0.91$ °C. This contrasted with studies on fowl spermatozoa (Hobbs and Harris, 1963a), where suspension and storage in a sodium citrate solution of $\triangle 0.79$ °C. gave good fertility results; even better were obtained in a solution of $\triangle 1.06$ °C. gassed with carbon dioxide (Hobbs and Harris, 1963b). Harris and Hobbs (1964) made an interesting, but puzzling, observation concerning the air space needed in containers in which semen was stored. In citrate-sodium bicarbonate diluents, gassed with carbon dioxide, there was an optimal size of air space for the retention of good fertilizing power; this was dependent upon the extent of dilution of the semen and upon the concentration of carbon dioxide. The implications of this phenomenon in all storage procedures might profitably be explored in the future. Yamane, Tsukunaga and Takahashi (1962) claimed reasonable fertility after storage of fowl semen in an egg yolk-citrate-glucose mixture with a freezing point depression of 1.03 °C. Saeki (1963) obtained good fertility after suspending semen in a simple saline diluent ($\triangle 0.61$ °C.) in the spring months of the year. Saline solutions of greater hypertonicity were apparently required when semen was taken in the autumn and centrifuged to free the spermatozoa from seminal plasma. Schindler and Nevo (1962) demonstrated that carbon dioxide reversibly inactivated fowl spermatozoa in semen diluted tenfold by Ringer's solution or seminal plasma.

Wilcox and Shaffner (1958) and Wilcox (1959b) showed that greatly improved fertility was obtained if fowl spermatozoa after storage *in vitro* in a phosphate buffer were resuspended, immediately prior to insemination, in a solution containing fructose. The addition of potassium (0.004 M.) or magnesium (0.001 M.) to the fructose did not further improve fertility (Wilcox, 1959a). Thus the requirements of the spermatozoa for survival *in vitro* may, under certain circumstances, be different from those enabling them to negotiate the first part of their life in the oviduct after storage. An ideal diluent may have to satisfy both needs.

Wilcox and Wilson (1961), El Zayat and van Tienhoven (1961b) and Lake (1960) obtained evidence which suggested that chloride can be harmful to the survival of fowl spermatozoa *in vitro*. It may be significant that the chloride concentration in vas deferens fluid is about one-third of that in blood plasma and *transparent fluid* (Lake and El Jack, 1964a).

Bull spermatozoa can oxidatively deaminate certain amino acids with the production of hydrogen peroxide (Tosic, 1951), which adversely affects their metabolism. No similar studies have been made with fowl spermatozoa. However, Wales, White and Lamond (1959) have shown that hydrogen peroxide *in vitro* affects the motility of fowl and bull spermatozoa more adversely than those of the dog, ram, rabbit or man. Fowl seminal plasma is devoid of catalase activity; if fowl spermatozoa produce hydrogen peroxide as a by-product of metabolism, this could be important in storage studies.

Antibiotics are often added to suspensions of spermatozoa *in vitro* to prevent the growth and accumulation of microorganisms. This is more important with the fowl than with the mammal, because of the greater chance of contamination with cloacal contents during the collection of semen (De Muelenaere and Quicke, 1958b; Gale and Brown, 1961; Hashimoto, 1964). Several investigators have studied the effects of various bactericidal compounds on the retention of fertility and motility of fowl spermatozoa (De Muelenaere and Quicke, 1958b; Wilcox and Shorb, 1958; Wales and White, 1960). There is general agreement that, unlike in mammals, penicillin and sulphanilamide adversely affect metabolism and fertilizing power. A mixture of oxytetracycline and dihydrostreptomycin appears to be the most useful combination for use with fowl spermatozoa. Similar results were obtained with turkey spermatozoa (Gale and Brown, 1961). Wilcox (1959c) showed that the beneficial effect of oxytetracycline in preserving the fertilizing power *in vitro* was not related to its antibacterial properties. He suggested that it acted by chelating harmful cations in the suspending medium. It might also have chelated calcium and magnesium ions, thus slowing down metabolic processes and extending the life of the spermatozoa. Auger and Wilcox (1964) investigated the effects of different anions (borate, citrate, glycine, glutamate, phosphate, tartrate) on the motility and fertilizing capacity of fowl spermatozoa stored *in vitro* for 72 hours, and found that borate and glycine did not sustain fertility. Tartrate was the best anion for retaining fertility; the addition of oxytetracycline and dihydrostreptomycin to the tartrate, glutamate and citrate diluents improved fertility, particularly with the latter two diluents.

D. CONCLUSIONS

It is possible to store bull semen successfully *in vitro* for several years at sub-zero temperatures, and for at least a week at 5 °C. However, work with other species of domesticated mammals, e.g. horse, pig and sheep, has not met with the same degree of success.

Within the last decade an increased amount of information has accumulated on the metabolism of fowl spermatozoa and the physical and chemical conditions which affect their survival *in vitro*. An ideal synthetic medium (diluent) and suitable physical conditions for maintaining the life of the spermatozoa *in vitro* for prolonged periods has not yet been found. The spermatozoa of poultry are normally able to live in the oviduct for several days (fowl) or weeks (turkey); this raises an important point in comparing the results achieved in storing bull and fowl semen *in vitro*. Bull spermatozoa can be stored for several years, but afterwards they are only required to survive in the oviduct for a few hours to effect fertilization. At present, similar results could be achieved with fowl semen stored for about one week, but the normal phenomenon whereby a succession of eggs in each hen is fertilized after a single insemination would not occur. Semen storage experiments with the fowl are not considered wholly successful unless this pattern of fertility can be achieved in each hen.

One problem in applying the results of laboratory studies on semen dilution and storage to practical poultry breeding is the likelihood of fowl semen being contaminated with urine and even faeces. In endeavouring to obtain the maximum amount of semen from males, extremely variable amounts of *transparent fluid* may be obtained and this will adversely affect the prolonged survival of spermatozoa *in vitro*.

Inseminations are carried out at frequent intervals (e.g. weekly) in poultry breeding. This raises two interesting points for consideration in the future. First, large amounts of *transparent fluid*, derived directly from blood plasma, are often included in fowl semen; if the vagina of the hen is permeable to such fluid, the possibility of immunological reactions affecting fertility might have to be considered. Secondly, synthetic diluents must be of such a composition that they do not disturb the environment in the oviduct where the spermatozoa are deposited, otherwise storage of spermatozoa in the female might be impaired.

TABLE I. Chemical composition and physical properties of *transparent fluid* and blood plasma of the domestic cock. Results are average values expressed in mg. per 100 ml. unless otherwise stated. Data to which no reference is given are as yet unpublished.

Constituent or property	Transparent fluid	Blood plasma	Reference number
Freezing point depression (°C.)	0.63	—	—
	—	0.6	1
pH	7.9	—	2
	7.5	—	3
	—	7.7	3
Calcium	8.8	11.1 (serum)	7
	—	11.4	1
Magnesium	2.88	—	—
	—	2.3	1
Sodium	369	—	—
	338.5	341.4 (serum)	7
	—	385	1
Potassium	19.3	17.6 (serum)	7
	—	22	1
Chloride	476.8	—	—
	—	430	1
Protein	0.4 gm. (defibrinated)	5 gm.	4
Glucose	202	252	5
Fructose	4	—	5
Total reducing substances	124	—	—
Acid phosphomonoesterase* ..	1620–5800	5	6
Alkaline phosphomonoesterase* ..	20–40	43	6
Lactic acid	23	—	5
	—	49.8	1
2-oxo-glutaric acid	—	1.8	1
Pyruvic acid	—	3.9	1

*Units of activity are expressed as mg. 4-nitrophenol liberated by 100 ml. of plasma in 60 min. at 37°C. in the appropriate buffer system.

1, Lake and El Jack (1964a); 2, Nishiyama (1952); 3, Nishiyama and Fujishima (1963); 4, Nishiyama (1957); 5, Schindler and Scharf (1963); 6, Bell and Lake (1962a); 7, Takeda (1959).

TABLE II. Chemical composition and physical properties of fowl and turkey semen containing variable amounts of *transparent fluid*. Results are average values (range in brackets) expressed in mg. per 100 ml. unless otherwise stated.

Constituent or property	Whole semen Fowl	Seminal plasma Fowl	Seminal plasma Turkey	Reference number
Freezing point depression (°C.)	—	—	0.653	1
	0.64	—	—	2
	0.81	—	—	28
	—	0.63	—	3
pH	—	7.2	—	4
	—	7.6	—	5
Calcium	—	8.4	—	27
Sodium	—	341	—	27
	—	—	338	1
Potassium	—	29.7	—	27
	—	—	113	1
Phosphorus, Total	44	—	—	6
Total acid-soluble ..	27	—	—	6
Phosphagens	—	Nil	—	11
Phosphorylcholine	Detected chromatographically	—	—	13
Glycerylphosphorylcholine ..	15 (0–40)	—	—	14
	Nil	—	—	13
Protein	1.82 gm.	0.93 gm.	—	7
	2.8 gm.	0.7 gm.	—	8
Nitrogen, Total	593	256	—	8
Total non-protein ..	149	141	—	8
Total protein ..	444	115	—	8
Ammonia	2	—	—	6
	7.5 (1.5–17.0)	—	—	9
	—	3.3	Nil	10
Urea	9.1 (1.8–22.5)	—	—	9
	—	29	4.5	10
Uric acid	40.5 (10.1–88.2)	37.5 (4–85.3)	—	9
Creatine	—	41	—	11
AMINO ACIDS:				
Glutamic acid	—	1178	958	10
	—	407	—	12
Aspartic acid	—	3	12.9	10
Alanine	—	4	7	10
Glycine	—	9.7	Nil	10
Asparagine/Glutamine ..	—	11	15	10
Serine	—	2	18	10
Arginine ..	—	18	—	11
	—	18.5	10.7	10
Threonine	—	11	6.6	10
Lysine	—	2.5	12.8	10
Valine	—	3.1	4.0	10
Isoleucine	—	Trace	Nil	10
Leucine	—	3.4	Trace	10
Histidine ..	—	3.5	Nil	10
Tyrosine ..	—	5.4	Trace	10
Ornithine ..	—	Trace	Trace	10
Phenylalanine	—	Nil	Trace	10
Methionine	—	11	Trace	10
Tryptophane	—	Nil	Nil	10
Taurine	—	5.3	Nil	10
Ethanolamine	—	Nil	1.1	10
Sialic acid (bound)	—	11.5	—	15
Volatile fatty acids (as acetic acid)	3	—	—	16
Glycerol	Nil (in spermatozoa)	2.8	—	17
Total reducing sugar	35	133	—	18
Total anthrone-reactive carbohydrate	57	—	—	6

TABLE II. (Contd.)

Constituent or property	Whole semen Fowl	Seminal plasma Fowl	Seminal plasma Turkey	Reference number
Total reducing substances ..	—	38 (0–125)	—	19
Glucose	(7.7–81)	—	—	6
	92	—	—	20
	—	108	—	18
Fructose	4	—	—	20
	—	2	4	21
Sorbitol	—	10	—	22
Inositol	16 (in 100 ml. spermatozoa)	20	—	17
Erythritol	9 (in 100 ml. spermatozoa)	Trace	—	17
Lactic acid	27 (13–34), 40	—	—	20
	—	77.4	—	19
Citric acid	Nil	—	—	14
Acid phosphomonoesterase* ..	—	(8,729–11, 732)	—	23
Alkaline phosphomonoesterase*	—	(29–46)	—	23
Catalase	—	Nil	—	24
N-amidinophosphokinase ..	—	Nil	—	11
Hyaluronidase	Nil or uncertain activity	—	—	25
Cytochromes a, a3, b and c ..	Present in spermatozoa	—	—	26

*Units of activity are expressed as mg. 4-nitrophenol liberated by 100 ml. of plasma in 60 min. at 37 °C. in the appropriate buffer system.

1, Brown (1959); 2, Schindler et al. (1955); 3, El Zayat and van Tienhoven (1961b); 4, Nishiyama (1952); 5, Wales and White (1958b); 6, Mann (1954); 7, Wales et al. (1961); 8, Pytasz and Klymiuk (1961); 9, Klymiukowna et al. (1960); 10, Graham et al. (1964); 11, White and Griffiths (1958); 12, Goldberg et al. (1961); 13, Dawson et al. (1957); 14, White and MacLeod (1963); 15, Hartree and Srivastava (1965); 16, Scott et al. (1961); 17, Ahluwahlia (1963); 18, De Muelenaere and Quicke (1958a); 19, Schindler et al. (1958); 20, Schindler and Scharf (1963); 21, Lorenz (1959); 22, King et al. (1958); 23, Wilcox (1961); 24, Wales et al. (1959); 25, Swyer (1947); 26, Goldberg and Norman (1961); 27, Takeda (1959); 28, Saeki (1963).

TABLE III. Chemical composition and physical properties of fresh fowl semen collected by massage. The seminal plasma contains little or no *transparent fluid*. Results are average values (range in brackets) expressed in mg. per 100 ml. plasma or spermatozoa unless otherwise stated. Data to which no reference is given are as yet unpublished.

Constituent or property	Spermatozoa	Seminal plasma	Reference number
Volume of spermatozoon ..	$9.2\mu^3$	—	12
Freezing point depression (°C.)	—	0.593	1
pH	—	7.0	—
Water content	—	96.4%	—
Specific gravity ..	—	1.011	—
Carbon dioxide (HCO_3^-) ..	—	119.6	2
Calcium	—	3.2 (2.1–4.1)	11
	—	4.2	1
Magnesium..	—	6.1	1
Sodium	—	294 (270–316)	11
	—	383	1

TABLE III. (Contd.)

Constituent or property	Spermatozoa	Seminal plasma	Reference number
Potassium	—	145 (109–188)	11
	—	50	1
Copper	—	0.032	7
Zinc	—	0.186 (0.06–1.7)	7
Iron	—	0.12	—
Chloride	—	132	1
Phosphorus, total	1566	7.5	4
total acid-soluble	173	2.4	4
apparent inorganic	51.8	1.5	4
true inorganic ..	24.0	—	4
lipid	216	5.0	4
deoxyribonucleic acid	1112	—	4
Protein	—	0.8 gm.	—
Nitrogen, total	—	360 (290–480)	—
total non-protein ..	—	160	3
Uric acid	—	7.8	—
Creatine	—	92	3
Glutamic acid, free	—	1068	3
Deoxyribonucleic acid ..	1.1×10^{-9} mg. per cell	—	8
	1.26×10^{-9} mg. per cell	—	9
Sialic acid (bound)	—	12	—
Total reducing substances ..	—	45	5
Glucose	—	Nil	6
Fructose	—	Nil	5
Sorbitol	—	Detected chromato-graphically	—
Inositol	—	10	—
Ascorbic acid	—	3	5
Ergothioneine	—	2	5
Lactic acid	—	34	1
Citric acid	—	Nil	7
Pyruvic acid	—	2.9	1
2-oxo-glutaric acid	—	21	1
Acid phosphomonoesterase* ..	—	15,000	10
Alkaline phosphomonoesterase*	—	37	10

*Units of activity are expressed as mg. 4-nitrophenol liberated by 100 ml. of plasma in 60 min. at 37°C. in the appropriate buffer system.

1, Lake and El Jack (1964a); 2, Lake and El Jack (1964b); 3, Lake and MacIndoe (1959); 4, Lake (1962c); 5, Lorenz (1959); 6, Lake (1957a); 7, Lake et al. (1958); 8, Vendrely et al. (1956); 9, Mirsky and Ris (1949); 10, Bell and Lake (1962a); 11, Takeda (1959); 12, Iversen (unpublished).

118   P. E. LAKE

REFERENCES

Abraham, K. A. and Bhargava, P. S. (1963) The uptake of radioactive amino acids by spermatozoa; the intracellular site of incorporation into proteins. *Biochem. J.*, **86**, 308–13.

Ahluwahlia, B. S. (1963) *Some biochemical aspects of fowl semen.* Ph.D. Thesis, University of Minnesota.

Auger, H. V. and Wilcox, F. H. (1964) The effect of various anions on the fertilizing capacity of fowl spermatozoa. *Poult. Sci.*, **43**, 834–9.

Bajpai, P. K. and Brown, K. I. (1963) The effect of some diluents on semen characteristics of turkeys. *Poult. Sci.*, **42**, 882–8.

Bajpai, P. K. and Brown, K. I. (1964) The effect of different temperatures on the metabolic activity, morphology and fertilizing capacity of turkey semen. *Poult. Sci.*, **43**, 1501–8.

Bell, D. J. (1957) Tissue components of the domestic fowl, 2. Blood urea. *Biochem. J.*, **67**, 33–6.

Bell, D. J. and Lake, P. E. (1962a) Tissue components of the domestic fowl, 5. Phosphomonoesterases in the seminal plasma of the cock. *Biochem. J.*, **82**, 277–81.

Bell, D. J. and Lake, P. E. (1962b) A comparison of phosphomonoesterase activities in the seminal plasmas of the domestic cock, turkey, tom, boar, bull, buck rabbit and of man. *J. Reprod. Fertil.*, **3**, 363–8.

Blackwood, U. B. and Harris, G. C. (1960) Reversible inhibition of 2, 5-alkyl benzimidazoles in chicken sperm. *Proc. Soc. exp. Biol. N.Y.*, **103**, 60–3.

Bobr, L. W., Lorenz, F. W. and Ogasawara, F. X. (1964) Distribution of spermatozoa in the oviduct and fertility in domestic birds. I. Residence sites of spermatozoa in fowl oviducts. *J. Reprod. Fertil.*, **8**, 39–47.

Bobr, L. W., Ogasawara, F. X. and Lorenz, F. W. (1964) Distribution of spermatozoa in the oviduct and fertility in domestic birds. II. Transport of spermatozoa in the fowl oviduct. *J. Reprod. Fertil.*, **8**, 49–58.

Bogdonoff, P. D. and Shaffner, C. S. (1954) The effect of pH on *in vitro* survival, metabolic activity and fertilizing capacity of chicken semen. *Poult. Sci.*, **33**, 665–9.

Brown, K. I. (1959) Electrolyte composition and freezing point depression of turkey seminal fluid. *Poult. Sci.*, **38**, 804–6.

Chubb, L. G. and Cooper, D. M. (1962) Amino acids in fowl seminal plasma. *J. Reprod. Fertil.*, **4**, 7–12.

Cooper, D. M. and Rowell, J. G. (1958) Relations between fertility, embryonic survival and some semen characteristics in the chicken. *Poult. Sci.*, **37**, 699–707.

Coulson, E. J. and Hughes, J. S. (1930) Collection and analysis of chicken urine. *Poult. Sci.*, **10**, 53–8.

Daly, M. M., Mirsky, A. E. and Ris, H. (1951) The amino acid composition and some properties of histones. *J. Gen. Physiol.*, **34**, 439–50.

Davis, R. E. (1927) The nitrogenous constituents of hen urine. *J. biol. Chem.*, **74**, 509–513.

Dawson, R. M. D., Mann, T. and White, I. G. (1957) Glycerylphosphorylcholine and phosphorylcholine in semen, and their relation to choline. *Biochem. J.*, **65**, 627–634.

De Muelenaere, H. J. H. and Quicke, G. V. (1958a) Studies on the biochemistry of cock semen. 1. Seminal sugars. *S. Afr. J. Agric. Sci.*, **1**, 67–74.

De Muelenaere, H. J. H. and Quicke, G. V. (1958b) Studies on the biochemistry of cock semen. 2. The problem of bacterial contamination. *S. Afr. J. Agric, Sci.*, **1**, 139–149.

De Muelenaere, H. J. H. and Quicke, G. V. (1960) Studies on the biochemistry of cock semen. 4. Respiration studies. *S. Afr. J. Agric. Sci.*, 3, 281–6.

El Zayat, S. and van Tienhoven, A. (1961a) Effect of glutamate and glycine on cock sperm metabolism. *Proc. Soc. exp. Biol. N.Y.*, 106, 803–6.

El Zayat, S. and van Tienhoven, A. (1961b) Effect of chloride ions on cock spermatozoa. *Amer. J. Physiol.*, 200, 819–823.

Fujii, S. (1963) Histological and histochemical studies on the oviduct of the domestic fowl with special reference to the region of uterovaginal juncture. *Arch. Histol. Japan*, 23, 447–459.

Fujii, S. and Tamura, T. (1963) Location of sperms in the oviduct of the domestic fowl with special reference to storage of sperms in the vaginal gland. *J. Fac. Fish. An. Husb. Hiroshima Univ.*, 5, 145–163.

Gale, C. and Brown, K. I. (1961) The identification of bacteria contaminating collected semen and the use of antibiotics in their control. *Poult. Sci.*, 40, 50–5.

Goldberg, E. and Norman, C. (1961) The metabolism of ejaculated spermatozoa from the fowl. *J. Cell. Comp. Physiol.*, 58, 175–180.

Goldberg, E., Pence, V. W. and Norman, C. (1961) The distribution of free amino acids in cock and bull seminal plasma and spermatozoa. *Amer. Zool.*, 1, 356 (Abstr.).

Graham, E. F., Johnson, L. A. and Fahning, M. L. (1964) A comparison of the free amino acids in seminal plasma of the bull, boar, cock, turkey and uterine fluids of the cow during oestrous. *Proc. Vth Internat. Congr. Anim. Reprod. and A.I. Trento*, Sec. III. 381–6.

Hamner, C. E. and Williams, W. L. (1961) The effect of light on the respiration of spermatozoa. *Biochem. Biophys. Res. Comm.*, 5, 316–9.

Hamner, C. E. and Williams, W. L. (1963) Effect of the female reproductive tract on sperm metabolism in the rabbit and fowl. *J. Reprod. Fertil.*, 5, 143–150.

Harris, G. C. and Hobbs, T. D. (1964) The effects of fluid to gas ratio, dilution rate, and CO_2 level on the fertilizing capacity of chicken spermatozoa stored in carbon dioxide extenders. *Poult. Sci.*, 43, 529–534.

Harris, G. C., Hobbs, T. D., Brown, J. E. and Warren, L. B. (1963) The storage of turkey spermatozoa in sodium citrate and carbon dioxide extenders. *Poult. Sci.*, 42, 536–8.

Harris, G. C. and Wilcox, F. H. (1962) The carbohydrate metabolism of chicken semen. *Poult. Sci.*, 41, 409–416.

Harris, G. C., Wilcox, F. H. and Shaffner, C. S. (1961) The storage of chicken and turkey spermatozoa by inhibition with 2-ethyl-5-methyl-benzimidazole (EBM). *Poult. Sci.*, 40, 777–81.

Hartree, E. F. and Srivastava, P. N. (1965) Chemical composition of the acrosomes of ram spermatozoa. *J. Reprod. Fertil.*, 9, 47–60.

Hashimoto, H. (1964) Comparison of bacterial contamination in fowl semen with various collecting methods. *J. Fac. Fish. An. Husb. Hiroshima Univ.*, 5, 545–50.

Hobbs, T. D. and Harris, G. C. (1963a) Effect of freezing point depression and pH on motility and fertility of chicken spermatozoa stored in sodium citrate extenders. *Poult. Sci.*, 42, 254–9.

Hobbs, T. D. and Harris, G. C. (1963b) Effect of freezing point depression and CO_2 on motility and fertility of chicken spermatozoa stored in carbon dioxide extenders. *Poult. Sci.*, 42, 388–93.

Iversen, S. (1964) Surface reflexion interference microscopy of bull spermatozoa. *Quart. J. Micr. Sci.*, 105, 245–6.

Iype, P. T., Abraham, K. A. and Bhargava, P. M. (1963) Further evidence for a positive role of acrosome in the uptake of labelled amino acids by bovine and avian spermatozoa. *J. Reprod. Fertil.*, 5, 151–8.

120   P. E. LAKE

Kamar, G. A. R. (1958) The collection of cock's semen without milking the copulatory organ. *Poult. Sci.*, **37**, 1382–5.

King, T. E., Isherwood, F. A. and Mann, T. (1958) Sorbitol in semen. *Proc. IV Internat. Congr. Biochem. Vienna.* 77.

Klymiukowna, B., Olbrychtowa, F. and Pytasz, M. (1960) Ammonia, urea and uric acid in the semen of the domestic fowl. *Med. wet.*, **16**, 547–9.

Kosin, I. L. (1944) Some aspects of the biological action of X-rays on cock spermatozoa. *Physiol. Zool.*, **17**, 289–319.

Kosin, I. L. (1958) Metabolism of turkey semen as affected by the environment of donor birds. *Poult. Sci.*, **37**, 376–388.

Krenis, L. J. and Strauss, B. (1961) Effect of size and concentration of latex particles on respiration of human blood leucocytes. *Proc. Soc. exp. Biol. N.Y.*, **107**, 748–750.

Lake, P. E. (1956) A retarding factor in the problem of fowl semen storage. *Proc. III Internat. Congr. Anim. Reprod. & A.I. Cambridge.* Sec. 3. 104–106.

Lake, P. E. (1957a) Fowl semen as collected by the massage method. *J. Agric. Sci.* **49**, 120–6.

Lake, P. E. (1957b) The male reproductive tract of the fowl. *J. Anat. Lond.*, **91**, 116–129.

Lake, P. E. (1960) Studies on the dilution and storage of fowl semen. *J. Reprod. Fertil.*, **1**, 30–5.

Lake, P. E. (1962a) Histochemical demonstration of phosphomonoesterase secretion in the genital tract of the domestic cock. *J. Reprod. Fertil.*, **3**, 356–362.

Lake, P. E. (1962b) Artificial Insemination in Poultry. In *The semen of animals and artificial insemination.* Ed. J. R. Maule. Chap. 19, 331–356. Commonwealth Agric. Bureaux, England.

Lake, P. E. (1962c) Phosphorus compounds in fowl spermatozoa. *Proc. XII World's Poult. Congr.*, 105–8.

Lake, P. E., Butler, E. J., McCallum, J. W. and MacIntyre, I. J. (1958) A chemical analysis of the seminal and blood plasmas of the cock. *Quart. J. exp. Physiol.*, **43**, 309–313.

Lake, P. E. and El Jack, M. H. (1964a) Further observations on the chemical composition of the seminal plasma of the domestic cock. *Proc. Vth Internat. Congr. Anim. Reprod. and A.I. Trento.* Sec. II. 359–363.

Lake, P. E. and El Jack, M. H. (1964b) The origin and composition of fowl semen. *B.E.M.B. Symposium on Avian Physiology* (in press).

Lake, P. E., Lorenz, F. W. and Reiman, W. D. (1962) Further investigations of the carbohydrate metabolism of cock spermatozoa. *Nature. Lond.*, **194**, 545–7.

Lake, P. E. and MacIndoe, W. M. (1959) The glutamic acid and creatine content of cock seminal plasma. *Biochem. J.*, **71**, 303–6.

Levine, R., Wolfson, W. Q. and Lenel, R. (1947) Concentration and transport of true urate in the plasma of the azotemic chicken. *Amer. J. Physiol.*, **151**, 186–191.

Liebe, W. (1914) Das männliche Begattungsorgan der Hausente. *Jen. Zeitschr. Naturwiss.*, **51**, 627–696.

Lorenz, F. W. (1958) Carbohydrate metabolism of cock spermatozoa. *Nature, Lond.*, **182**, 397–8.

Lorenz, F. W. (1959) Reproduction in the Domestic Fowl: Physiology of the Male. In *Reproduction in Domestic Animals.* Ed. H. H. Cole and P. T. Cupps. Vol. 2. 343–398. Academic Press, Inc. New York.

Lorenz, F. W. (1964) Recent research on fertility and artificial insemination of domestic birds. *Proc. Vth Internat. Congr. Anim. Reprod. and A.I. Trento.* Sec. III. 7–32.

Mann, T. (1954) *The Biochemistry of Semen.* Methuen and Co. Ltd., London.

Mann, T. (1964) *Biochemistry of Semen and of the Male Reproductive Tract.* Methuen and Co. Ltd., London.

Mirsky, A. E. and Ris, H. (1949) Variable and constant components of chromosomes. *Nature, Lond.*, 163, 666–7.

Nevo, A. C. (1965) Dependence of sperm motility and respiration on oxygen concentration. *J. Reprod. Fertil.*, 9, 103–7.

Nishiyama, H. (1952) On the hydrogen ion concentration of the transparent semen in the fowl. *Sci. Bull. Fac. Agric.Kyushu Univ.*, 12, 277–281.

Nishiyama, H. (1955) Studies on the accessory reproductive organs in the cock. *J. Fac. Agric.Kyushu Univ.*, 10, 277–306.

Nishiyama, H. (1957) On the characteristics of the transparent fluid. II. An electrophoretic study of proteins of the transparent fluid. *J. Fac. Agric.Kyushu Univ.*, 11, 63–8.

Nishiyama, H. (1961) On the quality and quantity of the cock semen obtained by different collection methods. *Mem. Fac. Agric.Kagoshima Univ.*, 4, 43–50.

Nishiyama, H. and Fujishima, T. (1961) On the ejection of the accessory reproductive fluid of the cock during natural copulation. *Mem. Fac. Agric.Kagoshima Univ.*, 4, 27–42.

Nishiyama, H. and Fujishima, T. (1963) On the hydrogen ion concentration of blood, blood plasma and blood serum of the cock. Relation to the hydrogen ion concentration of the accessory reproductive fluid of the cock. *Bull. Fac. Agric. Kagoshima Univ.*, 13, 162–172.

Nishiyama, H. and Ogawa, K. (1961) On the function of the vascular body, an accessory reproductive organ of the cock. *Jap.J. Zootech. Sci.*, 32, 89–98.

Norman, C., Goldberg, E. and Porterfield, I. D. (1962) The effect of visible radiation on the functional life-span of mammalian and avian spermatozoa. *Expt. Cell Res.*, 28, 69–84.

Norman, C., Goldberg, E., Porterfield, I. D. and Johnson, C. E. (1960) Studies on the physiology and biochemistry of germ cells. III. The effect of dinitrophenol on sperm. *Anat. Rec.*, 137, 384 (Abstr.).

Ogasawara, F. X. (1957) *Oxidative Metabolism of Fowl Spermatozoa as Influenced by Extracts of the Hen's Oviduct.* Ph.D. Thesis. Univ. California. Davis, California.

Ogasawara, F. X. and Lorenz, F. W. (1964) Respiratory rate of cock spermatozoa as affected by oviduct extracts. *J. Reprod. Fertil.*, 7, 281–8.

Owen, E. E. and Robinson, R. R. (1964) Urea production and excretion by the chicken kidney. *Amer.J. Physiol.*, 206, 1321–6.

Pitts, R. F. and Korr, I. M. (1938) The excretion of urea by the chicken. *J. Cell. Comp. Physiol.*, 11, 117–122.

Pytasz, M. and Klymiuk, B. (1961) Proteins and non-protein nitrogen in the semen of the domestic fowl. *Med. wet.*, 17, 437–440.

Saeki, Y. (1963) Effect of freezing point depression of diluent on the fertilizing ability of cock sperm. *Bull. Nat. Instit. Anim. Industry. Chiba*, 1, 1–7.

Saeki, Y. and Morichi, T. (1959) Action of semen inducing rupture of yolk membrane in chicken egg. *Proc. Soc. exp. Biol. N.Y.*, 101, 648–650.

Schindler, H. and Nevo, A. (1962) Reversible inactivation and agglutination of fowl and bull spermatozoa under anaerobic conditions. *J. Reprod. Fertil.*, 4, 251–265.

Schindler, H. and Scharf, S. (1963) The distribution of sugars, lactic acid and glutamic acid in the genital tract and body fluids of the cock. *Israel J. Agric. Res.*, 13, 163–172.

Schindler, H., Volcani, R. and Weinstein, S. (1958) Changes in pH during storage, buffering capacity, and glycolysis of cock and bull semen. *Poult. Sci.*, 37, 21–3.

Schindler, H., Weinstein, S., Moses, E. and Gabriel, I. (1955) The effect of various diluents and storage times on the fertilizing capacity of cock semen. *Poult. Sci.*, **34**, 1113–7.

Scott, T. W., White, I. G. and Annison, E. F. (1961) Fatty acids in semen. *Biochem. J.*, **78**, 740–2.

Scott, T. W., White, I. G. and Annison, E. F. (1962a) Oxidation of short-chain fatty acids (C_1-C_8) by ram, bull, dog and fowl spermatozoa. *Biochem. J.*, **83**, 392–8.

Scott, T. W., White, I. G. and Annison, E. F. (1962b) Glucose and acetate metabolism by ram, bull, dog and fowl spermatozoa. *Biochem. J.*, **82**, 398–404.

Srivastava, P. N., Adams, C. E. and Hartree, E. F. (1965) Enzymatic action of lipoglycoprotein preparations from sperm-acrosomes on rabbit ova. *Nature, Lond.*, **205**, 498.

Swyer, G. I. M. (1947) The hyaluronidase content of semen. *Biochem. J.*, **41**, 409–413.

Takeda, A. (1959) Studies on the cock semen. 1. Na, K and Ca levels of the seminal plasma. *Res. Rep. Fac. Text. Sericult. Shinshu Univ.*, **9**, 55–9.

Tosic, J. (1951) Hydrogen peroxide formation by spermatozoa and its relation to sperm survival. *Symp. Biochem. Soc. No.* 7. 22–3.

Tulloch, B. R. (1962) A modified technique for the collection of poultry semen. *S. Afr. J. Agric. Sci.*, **5**, 153–5.

van Tienhoven, A. (1960) The metabolism of fowl sperm in different diluents. *J. Agric. Sci.*, **54**, 67–80.

Vendrely, C., Knobloch, A. and Vendrely, R. (1956) Contribution à l'étude biochimique comparée de diverses desoxyribonucleoproteines d'origine animale. *Biochim. biophys. Acta*, **19**, 472–9.

Wales, R. G., Scott, T. W. and White, I. G. (1961) Biuret reactive materials in semen. *Austr. J. exp. Biol. Med. Sci.*, **39**, 455–462.

Wales, R. G. and Wallace, J. C. (1964) Effects of diluent composition on the metabolism of bull, dog, rabbit and fowl spermatozoa. *J. Reprod. Fertil.*, **8**, 361–373.

Wales, R. G. and White, I. G. (1958a) The effect of alkali metal, magnesium, and calcium ions on the motility of fowl spermatozoa. *Austr. J. Biol. Sci*, **11**, 589–597.

Wales, R. G. and White, I. G. (1958b) The interaction of pH, tonicity, and electrolyte concentration on the motility of fowl spermatozoa. *Austr. J. Biol. Sci.*, **11**, 177–186.

Wales, R. G. and White, I. G. (1959) The susceptibility of spermatozoa to temperature shock. *J. Endocrin.*, **19**, 211–220.

Wales, R. G. and White, I. G. (1960) The toxicity of some antibacterials to fowl spermatozoa. *Austr. J. biol. Sci.*, **13**, 361–370.

Wales, R. G. and White, I. G. (1961) The viability of fowl spermatozoa in dilute suspension. *Austr. J. Biol. Sci.*, **14**, 637–645.

Wales, R. G., White, I. G. and Lamond, D. R. (1959) The spermicidal activity of hydrogen peroxide *in vitro* and *in vivo*. *J. Endocrin.*, **18**, 236–244.

White, I. G. and Griffiths, D. E. (1958) Guanidines and phosphagens of semen. *Austr. J. exp. Biol. Med. Sci.*, **36**, 97–102.

White, I. G. and MacLeod, J. (1963) Composition and Physiology of Semen. Chapter 3. Proc. of conference on *Physiological Mechanisms concerned with Conception*. New York 1959. Pergamon Press, London.

Wilcox, F. H. (1958) Changes in the pH of semen of the domestic cock as affected by temperature and frequency of collection. *Poult. Sci.*, **37**, 444–9.

Wilcox, F. H. (1959a) The effect of different hydrogen ion concentrations during storage and at insemination and of added magnesium and potassium on the fertilizing ability of chicken semen. *Poult. Sci.*, **38**, 1159–61.

Wilcox, F. H. (1959b) Effect of the addition of carbohydrates after storage on the motility and fertilizing ability of chicken sperm. *Poult. Sci.*, **38**, 1162–8.

Wilcox, F. H. (1959c) Studies of the effect of oxytetracycline on chicken spermatozoa. *Amer. J. Vet. Res.*, **20**, 957–960.

Wilcox, F. H. (1960) Effect on fertility of temperature, handling methods, Lake's solution and the addition of egg white, egg yolk, and sugars to the diluent used in storing chicken semen. *Poult. Sci.*, **39**, 459–467.

Wilcox, F. H. (1961) Phosphatases in chicken semen. *J. Reprod. Fertil.*, **2**, 148–151.

Wilcox, F. H. and Clark, R. G. (1962) Semen dilution during storage and washing. *Poult. Sci.*, **41**, 1091–6.

Wilcox, F. H. and Shaffner, C. S. (1957) Effect of differences in salt and hydrogen ion concentration on the fertilizing ability of avian sperm. *J. Appl. Physiol.*, **11**, 429–434.

Wilcox, F. H. and Shaffner, C. S. (1958) The effect of different handling methods and added fructose on the fertilizing ability of chicken spermatozoa after storage. *Poult. Sci.*, **37**, 1353–7.

Wilcox, F. H. and Shaffner, C. S. (1960) Storage of turkey semen. *Poult. Sci.*, **39**, 1580–1.

Wilcox, F. H., Shaffner, C. S. and Wilson, H. R. (1961) Breed differences in storing chicken semen. *J. Heredity.*, **52**, 119–21.

Wilcox, F. H. and Shorb, M. S. (1958) The effect of antibiotics on bacteria in semen and on motility and fertilizing ability of chicken spermatozoa. *Amer. J. Vet. Res.*, **19**, 945–9.

Wilcox, F. H. and Wilson, H. R. (1961) The effect of the addition of potassium, magnesium and chloride ions to the diluent used in storing chicken semen. *Poult. Sci.*, **40**, 701–4.

Williams, W. L. and Hamner, C. E. (1963) Stimulation of respiration of rabbit, human and cock spermatozoa by light and certain chemicals. *J. Reprod. Fertil.*, **6**, 235–43.

Yamane, J., Tsukunaga, S., and Takahashi, T. (1962) A basic principle of make-up of the dilutor for fowl semen. *Zootec. e Vet.*, **17**, 523–7.

5

THE ULTRA-STRUCTURE OF MAMMALIAN
SPERMATOZOA

J. L. HANCOCK

Animal Breeding Research Organization, Edinburgh 9, Scotland

A. INTRODUCTION

The increasing attention which is being paid to the structural changes occurring in the mammalian spermatozoon as a preliminary to fertilization makes this an appropriate time to attempt to review present knowledge of sperm ultra-structure. This article will deal mainly with work which has appeared since Fawcett's (1958) review, although reference will be made to earlier work where necessary.

The most recent advances have been made possible by the development of techniques for preparing sections of individual cells suitable for electron microscopy. However it is sometimes possible to test the validity of conclusions about sperm ultra-structure against observations made with the light microscope. This attitude has been deliberately adopted wherever possible in this review.

One morphological type of mammalian spermatozoon is illustrated in Fig. 1A. Examples of this type are the spermatozoa of such differing

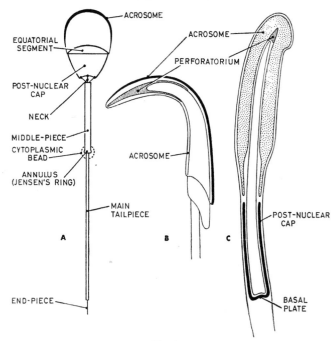

Fig. 1

A. General view of spermatozoon - ungulate type.
B. Rat sperm head showing acrosome and perforatorium (hatched).
C. Vertical section of ungulate sperm head showing the relationship of the acrosome (stippled), perforatorium (hatched) and the post-nuclear cap (heavy line). The post-nuclear cap is here shown to be continuous with the basal plate (but see text). The thickness of the head relative to its length is greatly exaggerated.

species as man, rabbit and the domestic ungulates: it consists of a paddle-shaped head and a long flagellum in which two distinct parts are recognizable, the middle-piece and the main tail-piece. The diagram includes a number of features which have been described by light microscopists and these will serve as points of reference. Species differences are most evident in the morphological features of the head and its cytoplasmic components. Fig. 1B shows the morphological type which is characteristic of many rodent spermatozoa. Here the head is a curved rod tapering markedly at its free extremity. Most studies of mammalian sperm structure refer to species with spermatozoa which are morphologically of one of these two types.

B. THE CELL MEMBRANE AND CYTOPLASMIC SHEATH

In all species a characteristic double 'plasma membrane' envelops the the whole of the spermatozoon. The firmness of the attachment of the cell membrane differs at different regions of the cell. In most species it seems to be particularly firmly attached to the posterior region of the head, and Saacke and Almquist (1964b) found that its attachment in the region of the annulus (Jensen's ring) was very constant. This observation could be explained by the occurrence of an invagination of the membrane at this point, such as is said to occur during the origin of the tail filaments (Sotelo and Trujillo-Cenoz, 1958).

The closeness of the attachment of the cell membrane of rabbit spermatozoa apparently changes during the epididymal journey (Bedford, 1964a). It is closely apposed to the acrosome in the most proximal part of the caput epididymis, but is frequently separated from the head over much of its surface in spermatozoa from the cauda epididymis and in ejaculated spermatozoa. Further loosening of the plasma membrane was observed in spermatozoa recovered from the uterus (Bedford, 1964b).

Fawcett (1958) concluded that the spermatozoon had no cytoplasmic sheath. There appears to be no recent evidence against this view.

C. THE HEAD

1. Nucleus

The prominence of the nuclear membrane varies considerably. Anberg (1957) found it difficult to demonstrate a nuclear membrane in human spermatozoa, but Nicander and Bane (1962a) describe a typical double membrane in the boar spermatozoon. The double-layered nuclear membrane of the bull spermatozoon is very clearly shown in the paper by Saacke and Almquist (1964a) and has been described in the rabbit by Bedford (1964b).

It is now agreed that in human, ungulate and rabbit spermatozoa the nucleus occupies the whole area of the head and is covered anteriorly only by a relatively thin cytoplasmic covering. Anberg (1957) and Fawcett (1958) have shown that earlier interpretations of the extent of the nucleus in human spermatozoa were erroneous. In many rodents the cytoplasmic cap covering the front of the head extends well beyond the margin of the nucleus.

In the mature ejaculated cell the chromatin is virtually homogeneous even at the highest magnifications in all species examined, although this homogeneity is lost soon after penetration of the ovum (Szollosi and Ris, 1961). Vacuolation of the nuclear material seems to be a fairly regular feature of human spermatozoa (Anberg, 1957; Rothschild, 1958). Vacuoles are much less common in other species but are occasionally observed in the rabbit (Bedford, 1964b) and bull (Saacke and Almquist, 1964a; Blom and Birch-Anderson, 1965). According to Saacke and Almquist the vacuoles may open on the surface of the nucleus. Bretschneider (1949) regarded these as artifacts of preparation in bull spermatozoa.

Fawcett (1958) observed that the vacuoles are not bounded by a nuclear membrane and that their variability in size, position and shape is in contrast to the constancy in structure of other nuclear parts. Fawcett concluded that the vacuoles of human spermatozoa have no functional significance; it is doubtful if this is true of other species.

2. Acrosome

It has long been recognized that the Golgi elements of the spermatid contribute to the formation of a cap-like structure which invests the front part of the sperm head. This cap will here be called the acrosome. Reasons for preferring this term have been given previously (Hancock, 1952). Although the cap has been shown to have a more complex structure than was believed to be the case then, the term has been used recently by Fawcett and Hollenberg (1963) as it is here, to mean the same as the 'acrosome system' (Leblond and Clermont, 1952) or the 'acrosome cap' (Fawcett, 1958; Blom and Birch-Anderson, 1965).

The general features of the acrosome of the intact spermatozoon are illustrated in Figs. 1A and B. Its structure as seen in sagittal and horizontal sections of the ungulate-type head is shown in Figs. 1C and 2A. The features of the ungulate acrosome in Fig. 1C resemble closely those shown by the rodent acrosome in transverse section (see Piko and Tyler, 1964).

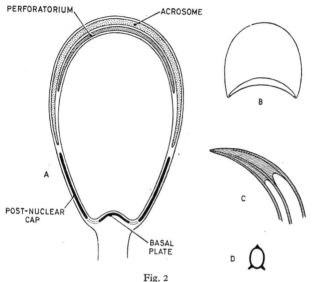

Fig. 2

A. Horizontal section of ungulate sperm head. The acrosome, perforatorium, sperm head and post-nuclear cap are identified as in 1C.
B. The outline of the *galea capitis* of ungulate spermatozoa.
C. The perforatorium of the rat spermatozoon.
D. Transverse section of rat perforatorium.

The acrosome is seen to be limited externally by an outer membrane, which is reflected forwards at the posterior boundary of the acrosome to form an inner membrane contiguous with the nuclear membrane. The space between the inner and outer membranes is occupied by an electron-dense matrix. These features have been described in the mature spermatozoa of man (Anberg, 1957), bull (Blom and Birch-Anderson, 1965), boar (Nicander and Bane, 1962a), rabbit (Hadek, 1963a,b), guinea pig (Fawcett and Hollenberg, 1963) and rat (Piko and Tyler, 1964). The acrosome in Fig. 1C is divided into an anterior thicker part and a posterior thinner portion, a feature first described by Nicander and Bane (1962a).

Fig. 1C also shows a local enlargement on one side of the acrosome near its anterior border. This is the sectional view of a horse-shoe shaped ridge which runs along the periphery of the acrosome. This

9

ridge is called here the *apical ridge*. It was first described by Blom and Birch-Anderson (1961) who called it the *apical body*, a term probably better avoided since it has also been applied to the structure now more generally called the *perforatorium* (Hadek, 1963a,b; Bedford, 1964b). The apical ridge is a constant feature of boar (Nicander and Bane, 1962a) and rabbit spermatozoa (Hadek, 1963a,b; Bedford, 1964b). It was clearly illustrated in ram spermatozoa by Randall and Friedlander (1950) although its true identity was then unknown.

In the bull, the ridge may be traversed in normal ejaculated spermatozoa by a 'vacuole' of low electron-density. Blom (1964b) illustrates (Fig. 307e) a transverse section of a head with two apical 'vacuoles' which are clearly the result of sectioning the apical ridge at two points. These vacuolations correspond in appearance to the areas of low electron density which are found in sections of the outer zone of the guinea pig spermatozoon. Bull, boar and rabbit spermatozoa evidently differ from guinea-pig spermatozoa in the degree of development of the apical ridge, but the observations of Fawcett and Hollenberg (1963) on the origin of the separate components of the guinea-pig acrosome cannot easily be reconciled with evidence of their probable origin in other species. Fawcett and Hollenberg apparently regarded the guinea-pig spermatid as exceptional because the pro-acrosome shows two distinct zones; they make no reference to Clermont and Leblond's (1955) demonstration that two zones can be differentiated, after suitable fixation, in the pro-acrosomes of ram, bull, monkey and rat spermatids. (The term 'pro-acrosome' as used here includes the 'cap' and the 'acrosome' referred to by Clermont and Leblond as separate components of the 'acrosome cap'.)

The apical ridge is almost certainly the inconspicuous feature of mature spermatozoa referred to by Clermont and Leblond (1955) as the 'acrosome'. If so, their conclusion that it originates from the inner zone of the pro-acrosome is contrary to the conclusion reached by Fawcett and Hollenberg (1963). Observations on the abnormal acrosome of 'knobbed' bull and boar spermatozoa (Bane, 1961; Blom and Birch-Anderson, 1962) have shown an enlargement and marked vacuolation of the apical ridge; these, together with Bedford's (1964a) observations on rabbit epididymal spermatozoa, support the view that the 'knobbed' defect is the result of failure of the apical ridge to complete its differentiation. Hancock and Trevan's (1957) findings on the origin of this defect are in better agreement with the conclusions of Clermont and Leblond (1955) than with those of Fawcett and Hollenberg (1963). The interpretation favoured here is that the outer zone of the pro-acrosome forms the major part of the acrosome, while the inner zone forms the apical ridge. The possibility that the pro-acrosome may also contribute to the perforatorium is referred to below.

Fawcett and Hollenberg (1963) have shown that morphological changes also occur in the acrosome of the guinea-pig spermatozoon during its epididymal journey, though, by contrast with the rabbit (Bedford, 1964a), the changes are in the direction of greater morphological differentiation. 'Vacuolation' of the apical ridge is a feature of rabbit spermatozoa from the proximal epididymis, but is absent from the majority of ejaculated spermatozoa. In the guinea-pig, 'vacuolation' of the horseshoe-shaped zone considered here to be the apical ridge, was found to be present in spermatozoa from the distal epididymis but was absent from those in the more proximal part. (Note that the Figs. 3A and 3B in Bedford's paper are labelled incorrectly.) At first glance it may seem natural to interpret differences between spermatozoa from the proximal and distal epididymis as evidence of differentiation towards the form found in the distal regions; but this need not necessarily be so. The rate of differentiation of spermatozoa in the epididymis may vary; and it is possible that, in Fawcett and Hollenberg's experiments, differentiation had been accelerated in the proximal samples or delayed in the distal ones.

It is not yet clear to what extent the acrosome of the bull and boar is modified during the epididymal journey, but the differences in acrosome structure between normal and 'knobbed' spermatozoa are already evident in spermatozoa from the testis (Hancock and Trevan, 1957).

3. Perforatorium

Fawcett (1958), Austin and Bishop (1958) and Bishop and Walton (1960) have summarized the evidence for the existence of a structure, the perforatorium, separate from the acrosome and distinguished from it by its mode of origin, site and cytological characteristics. The recent description by Piko and Tyler (1964) of the perforatorium of the rat agrees except in minor details with that given by Clermont, Einberg, Leblond and Wagner (1955). It appears to be a pyramidal structure engaging the nucleus posteriorly by three prong-like extensions (Figs. 1B, 2C,D); Piko and Tyler say that not all of it lies within the acrosome.

At the time of Bishop and Walton's review there was no evidence of the existence of a comparable structure in spermatozoa of the rabbit and the domestic ungulates. Since then a number of structures which may be the homologue of the perforatorium have been described in the rabbit (Moricard, 1960, 1961; Hadek, 1963a,b; Bedford, 1964b), bull (Blom and Birch-Anderson, 1965), boar, dog, stallion and ram (Bane and Nicander, 1963). Its appearance in sagittal section is shown in Fig. 1C, where it is seen as a cone-like projection lying in a recess of the overlying acrosome. Hadek says that the perforatorium (which he refers to as the 'apical body') is embedded in a layer of cytoplasmic origin; he also says that Fawcett (1958) referred to this layer as 'the intermediate layer of the head cap' but it seems more likely that Fawcett was referring to the material between the inner and outer acrosome membranes. Bedford also referred to the structure as the 'apical body', but suggested that it might be the homologue of the perforatorium. From its appearance in section it seems likely that it is a modification of the inner membrane of the acrosome rather than of the nuclear membrane.

In ungulate-type spermatozoa the lateral limits of the perforatorium have not been very clearly defined, but Bedford (1964b) and Blom and Birch-Anderson (1965) show it as a crest extending the full width of the sperm head (see Fig. 2A). The small component of the ram acrosome described and illustrated by Randall and Friedlander (see their Plate IIa) is probably the perforatorium.

4. Galea capitis and equatorial segment

In the past certain difficulties have confronted attempts to integrate findings made with the electron microscope and the light microscope. Two features of the spermatozoon which have been described by light microscopists have been the subject of particular controversy.

The galea capitis is a semilunar-shaped structure (see Fig. 2B) found free in bull semen after prolonged sexual rest, and in pathological ejaculates of bull, stallion and ram. It has also been seen in the ejaculates of rabbits a few days after the application of ice to the scrotum over the epididymis (unpublished observation). It can be detached intact by treatment of spermatozoa with anionic detergents (Hartree and Srivastava, 1965).

The equatorial segment (see Fig. 1A) is an area of the sperm head whose posterior boundary is the common boundary of the acrosome cap and the post-nuclear cap. The identity of its curved anterior boundary has been the source of considerable controversy: in Fig. 3, for instance, are shown seven different diagrammatic reconstructions of the sperm head based on interpretations offered by various investigators.

In Fig. 3A a smaller cap, believed to be the *galea capitis*, is shown lying outside a larger cap: on this interpretation the equatorial

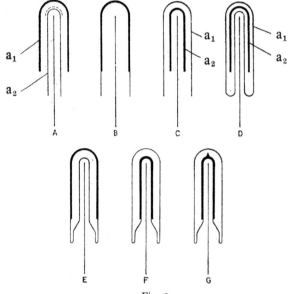

Fig. 3

Diagrammatic representations of different interpretations of the relationships of the components of the acrosome showing the origins of the *galea capitis* and equatorial segment.
The component from which the *galea capitis* is supposed to be derived is shown as a heavy line.

A. The larger component (a₂) is covered by the smaller component (a₁) from which the *galea capitis* is derived (Randall and Friedlander, 1950).
B. The acrosome is shown as a single cap. The *galea capitis* is formed as the result of deformation and detachment of this cap (Hancock, 1952).
C. The outer component (a₁) is larger than the inner component (a₂). The *galea capitis* is the detached inner component (Hancock, 1957).
D. The larger component (a₁) includes within its double walls the smaller component (a₂) which when detached forms the *galea capitis* (Bishop and Walton, 1960).
E. The acrosome is a double layered cap. The *galea capitis* is the detached *outer* membrane of the thicker anterior part (Blom and Birch-Anderson, 1965; Saacke and Almquist, 1964a).
F. The *galea capitis* is the detached *inner* membrane of the thicker part of the cap.
G. The *galea capitis* is the detached perforatorium, alone or in conjunction with the inner membrane of the acrosome.

With the interpretations in Figs. A–D the equatorial segment is the area of overlap between the larger and smaller (heavy line) components of the acrosome. In Figs. E, F, G the equatorial segment is the area covered by the thinner posterior part of the acrosome.

segment is the area of overlap between the smaller *galea capitis* surrounding the larger outer acrosome cap. This interpretation (Randall and Friedlander, 1950) was rejected, because observations on living spermatozoa with the light microscope showed that the equatorial segment was absent from living bull spermatozoa and appeared only after death of the cell. Hancock (1952) suggested that the acrosome cap and *galea capitis* were a single structure whose different forms in living and dead cells explained the absence of the equatorial segment from living cells. This view (Fig. 3B) had to be abandoned because it could not explain the observation of an equatorial segment in the living spermatozoa of the boar. A third interpretation was offered (Fig. 3C). Here, the existence of two separate components was accepted but it was stressed that the semilunar *galea capitis* must be the inner, not the outer of the two as suggested by Randall and Friedlander. A fourth interpretation, prompted by Burgos and Fawcett's (1955) observations, maintains that the semilunar structure is situated between the inner and outer layers of a double layered cap resembling that shown in outline in Fig. 3D (Bishop and Walton, 1960).

The interpretations outlined so far were based largely on findings made with the light microscope, and on electron microscopy of intact spermatozoa, at a period when no direct evidence of the existence of two separate components of the acrosome was available from sections of spermatozoa. New information on the structure of the sperm head has evoked some new answers to these questions. Nicander and Bane (1962a), Saacke and Almquist (1964a) and Blom (1964a) have all concluded that the equatorial segment coincides with that area of the head covered by the thinner posterior part of the acrosome. If this view is correct there should be variation between sections in the length of the thinner posterior part of the acrosome, corresponding to the continuous variation in the vertical diameter of the equatorial segment. It should also be possible to correlate differences in the vertical diameter of the equatorial segment of say bull and boar spermatozoa, with differences in the dimensions of the posterior part of the acrosome. So far there is no conclusive evidence of this kind.

Blom (1964a), Blom and Birch-Anderson (1965) and Saacke and Almquist (1964a) agree that the *galea capitis* is the outer membrane of the thicker walled anterior portion of the acrosome, which when detached leaves both membranes intact over the equatorial segment and the inner membrane intact over its whole length. Neither Saacke and Almquist nor Blom and Birch-Anderson have examined the validity of their conclusion in the light of other evidence; their view is liable to some of the objections which have been raised (Hancock, 1957) to the rather similar interpretation put forward by Randall and Friedlander (1950). (Randall and Friedlander showed a shadowed sperm head with features clearly compatible with the new interpretation of the equatorial segment.)

There can be no doubt that the outer membrane of the thicker anterior part of the acrosome is particularly vulnerable to degenerative changes; but it is less certain that this disrupted membrane is detached intact as the *galea capitis*. In both bull and boar spermatozoa, when the features of the intact cell are preserved the head is invested with a cap which has a straight posterior border and which stains distinctly with Schiff's reagent after treatment with periodic acid (PAS). Death of the cell causes disruption of the cap and loss of reactivity to PAS, but a Giemsa-positive semilunar area of the head is left behind identical in outline with the *galea capitis*. This could be an area of the nuclear surface whose typical staining affinity is exposed only after loss of the *galea capitis*, but this seems less likely in view of the observation that the spontaneously detached *galea capitis* is itself Giemsa-positive (Hancock, 1952), and that spermatozoa with and without the Giemsa-positive semilunar area are found in smears of semen aged *in vitro* (Hancock, 1957).

The observations with the light microscope, however, are compatible with the view that the *galea capitis* corresponds to the inner membrane of the thicker part of the acrosome, anterior to the equatorial segment (Fig. 3F), and that this is still *in situ* when the outer membrane of the acrosome has been disrupted and removed. In the spermatid, the inner membrane of the acrosome is more prominent where it lies over the face of the nucleus than is the outer membrane which lines the roof of the archoplasmic vacuole. This may be evidence of some modification of the inner membrane of the acrosome sufficient to maintain an area of structural integrity in dead spermatozoa, when the rest of the acrosome is disrupted.

The identification of a second structure, the *perforatorium*, makes possible another interpretation, namely that the perforatorium corresponds to the *galea capitis*. The present location of the lateral and posterior limits of the perforatorium are against this suggestion, but in its staining affinity for iron haematoxylin the semilunar region of the boar spermatozoon shows at least one of the distinguishing features of the perforatorium of rodent spermatozoa.

The finding of the perforatorium raises again the question of the fate of the inner component of the developing acrosome of the spermatid. If, as is argued above, the apical ridge of the acrosome arises from this inner component, then the perforatorium may be formed at this time, perhaps as a modification of the inner membrane of the acrosome. Blom and Birch-Anderson's (1965) observation that the perforatorium in knobbed spermatozoa is abnormal (*see* Fig. 2a, Blom and Birch-Anderson, 1962) may be evidence that the development of the apical fold and perforatorium are inter-related.

5. Post-nuclear cap

Fawcett (1958) concluded that a post-nuclear cap had not been demonstrated in any mammalian spermatozoa studied up to that time. Since then there have been repeated observations of a special limiting membrane covering the part of the nucleus not covered by the acrosome. Anberg (1957) failed to identify a post-nuclear cap in the human spermatozoon, but in the boar Nicander and Bane (1962a) described a layer of dense material adherent to the inner surface of the cell membrane and staining with phosphotungstic acid. Blom and Birch-Anderson (1965) say that the posterior half of the bull spermatozoon is covered by an electron-dense post-nuclear cap with a characteristic structure of longitudinally disposed elements; in this respect it resembles the post-nuclear cap described by Das (1962) in the developing spermatozoon of *Microtus pennsylvanicus*, though Das himself identified the post-nuclear cap with the manchette of the spermatid.

Bedford finds the post-nuclear cap less clearly defined than the acrosome in the rabbit, but comments on its spongy appearance in lead-treated and uranyl acetate or permanganate-treated material. Hadek (1963b) also claims to have demonstrated a post-nuclear cap in rabbit spermatozoa. Saacke and Almquist (1964a) depict a membrane closely attached to the inner surface of the cell membrane over the posterior part of the head, and call this the post-nuclear cap. It seems doubtful whether the structure described by Mathur (1962) as the post-nuclear cap, corresponds to the post-nuclear cap of other authors.

D. STRUCTURAL CHANGES IN SPERMATOZOA BEFORE AND AFTER FERTILIZATION

Moricard (1960) examined rabbit ova in which the opportunities for penetration by supplementary spermatozoa had been increased by previous insemination directly into the oviduct. His observations were limited to spermatozoa in the zona pellucida or in the perivitelline space: the fertilizing spermatozoon was not observed. Moricard described the perforatorium as a comma-shaped structure 200 to 300 mμ long in spermatozoa in the zona pellucida; he noted the absence of the acrosome from spermatozoa in the perivitelline space. Hadek (1963a) reported morphological differences between ejaculated spermatozoa and spermatozoa exposed to rabbit ova *in vitro* and *in vivo*. Exposure to ova *in vitro* was said to be followed only by swelling of the acrosome, whereas spermatozoa found in the vicinity of the vitelline membrane (following penetration of the zona pellucida *in vivo*) showed loss of all but the inner membrane of the acrosome, and elongation of the 'apical body' (perforatorium). Finally, by the time it reached the vitellus, the spermatozoon was covered only by the cytoplasmic layer which Hadek believes to be situated within the inner acrosome membrane.

Hadek's interpretation of the changes in the acrosome which he observed are open to the criticism that some of the changes may have been due to cell death. Austin and Bishop (1958) pointed out that the morphological changes which occur in the acrosome after death of the cell (Hancock, 1952) resemble closely those which they described as characteristic of 'capacitated' spermatozoa; Bedford (1963) has shown that the same *post-mortem* changes occur in rabbit spermatozoa.

Bedford (1964b) found that the majority of uterine spermatozoa have the plasma membrane and acrosome intact; he could find no structural change clearly associated with contact with the female tract, although there was some evidence of a loosening of the attachments of the plasma membrane to the acrosome. Bedford found no significant alteration in the perforatorium (apical body) and is sceptical of the validity of Hadek's observations.

Dickman (1964) has recently observed with the light microscope an 'acrosome filament' on the heads of rabbit spermatozoa in the zona pellucida, and Dickmann and Dziuk (1964) have described a similar structure on the heads of boar spermatozoa in the zona pellucida of pig ova. The 'acrosome filament' photographed by Dickmann in the zona pellucida of rabbit ova is obviously of much greater length than the perforatorium seen in electron micrographs of sectioned ova, but there is no reason to suppose that any one section would include the whole length of the perforatorium. The existence of the acrosome filament has yet to be confirmed by electron microscopy.

Szollosi and Ris (1961) have described the rat spermatozoon during penetration of the egg; their description is said to apply also to the golden hamster spermatozoon. Soon after penetration, when the spermatozoon is lying tangentially on the surface of the vitellus, the sperm plasma membrane is lost on the side nearest to the vitellus, remaining intact along the outer side. The egg and sperm plasma membranes become confluent at the base of two folds, one of which forms near the apex of the head, the other in the tail region. In their diagrammatic representation of these events, Szollosi and Ris show the sperm plasma membrane remaining as a discrete area of the egg membrane at the site of penetration. They make no reference to either the acrosome or the perforatorium, both of which have presumably been lost by this time.

The sequence of events described by Piko and Tyler (1964) for the rat is as follows. The contents of the acrosome have been lost by the time the spermatozoon reaches the perivitelline space, and the outer acrosome membrane fuses with the sperm plasma membrane to form isolated vesicles. Villi from the vitellus attach to the sperm plasma membrane, immobilizing the spermatozoon, and fusion of the egg and sperm plasma membranes then exposes the sperm nucleus to the egg cytoplasm. Fusion of the inner acrosome membrane and the egg plasma membrane eventually occurs, but only after the post-nuclear cap and underlying nuclear membrane have disintegrated, leaving the nucleus exposed. Piko and Tyler concluded that the sperm plasma membrane is unlikely to remain as part of the egg plasma membrane after incorporation of the sperm into the egg, as described by Szollosi and Ris. Despite this difference the two accounts have much in common.

The description of the fusion of the plasma membrane and outer acrosome membranes during fertilization could apply equally to the striking degenerative changes in the outer acrosome membrane which are so clearly illustrated by Saacke and Almquist (1964a). It seems that the changes which occur in the acrosome as a preliminary to fertilization are mimicked by those which occur after death of the cell. These changes are presumably normally inhibited in the living cell, and released only at the time of fertilization.

In spite of the progress which has been achieved, we cannot yet be said to possess a coherent picture of the structural changes in the plasma membrane, acrosome and perforatorium which are involved in penetration of the cumulus oophorus, the zona pellucida, and the vitelline membrane.

E. THE FLAGELLUM

1. Axial fibre bundle

Although recent work has contributed new details of the structural organization of the sperm tail (Telkka, Fawcett and Christensen, 1961; Fawcett, 1962), it has not been necessary to modify greatly the earlier observations made with the electron microscope on sectioned spermatozoa (see Bradfield, 1955; Fawcett, 1958), which established the characteristic pattern of the components which form the axial fibre bundle. The basic pattern consists of a central pair of fibrils with one or two (according to the level of the section) concentric outer rings, each of nine fibrils. The general pattern, illustrated in Fig. 4, consists of an outer peripheral ring of nine 'coarse' fibres, an inner ring of nine 'fine' fibres, and two 'central' fibres.

2. Axial filament complex

This is the term usually applied to the inner ring of nine fibres and the central paired fibres. The fibres of the inner ring lie opposite to the corresponding coarse fibres of the outer ring. Each fine fibre consists of two subfibres which differ in density. The relative positions of the two subfibres is constant; the arrangement shown in Fig. 4 is characteristic of sections viewed from the caudal end looking towards the head. The members of each pair of subfibres do not lie on the same circumference: the denser member of the pair (subfibre A) is smaller and lies nearer the axis of the tail than does the larger, less dense subfibre B. Subfibre A carries two *arms* directed towards the adjacent doublet. Areas of higher density, referred to as *spokes*, join the denser of the two members of the doublet to an area of higher density surrounding the central pair. These features were originally described by Afzelius (1959) in the sea urchin and have since been recognized in several mammalian species (Fawcett, 1962).

A convention for the numbering of the fibres was introduced by Bradfield (1955), and modified recently by Fawcett (1962). The single coarse fibre of the outer ring on the axis which separates the two central fibrils is termed fibre 1, and the remaining fibres are numbered by counting in the direction pointed by the arms on subfibre A. Cleland and Rothschild (1959) numbered the fibres in the bandicoot sperm tail differently: fibres 1 and 6 numbered according to their method correspond to fibres 3 and 8 as numbered above.

Few observers have been able to relate the axes of the tail to those of the head, but Fawcett (1962) concluded that the axis of the two central fibres is at right angles to the longer transverse axis of the head. In the bat spermatozoon he showed that it is possible to fix with some certainty the relationship of the two axes. In transverse section, the end-to-end junctions of the semicircular units of the mitochondrial sheath lie on the axis of the two central fibres. In longitudinal section the mitochondrial junctions lie on the vertical longitudinal head axis. If one considers the two faces of the head to be dorsal and ventral, then the dorso-ventral axis of the head is the axis of the two central fibres. Nicander and Bane (1962a) imply that the axes of the head and tail are similarly related in the boar. Kojima (1962) referred to a dorsal and ventral surface of the bull sperm head, and his summarized observations suggest that the relationships of the two axes are the same in the bull as in the bat.

These findings contrast with those of Cleland and Rothschild in the bandicoot. They concluded that the transverse axis of the head was parallel to the axis of the two central fibrils. The longitudinal columns of the fibrous sheath of the bandicoot spermatozoon (see below) can apparently be identified with the light microscope and their axes related to the head axis. This interpretation of the relationship of the head and tail axes of the bandicoot makes it necessary to postulate that the waves of motility propagated along the bandicoot sperm tail are in a plane at right angles to that observed in the bull spermatozoon.

Cleland and Rothschild also say that the paired fibres of the inner ring are not equidistant from one another. The arrangement which they described is illustrated in Fig. 4A. The axis of the two central fibres intersects only one of the peripheral ring fibres; in the lower left (XY^1) quadrant there are two fibres neither of which touches the axis; and in the lower right quadrant (X^1Y^1) the axes intersect two fibres and there is a single fibre between them. This arrangement, or its mirror image, was believed by Cleland and Rothschild to be a basic pattern common to the spermatozoa of several species including the bandicoot. A feature of this pattern is that the fibrils are not spaced at regular intervals. The pattern illustrated in Fig. 4B shows the fibres equally spaced; here, the axis of the central fibres intersects two of the inner ring fibres.

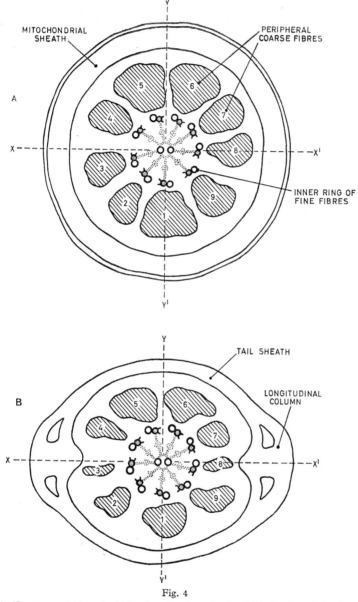

Fig. 4

A. Transverse section of middle-piece showing mitochondrial sheath, peripheral coarse fibres and axial filament complex.

B. Transverse section of tail showing fibrous sheath and its longitudinal columns, peripheral coarse fibres and axial filament complex. The arrangement of the inner ring of fibres is different from that shown in A (see text).

Inspection of a number of recent electron micrographs of sectioned sperm tails of guinea-pig, bull and boar sperm suggests that they do not conform rigidly to either pattern. (See Fawcett, 1962, Fig. 7; Nicander and Bane, 1962a, Fig. 10; Saacke and Almquist, 1964b, Figs. 8 and 9.)

Fawcett (1958) made no comment on the origin of the inner ring of fibres. According to Kojima (1962) the inner ring of nine and the central pair all originate from a centriole in the neck. According to Saacke and Almquist (1964b) they arise by division of the coarse fibres. Nicander and Bane traced the central pair to the proximal centriole but could not identify the source of the inner ring. Nagano (1963), in a study of the spermatogenic disturbances which follow artificial cryptorchidism, has reported that the central fibres are the first to show degenerative changes.

3. Peripheral ring

The nine coarse fibres of the outer ring vary in cross-sectional shape and area in different parts of the tail, and at any one level there are differences between individual fibres. Bradfield (1955) found that the tail was symmetrical about an axis through fibre 1, between the central pair of fibrils and between coarse fibres 5 and 6; he concluded that fibrils 1, 5 and 6 were characteristically larger than the remaining six fibres. It is now clear that there is no uniform distinction of size between these three fibres and the rest. The pattern observed by Bradfield seems to be common in rodents (Telkka *et al.* 1961), but in other species it is a common finding that fibres 1 and 9 are similar in size so that the tail is markedly asymmetrical about the axis which divides the two central fibres. The axis of the two pairs of coarse fibres is parallel to the horizontal axis of the head.

This pattern of two large fibres disposed laterally on each side of the axial filament has been described in the bull middle-piece by Blom and Birch-Anderson (1960), Rahlman (1961), Kojima (1962) and Saacke and Almquist (1964b). In the boar all the fibres are said to be of the same diameter at the proximal end of the middle piece (Nicander and Bane, 1962a); at the distal end of the middle piece and in the main tail piece fibres 1, 5 and 6 are larger than the rest, and fibre 9 is intermediate in size between these three and the rest. In both bull and boar, fibres 1 and 9 fuse to form one of the main stems and fibres 5 and 6 fuse to form the other. The smaller coarse fibres retain their individuality until they fuse with the heads of the main stems. The number of the smaller coarse fibres is uncertain. Kojima says the bull spermatozoon has five, Saacke and Almquist say it has four. According to Kojima two fibres contributing on each side to the main stems are twisted one round another. Saacke and Almquist's reconstruction of the neck of bull spermatozoon does not incorporate this feature.

Bawa (1963) found up to 14 coarse fibres in a few sections of human spermatozoa, but the majority had the normal complement of nine as recorded by Anberg (1957).

4. Main tail piece

All of the nine coarse fibres persist beyond the middle piece into the tail piece for a varying distance. In the rat, fibres 3 and 8 terminate first, followed by fibres 4 and 7, then fibres 2 and 9, and lastly the 3 largest fibres 1, 5 and 6 (Telkka et al. 1961). Fibres 3 and 8 also terminate first in the boar (Nicander and Bane, 1962a) and in man (Anberg, 1957), but Saacke and Almquist (1964b) say that in the bull spermatozoon fibres 3 and 8 disappear last. In the main tail-piece the outer and inner rings of fibres are contiguous. If bending of the tail occurs, as it is believed to do, in the plane of the horizontal transverse axis of the head, the largest fibres in the bull and boar are in a position to contribute most.

Cleland and Rothschild have noted some points of difference between the peripheral fibrils of the bandicoot and those of other mammalian spermatozoa: a particularly striking structural feature is the presence of laminae connecting the peripheral fibres with those of the inner ring.

F. THE MITOCHONDRIAL HELIX

The mid-piece is characterized by the presence of a mitochondrial helix which surrounds the axial fibre bundle. There have been differences in opinion as to whether or not the mitochondria retain their individuality or become fused; Fawcett (1958) concluded that the former was the more likely, and more recently (Fawcett, 1962) he has remarked on the species variation in the form and arrangement of the elements. The mitochondria may be spherical or cylindrical and are arranged in one or more helically disposed chains around the middle-piece. Marked morphological changes occur in the mito-chondria after death, and may explain some differences of results.

For instance, Blom and Birch-Anderson (1960) remarked that cristae
were rarely observed in the mitochondria of bull spermatozoa which
had been stored at 4°C for 48 hours before fixation, but they later
showed (Birch-Anderson and Blom, 1963) that the mitochondria
of freshly fixed bull spermatozoa had the usual pattern of cristae.
They originally (Blom and Birch-Anderson, 1960) distinguished a
pars spiralis, comprising the helical region, from the terminal part of
the mitochondrial chain which follows a straight course in the neck
region (*pars ascendens*), but more recently (Blom and Birch-Anderson,
1965) they revised an earlier view that the mitochondrial chain
reached the head. In the boar the helix at its proximal end stops
short of the sperm head, but reaches it in the stallion (Nicander and
Bane, 1962a).

There is very clear evidence from macerated preparations of whole
spermatozoa that the bull spermatozoon has a helix of two or three
strands (*see* Hodge, 1949, Fig. 10; note that Fig. 10 is a bull spermatozoon although the remaining illustrations are of human spermatozoa), but this helix is not the mitochondrial helix although it may
mark its original site. Challice (1953) concluded from a study of
sectioned material that the helix of the rat spermatozoon was double.
Wu and Newstead (1963) have described a double helix in bull
spermatozoa. Blom and Birch-Anderson (1960) have described a
spiral of about one hundred turns in the bull spermatozoon. They
suggest that the mitochondrial helix is a single chain which is
doubled to form a loop with its two free ends terminating near the
head; this is in effect a double helix. Saacke and Almquist (1964b)
found the helix to be composed of 'one or more' strands, and suggested that some strands apparently failed to reach the end of the middle
piece, while others had their origin at intermediate points between
the proximal and distal ends of the middle-piece. In contrast to
Anberg (1957), Rothschild (1958) found evidence of one or two
mitochondrial spirals in sectioned human spermatozoa.

G. THE FIBROUS SHEATH

A fibrous sheath surrounds the axial fibre bundle in the principal
tail piece. This sheath was believed by earlier workers to consist
of spirally disposed fibres and was known as the cortical helix or tail
helix. Fawcett (1958) suggested that these terms were inappropriate
in view of his evidence which argued against the existence of a spiral.
More recently Fawcett (1962) has provided further evidence against

the view that the windings of the sheath are helical in form. He describes and illustrates inter-connecting strands between contiguous transverse strands, and Nicander (1962) has recorded similar findings in the developing fibrous sheath of rat spermatids. Telkka *et al.* found that the organization of the fibrous sheath is basically similar in the rat, guinea-pig, bat, monkey and man. Their findings show a sheath consisting of semicircular ribs which have a common junction with two lateral longitudinal pillars. The ends of the ribs are bifurcated and the bifurcations of the opposed fibres embrace the longitudinal pillars.

There is now more or less general agreement that the tail sheath is strengthened by two longitudinal pillars which lie one on each side of the tail in the plane of the two central fibrils. The pillars lie not quite opposite to fibres 3 and 8 at points on the tail where these fibres still persist. The pillars are inconspicuous in the boar spermatozoon (Nicander and Bane, 1962a). Schultz-Larsen and Hammen (1956) failed to identify them in human spermatozoa and suggested that they were artifacts of sectioning, but Telkka *et al.* convincingly refuted this, and there is now positive evidence that pillars exist in the human spermatozoon also (Fawcett, 1962). The two 'resistant fibres' described by Hodge in the human spermatozoon may not have been, as he suggested, the homologues of the two central fibres found in fowl spermatozoa, but the longitudinal columns of the fibrous sheath. His illustration shows two fibres with what appear to be transverse processes attached, fitting the description given by Telkka *et al.* Cleland and Rothschild (1959) refer repeatedly to the gyres of the fibrous sheath in their description of the bandicoot sperm tail. The spiral sheath proper is said to be a single gyred spiral re-inforced by two pyramidal spiral sheath thickenings, while a trilaminar tail sheath membrane separates the spiral sheath within from an external tail sheath of varying electron-density. Both Saacke and Almquist (1964b) and Kojima have found some evidence of a spiral disposition of the sheath fibres of the bull spermatozoon.

H. THE ANNULUS (JENSEN'S RING)

Fawcett (1958) points out that the structure of the annulus at the distal end of the middle-piece shows none of the characteristic features of a centriole, and doubts whether it can properly be regarded as such; but Gatenby (1959) does not accept this conclusion unreservedly. Fawcett describes two components of the annulus of the

10

spermatid: a smaller dense homogeneous ring embedded in the posterior margin of a larger ring which has a granular appearance. Blom and Birch-Anderson (1960) and Saacke and Almquist (1964b) have since described the annulus of the mature bull spermatozoa in some detail; neither description refers to any evidence of a double structure. Both show its cross-section to be an isosceles triangle with the apex directed caudally. Nicander and Bane (1962a) describe but do not illustrate a distinct distal ring in the boar spermatozoon.

I. THE CYTOPLASMIC BEAD

This feature, which represents the residual cytoplasm of the spermatid, is commonly found at the neck of the spermatozoon ('proximal bead') or at the distal end of the middlepiece ('distal bead').

Discrete cytoplasmic beads, such as are commonly found in ungulate spermatozoa, are apparently not usual in human spermatozoa, where the amount of residual cytoplasm is relatively large and amorphous (Hodge, 1949). Anberg (1957) described a number of vesicles in the cytoplasm around the middle-piece of the human spermatozoon, though he does not refer specifically to the cytoplasmic bead. Descriptions of the bead in other species agree that it is bounded by the cell membrane, and that it contains flattened vesicles and tubules derived from the Golgi elements and possibly also from the endoplasmic reticulum. The vesicles tend to be concentrated in the peripheral part of the bead. These structures have been described in the boar by Nicander and Bane (1962a), and in the bull by Bloom and Nicander (1961), Kojima and Ishikawa (1963) and Birch-Anderson and Blom (1963). The latter authors also identified the isolated vesicular elements free in the seminal plasma, presumably after their release from the disintegrated bead.

No difference in structure between proximal beads and distal beads has been recognized, and no structural modifications of the middle-piece have been identified which could be associated with the migration of the cytoplasmic bead.

J. THE NECK

This term has long been used by light microscopists to denote the rather ill-defined region at the junction of the head and middle-piece.

It has now been found to have a complicated structure which includes one typical centriole, and a complex organelle by which the axial fibre bundle is articulated with the head. The precise organization of these structures is difficult to specify in the mature spermatozoon (see Fawcett, 1958; Rothschild, 1962). The salient features of the neck region as seen in whole (unsectioned) spermatozoa are well shown in Bretschneider's (1949) electron micrographs of bull and dog spermatozoa. Articulating with the posterior region of the sperm head is a flattened plate-like structure which in the bull has a raised centre. Posteriorly the plate is joined by a number of columnar structures with distinct transverse striations. These communicate, through a dense cylindrical area in which no detail is discernible, with nine stout fibres, below which are situated the peripheral fibres seen in the sectioned flagellum. Fawcett (1958) described a funnel-shaped structure, fixed at its expanded end to the head and continuous at the other end with the fibres of the flagellum. This structure is clearly that illustrated by Bretschneider. The connecting piece had a dense wall of nine coarse longitudinal fibres, with a distinct periodic structure giving them a banded appearance, continuous posteriorly with the outer ring of nine unstriated coarse tail

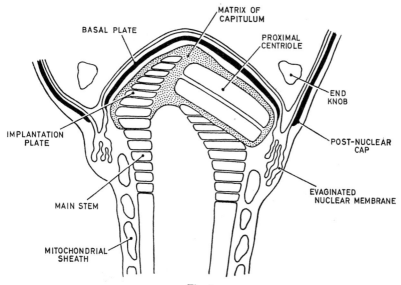

Fig. 5

Horizontal section of neck region showing the relationship of the main stems, implantation plate and the proximal centriole. The centriole is sectioned longitudinally. No attempt is made to show its detailed structure.

fibres. Fawcett judged the connecting piece to be a modified basal body representing the distal centriole.

Work on sectioned spermatozoa has added some new details, but it is still not easy to integrate these into a convincing and clear picture. Diagrammatic representations of the region as seen in vertical and transverse sections are shown in Figs. 5, 6 and 7. The terminology is that used by Anberg (1957), Blom and Birch-Anderson (1960, 1965), and Nicander and Bane (1962a).

Fig. 5 shows a longitudinal section of the neck, in the plane of the sperm head. Articulating with the *basal plate* which lies below the posterior boundary of the nucleus is the articular head or *capitulum*, supported by two laminated columns one on each side: these are the *main stems*. Their expanded upper ends form two *implantation plates*, one on each side. The plate on the left reaches almost to the articular surface: the other stops at the inferior boundary of the *proximal centriole*. This is shown as a hollow cylinder sectioned sagitally. The right implantation plate is assumed to be hollowed out to accommodate the centriole. On this interpretation both the left and right columns would reach the upper boundary of the capitulum in tangential sections.

Fig. 6 shows a transverse section of the neck region distal to the centriole. The two main stems are seen in section, one on each side, and five smaller stems are shown, three on one side of the main axis of the head and two on the other.

In Fig. 7 the neck is seen in longitudinal section vertical to the plane of the head. The wall of the proximal centriole consists in transverse section of nine elements, each with three tubular structures.

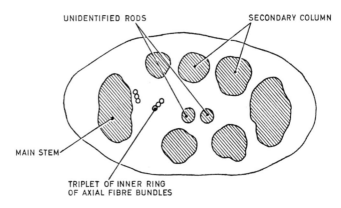

UNIDENTIFIED RODS   SECONDARY COLUMN

MAIN STEM

TRIPLET OF INNER RING
OF AXIAL FIBRE BUNDLES

Fig. 6 Transverse section of lower neck region.

The plane of the section passes through one of the smaller laminated columns, which is shown to embrace the centriole.

An evagination of the nuclear membrane projects backwards from the posterior border of the head, reaching almost to the mitochondrial sheath. Thus the deeper structures of the neck region are covered by this collar of nuclear membrane, and by the plasma membrane which lies over it.

This description accommodates a number of the features of the human spermatozoon described by Anberg, although it leaves un-

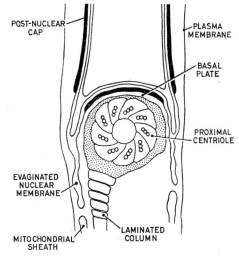

Fig. 7

Vertical section of neck region showing proximal centriole in transverse section. This section is shown to pass through only one of the smaller laminated columns which join the capitulum.

explained Anberg's observations of a series of circular bands round the neck of fragmented spermatozoa (see Anberg's Fig. 8). Blom and Birch-Anderson (1960) apparently failed to resolve the detailed structure of the attachments to the bull sperm head. They say that two *main stems* are formed each by the fusion of two coarse fibres, the heads of the main stems forming two *implantation plates* which attach to the basal plate at the posterior boundary of the head. These two plates are united into a single capitulum. The attachments of the five secondary fibres were unidentified. In three spermatozoa only, they identified a structure corresponding to the proximal centriole. There are two figures (Fig. 8 and Fig. 10) in their paper, however, in each of which is discernible a structure which could be the proximal centriole in vertical longitudinal section (compare Nicander and Bane 1962a, Plates 4 and 5, and Blom and Birch-Anderson, 1965, Plate 8e). Blom (1964b) suggested that the two implantation plates fuse with the proximal centriole to form a single structure attached to the basal plate.

Nicander and Bane (1962a) say that in the boar a thick dense *basal plate* lies at the posterior border of the head, outside the nuclear membrane, as described by Anberg (1957) in man, and provides an articular surface, the *implantation groove*, on its distal face. Two *implantation plates*, formed by the coalescence of fibres 5 and 6 and of fibres 1 and 9, articulate into the implantation groove.

Nicander and Bane were apparently able to trace the central pair of tail filaments into the proximal centriole, but did not observe the termination of the doublets of the inner ring. The proximal centriole was found to be a typical cylindrical structure with dense walls and a less dense centre, with nine tubular triplets set in the walls. Its long axis lay near the plane of the head and at rather less than 60° to the tail axis, and it was in close contact with all fibres except those forming the implantation plate on the opposite side. This asymmetry of the centriole and its attachments is apparently related to an asymmetry of the articular surface in the boar, and is responsible for the abaxial insertion of the tail which is a notable feature of boar spermatozoa (Hancock, 1957). In the anterior part of the neck the doublets of the inner ring were continued as triplets, looking very similar to those in the proximal centriole (see Figs. 6 and 7). The cross striations on the main stems reached only part of the way across the fibres; these striations run from the mesial surface of the fibres in the more cephalic part, and from the lateral surface in the distal part of the main stems.

The peculiar folding of the nuclear membrane in the neck region was first observed in the boar spermatozoon by Nicander and Bane (1962a). A similar formation has now been found in the bull spermatozoon (Blom and Birch-Anderson, 1965). A component of the double nuclear membrane is said to form the upper boundary of the basal plate. Nicander and Bane also described two unidentified rods in the neck region.

Kojima (1963) described two main stems on each side of the neck, with five smaller secondary fibres, three dorsal and two ventral. Each main stem is said to be composed of fifteen neck platelets. Each of the main stems divides into two medium stems and the members within each pair cross, so that their relative positions are reversed in their distal as compared with their proximal portions. Saacke and Almquist (1964b) summarized their findings in clear diagrammatic form. They recognized two separate implantation plates, but were uncertain how many fibres contributed to the two plates; at least four others were seen to enter the base of the head. They describe a common insertion of the laminated fibres into a single cap-like structure articulating with the recess in the head, but could find no evidence to support Wu and McKenzie's (1955) observation that articular strands project into the inner structure of the sperm head.

In all the above papers the position of the distal centriole is virtually ignored, although Blom and Birch-Anderson identify it with the annulus, which they describe clearly. Nicander and Bane (1962b) refer to the 'modified distal centriole' in the caption to one of their figures, but make no reference to it in the text. From this figure it seems likely that they accept Fawcett's interpretation and do not regard the terminal ring (annulus) as the distal centriole.

Fawcett (1958) has summarized some of the conflicting views which have been put forward about the behaviour of the centrioles during spermatogenesis. The typical centriole is a cylinder composed of nine longitudinally arranged elements. Burgos and Fawcett (1956) described two centriolar structures in the toad spermatid. The one nearer the nucleus lay with its long axis at right angles to that of the other, which was the filament-forming centriole and had its axis parallel to that of the flagellum. According to Fawcett (1958) the proximal centriole of the mammalian spermatozoon is typically an unmodified cylindrical centriolar structure lying at the base of the head, with its long axis at right angles to the sperm tail, and no second structure of undoubted centriolar origin exists in the neck of the mature spermatozoon.

Gatenby (1959), however, says that the unmodified centriole lying across the base of the head of the mammalian spermatid is the homologue, not of the similarly placed centriole of the toad, but of the longitudinally placed filament-forming centriole. The annulus, in spite of its atypical structure, could then be the distal centriole.

ACKNOWLEDGEMENTS

I have to thank Professor Alan Bane, Royal Veterinary College, Stockholm, and Dr. Erik Blom, State Serum Institute, Copenhagen, for their comments on the manuscript which they kindly read. I am grateful to Drs. Blom and Birch-Anderson for the opportunity to read in proof their paper 'The ultra-structure of the bull sperm'. I have to thank Mr. E. D. Roberts and Miss Sharman Currie for the line drawings.

REFERENCES

Afzelius, B. (1959) Electron microscopy of the sperm tail. Results obtained with a new fixative. *J. biophys. biochem. Cytol.* **5**, 269.
Anberg, A. (1957) The ultra-structure of the human spermatozoon. *Acta Obstet. Gynec. Scand.* **36**, Suppl. 2, 1–133.
Austin, C. R. and Bishop, M. W. H. (1958) Some features of the acrosome and perforatorium in mammalian spermatozoa. *Proc. Roy. Soc. B*, **148**, 234.
Bahr, G. F. and Teitler, E. (1964) Study of bull spermatozoa. Quantitative electron microscopy (samples collected in centrifuge tubes and immediately chilled on ice). *J. Cell. Biol.* **21**, 175.
Bane, A. (1961) Acrosome abnormality associated with sterility in boar. *Proc. IV Int. Congr. Anim. Reprod.* **4**, 810.
Bane, A. and Nicander, L. (1963) The structure and formation of the perforatorium in mammalian spermatozoa. *Int. J. Fertil.* **8**, 865.
Bawa, S. K. (1963) Outer coarse fibres of the mammalian spermatozoa tail—an electron microscopy study. *J. Ultrastruct. Res.* **9**, 475.
Bedford, J. (1963) Morphological reaction of spermatozoa in the female reproductive tract of the rabbit. *J. Reprod. Fertil.* **6**, 245.
Bedford, J. (1964a) Changes in the fine structure of the rabbit sperm head during passage through the epididymis. *Proc. V. Int. Congr. Anim. Reprod., Trento,* **3**, 397.
Bedford, J. (1964b) Fine structure of the sperm head in ejaculate and uterine spermatozoa of the rabbit. *J. Reprod. Fertil.* **7**, 221–228.
Birch-Anderson, A. and Blom, E. (1963) Concentrating ejaculated sperm for electron microscopy. *Nature,* **199**, 201–203.
Bishop, M. W. H. and Walton, A. (1960) Spermatogenesis and the structure of mammalian spermatozoa. In Marshall's *Physiology of Reproduction.* Ed. A. S. Parkes. **1** (2), 1–101.
Blom, E. (1964a) The *galea capitis* as part of the acrosome cap in the bull sperm. *Proc. V Int. Congr. Anim. Reprod.,* Trento, **4**, 655.
Blom, E. (1964b) Spermatic ultra-structure (bovine). In *Sterility,* W. W. Williams, Springfield.
Blom, E. and Birch-Anderson, A. (1960) Ultra-structure of the bull sperm. I. The middle piece. *Nord. Vet. Med.,* **12**, 261–279.
Blom, E. and Birch-Anderson, A. (1961) An apical body in the galea capitis of the normal bull sperm. *Nature,* **190**, 1127–8.
Blom, E. and Birch-Anderson, A. (1962) Ultra-structure of the sterilizing knobbed-sperm defect in the bull. *Nature,* **194**, 989–990.
Blom, E. and Birch-Anderson, A. (1965) The ultra-structure of the bull sperm. II. The sperm head. *Nord. Vet. Med.,* **17**, 193–212.
Bloom, G. and Nicander, L (1961) On the ultra-structure and development of the protoplasmic droplet of spermatozoa. *Z. Zellforsch,* **55**, 833–844.
Bradfield, J. R. G. (1955) Fibre patterns in animal flagella and cilia. *Symp. Soc. Exp. Biol.* **9**, 306.

Bretschneider, L. H. (1949) An electron microscopical study of bull sperm. IV (The sperm of bull, horse and dog.) *Proc. Kon. Ned. Akad. Wet.* **52** (5), 1.

Burgos, M. H. and Fawcett, D. W. (1955) Studies on the fine structure of the mammalian testis. I. Differentiation of the spermatids in the cat (*Felis domestica*). *J. biophys. biochem. Cytol.* **1**, 287–299.

Burgos, M. H. and Fawcett, D. W. (1956) An electron microscope study of spermatid differentiation in the toad *Bufo arenarum* Hensel. *J. biophys. biochem. Cytol.* **2**, 223.

Challice, C. E. (1953) Electron microscope studies of spermiogenesis in some rodents. *J. Roy. Micr. Soc.* **73**, 115.

Cleland, K. W. and Rothschild, Lord (1959) The bandicoot spermatozoon: an electron microscope study of the tail. *Proc. Roy. Soc.* (London) B, **150**, 24.

Clermont, Y. and Leblond, C. P. (1955) Spermiogenesis of man, monkey, ram and other mammals as shown by the 'periodic acid—Schiff' technique. *Am. J. Anat.* **96**, 229.

Clermont, Y., Einberg, E., Leblond, C. P. and Wagner, S. (1955) The perforatorium an extension of the nuclear membrane of the rat spermatozoon. *Anat. Rec.* **121**, 1.

Das, C. M. S. (1962) Ultra-structure of the post-nuclear cap in the developing sperms of *Microtus pennsylvanicus*. *Proc. Zool. Soc.* (Calcutta) **15**, 75.

Dickmann, Z. (1964) The passage of spermatozoa through and into the zona pellucida of the rabbit egg. *J. Exp. Biol.* **41**, 177.

Dickmann, Z. and Dziuk, P. J. (1964) Sperm penetration of the zona pellucida of the pig egg. *J. Exp. Biol.* **41**, 603.

Fawcett, D. W. (1958) The structure of the mammalian spermatozoa. *Int. rev. Cytol.* **195**, 233.

Fawcett, D. W. (1962) Sperm tail structure in relation to the mechanism of movement. *Proc. Symp. Sperm. Mot. Am. Ass. Adv. Sci.* **72**, 147–169.

Fawcett, D. W. and Hollenberg, R. D. (1963) Changes in the acrosome of guinea pig spermatozoa during passage through the epididymis. *Z. Zellforsch.* **60**, 276–292.

Gatenby, J. B. (1959) The electron microscopy of centriole, flagellum and cilium. *J. Roy. Microsc. Soc.* **79**, 299.

Hadek, R. (1963a) Submicroscopic changes in the penetrating spermatozoa of the rabbit. *J. Ultrastruct. Res.* **8**, 161.

Hadek, R. (1963b) Study on the fine structure of rabbit sperm head. *J. Ultrastruct. Res.* **9**, 110–122.

Hancock, J. L. (1952) The morphology of bull spermatozoa. *J. exp. Biol.* **29**, 445.

Hancock, J. L. and Trevan, D. J. (1957) The acrosome and post-nuclear cap of bull spermatozoa. *J. Roy. Microsc. Soc.* **76**, 77.

Hancock, J. L. (1957) The morphology of boar spermatozoa. *J. Roy. Micr. Soc.* **76**, 84.

Hartree, E. F. and Srivastava, P. N. (1965) Chemical composition of the acrosomes of ram spermatozoa. *J. Reprod. Fertil.* **9**, 47.

Hodge, A. J. (1949) Electron microscopic studies of spermatozoa. II. The morphology of the human spermatozoon. *Austral. J. Sci. Res.* (B) **2**, 368.

Kojima, Y. (1962) Electron microscopic study of the bull spermatozoa. *Jap. J. Vet. Res.* **10**, 72–74.

Kojima, Y. and Ishikawa, T. (1963) Etude au microscope électronique de la gouttelette protoplasmique observée dans le spermatozoïde chez les taureaux. *Jap. J. Vet. Res.* **11**, 152–157.

Leblond, C. P. and Clermont, Y. (1952) Spermiogenesis of rat, mouse, hamster and guinea-pig as revealed by the 'periodic-acid fuchsin sulphurous acid' technique. *Amer. J. Anat.* **90**, 167.

Mathur, R. S. (1962) The centriole complex of the rat. An electron microscope study. *J. Roy. Micr. Soc.* **81**, 19.

Moricard, R. (1960) Observations de microscopie électronique sur des modifications acrosomiques lors de la pénétration spermatique dans l'oeuf des mammifères. *C. R. Soc. Biol.* **154**, 2187.

Moricard, R. (1961) Superpénétration spermatique de la membrane pellucide et observations en microscopie électronique d'oeufs fécondés de lapine. *Proc. IV Int. Congr. Anim. Reprod.* The Hague. **IV**, 736.

Nagano, T. (1963) Fine structural changes in the flagellum of the spermatid in experimental cryptorchidism of the rat. *Exp. Cell. Res.* **18**, 337.

Nicander, L. (1962) Development of the fibrous sheath of the sperm tail. *Proc. Fifth Int. Congr. Electron Microscopy* pt. 4.

Nicander, L. and Bane, A. (1962a) Fine structure of boar spermatozoa. *Z. Zellforsch.* **57**, 390–405.

Nicander, L. and Bane, A. (1962b) New observations on the fine structure of spermatozoa. *Int. J. Fertil.* **7**, 339–344.

Piko, L. and Tyler, A. (1964) Fine structural studies of sperm penetration in the rat. *Proc. Vth Int. Congr. Anim. Reprod.* Trento, **2**, 372.

Rahlman, D. F. (1961) Electron microscopic structure of mature bovine spermatozoa. *J. Dairy Sci.* **44**, 915.

Randall, J. T. and Friedlaender, M. H. G. (1950) The microstructure of ram spermatozoa. *J. Exp. Cell. Res.* **1**, 1.

Rothschild, Lord (1958) The human spermatozoon. *Br. Med. J.* **i**, 301.

Rothschild, Lord (1962) Spermatozoa. *Br. Med. J.* **ii**, 743–749, 812–817.

Saacke, R. G. and Almquist, J. O. (1964a) Ultra-structure of bovine spermatozoa. I. The head of normal ejaculated sperm. *J. Dairy Sci.* **115**, 143–161.

Saacke, R. G. and Almquist, J. O. (1964b) Ultra-structure of bovine spermatozoa. II. The neck and tail of normal ejaculated sperm. *J. Dairy Sci.*, **115**, 163–172.

Schultz-Larsen, J. and Hammen, R. (1956) The submicroscopic morphology of human spermatozoa. *Dan. Med. Bull.* **3**, 141.

Sotelo, J. R. and Trujillo-Cenoz, O. (1958) Electron microscope study of the kinetic apparatus in animal sperm cells. *Z. Zellforsch.* **48**. 565.

Szollosi, D. G. and Ris, H. (1961) Observations on sperm penetration in the rat. *J. biophys. biochem. Cytol.* **10**, 275.

Telkka, A., Fawcett, D. W. and Christensen, A. K. (1961) Further observations on the structure of the mammalian sperm tail. *Anat. Rec.* **141**, 231–236.

Wu, S. H. and McKenzie, F. F. (1955) Microstructure of spermatozoa after denudation as revealed by the electron microscope. *J. Anim. Sci.* **14**, 1152.

Wu, S. H. and Newstead, J. D. (1963) Electron microscope studies of bovine epididymal spermatozoa. (Abstr.) *J. Anim. Sci.* **22**, 867.

6

PHEROMONES AND MAMMALIAN REPRODUCTION

W. K. WHITTEN

National Biological Standards Laboratory, Canberra, Australia

A. INTRODUCTION

The term pheromone was proposed by Karlson and Butenandt (1959), and has since been widely accepted to describe chemical substances used for animal communication. It replaces the older and less accurate word ectohormones. Kalmus (1964) has suggested some minor changes to the original definition so that it now reads: 'Pheromones are substances, or mixtures of substances, which are produced to the exterior by an animal and may be received by a second individual of the same species, in which they produce one or more specific reactions.' They may act by stimulating chemical receptors, for example the olfactory receptors, or they may function after ingestion.

Wilson and Bossert (1963) further classified pheromones according to the type of response they produce. If the pheromone elicits a more or less immediate but reversible change in behaviour it is said to be a 'releaser pheromone', whereas if the principal function of the pheromone is to initiate a chain of physiological events in the recipient then the term 'primer pheromone' is used. This effect may be either inhibitory or stimulating. A pheromone may exhibit both releaser and primer actions, and its function may then depend on the context in which it is produced or received. The 'queen substance' of the honey bee is an example of such a combination. It inhibits oogenesis in the workers and prevents them from rearing other queens in the hive, but it also acts as a sex attractant to drones during the queen's nuptial flight (Butler, 1964).

There is evidence that both types of pheromones function in mammals, but we know very much less about mammalian than about insect pheromones. The present article will attempt to indicate the gaps in our knowledge of mammalian pheromones, and to relate the findings to the principles of chemical communication which have been established from the work with insects.

B. PRIMER PHEROMONES

A field of science often yields independently to attacks from different quarters. Within the last decade this has happened in the field of mammalian primer pheromones from work in Holland by Lee and Boot, in England by Bruce and Parkes, in America by Bronson, Marsden and Eleftheriou and by the author in Australia. The field is very new, and progress is slow because the techniques are tedious. The aim is to establish the following:-

   (i) The nature of the responses produced by the pheromones, and to quantitate them as methods of assay.

  (ii) That the responses are elicited by products to the exterior, e.g. urine.

 (iii) The sources and pathways of production.

 (iv) The receptor mechanisms involved, e.g. olfaction.

  (v) The target organs or systems.

 (vi) The chemical structures of the pheromones and to confirm these by synthesis.

(vii) That the synthetic compounds produce complete responses. In order to prove that a primer pheromone functions, it is necessary to establish both (i) and (ii) above.

As will be seen, few mammalian studies have shown that pheromones are present and no pheromone has been identified chemically. However, much indirect evidence has been obtained and this will be discussed. The outstanding problem with mammalian studies is to identify the receptor(s) involved and to develop a rapid method of assay, such as has been done with electro-antennograms in insects. So far only gross effects have been studied and the response determined by statistical assessment of quantal results.

1. Effects in mice

Most of the conclusive evidence for mammalian primer pheromones has been derived from studies with laboratory mice (*Mus musculus* L.) during the last decade. This may in part reflect the increasing attention which has been given to the design, ventilation and hygiene of experimental animal quarters.

Female mice subjected to normal diurnal light cycles exhibit a relatively short oestrous cycle of 4 to 6 days' duration. Behavioural oestrus with mating occurs for a few hours on each side of midnight of the last day, and ovulation, which is usually spontaneous, occurs at about 3 a.m., towards the end of the period of oestrus (Whitten and Dagg, 1961). Later that morning a characteristic change in the smear from the vagina occurs, indicating a transition from oestrus to metoestrus. The cell type changes from purely cornified epithelial cells to a mixture of cornified cells and leucocytes. Successful copulation is accompanied by the formation of a copulation plug, a horny mass of coagulated ejaculum which often completely fills the vagina and may adhere to its walls for some 30 hrs.

In the absence of copulation or some such stimulus the short 4–6 day cycle recurs, and is characteristically free of any luteal phase. Corpora lutea are formed but do not secrete significant amounts of progesterone. However, if sterile mating takes place the cycle is extended to 10–15 days, and activation of the organized corpora lutea occurs. Luteal function can be demonstrated by the formation of a decidual reaction in response to uterine trauma. Such cycles are referred to as pseudopregnancies and occasionally may occur spontaneously. Cycles in which the oestrous phase is prolonged for three or more days may also be observed.

Pregnancy normally lasts for 19 or 20 days with implantation on the 5th day. A post-partum oestrus occurs in which ovulation and mating are not limited to the period of dark.

2. Shortening of the oestrous cycle and prevention of spontaneous pseudopregnancy

Merton (1938) first suggested that the presence of males may prevent a prolongation of the oestrous cycle of mice, but it was twenty years before this hypothesis was tested (Whitten, 1958). The experiment will be described in full to indicate the nature of the observations. The technique adopted was to compare the mean length of oestrous cycles of mice caged individually with those of mice in whose cage a male was confined within a wire basket. Three consecutive cycles were observed in half of the animals under one set of conditions and then the conditions were reversed, so that the animals acted partly as their own controls. The change-over for each animal was made during metoestrus. Other precautions were taken to control variables. The cages were similarly placed in small rooms identically lit and individually but equally ventilated. The cages were of smooth stainless steel, and were carefully cleaned. The vaginal smears were taken each morning from the mice caged without males first, so as not to transfer any male mouse odours.

The results are reproduced in Table I. The distribution is obviously not normal, but with each treatment is positively skewed. Moreover, the observations made in the absence of a male seem to have a secondary mode at 11 days which may result from the occasional occurrence of pseudopregnancy or prolonged dioestrus. To permit an analysis of variance all values of 10 days or more were rejected, because they represented obvious departures from normal oestrous cycles. All the discarded values were confined to observations made in the absence of a male, which itself represents a significant difference between the treatments. Despite the rejection of these high values the effect of the male was highly significant (P < 0.001) and departures from normal distribution could be safely neglected. The difference between the groups, which represents the order of treatment, was not significant.

Similar findings were obtained with two inbred strains of mice. Moreover, the same difference was observed if the male was separated by a double-layered basket so that tactile stimulation was completely

TABLE I

DURATION OF OESTROUS CYCLE IN PRESENCE AND ABSENCE OF MALES

	Duration of cycle (days)					
	Males present			Males absent		
	1st	2nd	3rd	4th	5th	6th
	4	4	4	8	16	4
	4	4	4	5	4	4
	4	6	5	11	13	13
	5	5	5	7	5	8
	4	4	4	6	5	5
Males present for first three	4	5	5	7	11	6
cycles observed, absent for	5	4	5	7	7	6
second three cycles (12 fe-	5	4	4	5	5	5
males)	4	4	4	6	6	5
	5	5	5	5	5	15
	5	9	7	5	6	7
	5	5	5	8	9	6
Mean	4.5	4.9	4.8	6.3	5.8	5.6
	4th	5th	6th	1st	2nd	3rd
	4	4	4	6	8	10
	4	4	5	6	13	7
	6	5	6	10	11	6
	4	4	4	6	6	5
	5	5	4	6	6	7
Males absent for first three	4	4	4	5	5	5
cycles observed, present for	5	5	5	6	6	6
second three cycles (14 fe-	6	4	5	8	11	7
males)	5	4	4	5	5	5
	4	4	4	5	5	5
	5	5	4	5	5	5
	4	4	4	5	8	6
	4	4	4	6	5	6
	5	4	5	5	5	5
Mean	4.6	4.3	4.4	5.7	5.8	5.8

Cycles of 10 days or more were omitted from calculations
(From Whitten (1958) *J. Endocr.*, **17**, 307–13)

eliminated. It also occurred if the female mice were blinded, or if their ear drums were completely ruptured.

These findings indicate that visual, tactile or auditory perception is not essential for the effect to occur. It was not possible to test in the same way for olfactory or vomeronasal chemoreception, since mice from this strain do not exhibit oestrous cycles when the olfactory bulbs are completely ablated (Whitten, 1956b). Removal or denervation of the vomeronasal organs prevented the shortening of the oestrous cycles by the presence of males, but so did sham operations (Whitten, 1963), so no conclusion could be drawn regarding the function of these organs.

Table I also shows that there is no carry-over of the effect from one treatment to the succeeding one. This is shown by the fact that the first cycle of each treatment was not significantly different from the remaining two. Thus, the stimulus is effective only during the cycle in which it acts.

In order to prove that the effect is produced by a pheromone, experiments are now in progress using the technique of Marsden and Bronson (1964), in which male mouse urine is applied to the external nares.

Further experiments were carried out in which the female was exposed for only a portion of a cycle. Only in animals which were exposed to males immediately after metoestrus, for a period of 48 hours, was it possible to demonstrate a clear-cut reduction in the length of the oestrous cycle. No effect was observed with 12 hours' exposure, and a doubtful result was obtained with 24 hours. Moreover, when the exposure to the male was delayed for 24 hours after the detection of metoestrus, but then continued until the end of the cycle, no significant shortening was observed. In view of the ready fatigue of the olfactory sense in man it might be supposed that adaptation to the stimulus would preclude so long an action. However, such fatigue has not been demonstrated in any mammal other than man (Adrian, 1950).

These experiments suggest that the stimulus from the male is effective during the period of follicle growth and thus differs from the ovulatory stimulus required in those species in which ovulation is not spontaneous. The effect produced by the male may be to initiate follicle development earlier, or to increase its rate, or both. The effect may also influence pre-ovulatory swelling and ovulation.

The prolonged dioestrus or pseudopregnancy which occasionally occurs in isolated females was prevented by the presence of males. On the other hand, pseudopregnancy resulting from sterile mating was not influenced by the continued presence of the sterile male.

3. The occurrence of pseudopregnancy in grouped mice

Lee and Boot (1955, 1956) observed a higher incidence of prolonged oestrous cycles with vaginal mucification among older mice when the mice were kept four to a cage than when they were housed individually. The abnormal cycles were proved to be pseudopregnancies by demonstrating that decidual reactions followed uterine trauma, and that transfer of fertile ova resulted in successful pregnancies.

The incidence of pseudopregnancy was decreased if the olfactory bulbs were removed, but not if body contact between the animals was prevented. It was therefore suggested that an odour was responsible for the occurrence of pseudopregnancy.

Dewar (1959) confirmed the spontaneous occurrence of pseudopregnancies in grouped mice by observing vaginal mucification, body weight changes and mammary development. He also observed male-like mounting activity on the part of the females, and suggested that this might be a factor in the production of 'spontaneous' pseudopregnancy.

4. The occurrence of anoestrus in grouped mice

The findings of Lee and Boot (1955, 1956) stimulated an investigation of grossly irregular cycles in Walter and Eliza Hall strain of mice caged in groups of about 30 (Whitten, 1957). The irregular cycles appeared to be unrelated to any form of stress because the animals maintained growth and sleek appearance, and exhibited no evidence of an order of social dominance. Also more than 90% were capable of fertile mating within 5 days if paired with males.

The following account of an experiment carried out by the author (Whitten, 1959) illustrates the degree of suppression of oestrus. Sixty female mice were divided at random into two lots of 30. One lot was housed in a single large cage, while the mice from the second lot were caged individually. Beginning 10 days later, vaginal smears were taken daily for 16 days. At the completion of this period the housing conditions were reversed and after a similar lag of 10 days the vaginal smears were again observed for an additional 16 days. During both periods of observation the number of times that each mouse exhibited an oestrous vaginal smear was recorded. An oestrous smear was considered to be one in which all the cells were fully cornified and which was followed next day by one containing leucocytes, typical of metoestrus. The mean scores together with standard errors are given in Table II. Analysis of variance of the data shows that grouping produced a highly significant reduction of the incidence of oestrus (P < 0.001). The difference was sufficiently great to ignore any

11

possible departure from normal distribution. There was no significant difference between the two lots, which shows that oestrous cycles returned promptly after segregation and were suppressed shortly after grouping.

TABLE II

PERIODICITY OF OESTRUS IN MICE LIVING SINGLY
OR IN GROUPS

No. of females	Treatment		Mean frequency of occurrence of oestrus during 16 days ± S.E.
30	A	Caged individually then caged as a group	2.90 ± 0.14 0.57 ± 0.12
30	B	Caged as a group then caged individually	0.83 ± 0.15 2.57 ± 0.24

Analysis of variance: grouped v. individual, P < 0·001; A v. B, P > 0·05
(From Whitten (1959) *J. Endocr.*, **18**, 102–7)

A reduction in the incidence of oestrus has been consistently observed in grouped mice, and was still evident in a group maintained for 3 months. The vaginal smears of most grouped animals were mucified, and this condition frequently persisted for 40 days or more. This mucification was probably similar to that observed by Robson and Wiesner (1932) following a dose of oestrogen too small to elicit vaginal cornification. In each group a few animals continued to exhibit regular oestrous cycles and in these the oestrous phase appeared to be prolonged. There was no evidence to suggest that these were in any way socially dominant, but they might be the source of a pheromone. Regular short oestrous cycles occurred when a male was confined in the cage with a group of female mice, but were not observed if the male was castrated (Bruce, personal communication; Whitten, unpublished).

Mice in the large groups congregated in masses. It therefore seemed possible that mechanical stimulation of the mammary area might have reduced the secretion of gonadotrophin by the pituitary (Selye, Collip and Thompson, 1934). But when contact between the mice was prevented by subdividing the large cage into 30 small compartments, suppression of oestrus still occurred.

The suppression also persisted after section of the optic nerves or rupture of the ear drums. This again suggests but does not prove that the effects are produced by a pheromone probably acting through a remote chemical sense, e.g. olfaction.

There is some similarity between this effect and that described by Lee and Boot (1955, 1956). However, the following observations clearly indicate that the prolonged cycles are not due to the occurrence of pseudopregnancies:—

(i) Vaginal mucification often persisted for more than 40 days compared with about 10 days during pseudopregnancy.

(ii) Many of the uteri of the grouped mice were atrophic.

(iii) The ovaries of the grouped mice generally contained atrophic corpora lutea, but occasionally no evidence of luteal tissue was found.

(iv) When the uteri of a large number of grouped mice were traumatized as for a progesterone assay (Astwood, 1939), only one animal developed a decidual reaction.

The additional evidence for the occurrence of anoestrus is as follows:—

(i) The mean weight of the ovaries was significantly reduced.

(ii) Fewer mice had ova from a recent ovulation in their oviducts.

(iii) Fewer mice exhibited vaginal oestrus.

We may therefore conclude that while Lee and Boot (1956) demonstrated pseudopregnancy when mice were kept in groups of 4, Whitten (1959) observed anoestrus in groups of 30. If we assume that females produce primer pheromones which modify the oestrous cycle, we may ask whether these different effects are due to different pheromones or to a difference in response by the strains of mice used, or whether there is a quantitative difference in the nature of the pheromonal stimulus.

Everett (1956, 1964) postulated that a reciprocal relationship exists between the secretion of follicle-stimulating hormone (FSH) and luteotrophin, so that pseudopregnancy results only when the secretion of FSH is reduced. If this is correct, then the effect of grouping observed by Lee and Boot (1956) resulted from an inhibition of FSH secretion. If the conditions producing the inhibition are intensified (30 instead of 4 mice per cage), further depression of FSH production resulting in anoestrus might be expected.

5. Synchronization of oestrus and mating

As pointed out above, the presence of a male for 48 hours during the early part of a cycle results in a shortening of that cycle. When a group of mice is paired with males a proportion of the females will be in that phase of their cycles during which they will respond to the males by a shortened cycle. As a result, one would expect more mice to mate after 48 hours than on the first two nights after pairing. Experiments have shown that a peak of incidence of mating occurs on the third night if previously isolated females are paired with males (Whitten, 1959; Lamond, 1959).

A much more significant peak of oestrus on the third night occurred if the mice had been grouped before pairing with males. Moreover, if the mice were paired but the male confined within a basket for 2 days and then released, the synchrony of oestrus occurred on the first night after his release—that is, as before, on the third night after the female was paired (Whitten, 1956a).

Housing the females for 2 days in cages recently occupied by males altered the timing of oestrus, which suggests that synchronization is caused by a pheromone. Proof has recently been provided by Marsden and Bronson (1964). These workers applied male urine to the nares of grouped mice regularly for 2 days and observed synchronization of oestrus during the following night.

It thus appears that marked synchronization results from the effects of two pheromones, the first acting in grouped females and causing anoestrus, the second from males, releasing the females from this inhibition and stimulating short cycles. The results are summarized in Fig. 1.

6. Block to pregnancy by strange males

The most spectacular effect produced by primer pheromones was discovered by Bruce (1959). She observed that if the stud male was removed from a recently mated female mouse, and a male from a different strain was introduced on the following day for 2 or 3 days, 70–80% of the newly mated females returned to oestrus within a week. In other words the cycle proceeded as though the first mating had not occurred. If a fertile mating occurred with the strange male, then all offspring after such double mating were sired by the second male, and the original pregnancy from the stud male was blocked.

The effect was still observed if body contact with the male was prevented (Bruce, 1960). In addition, Bruce and Parkes (1961a) and

Parkes and Bruce (1962) have provided the best evidence yet that a product released to the exterior can elicit the full response. Recently mated female mice were transferred twice daily for 3 days to cages which had been previously occupied by 5 alien males. The degree of pregnancy block which resulted was as high as with exposure to males themselves. However, transfer only once daily was much less effective. This gives some indication of the stability or persistence of the pheromone.

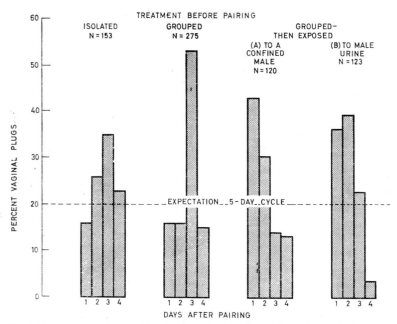

Fig. 1: Frequency distribution of vaginal plugs in days after pairing. The females had been previously isolated, grouped, or grouped but exposed to confined males or male urine. Values are expressed as percentages of the total number of vaginal plugs occurring within 4 days. Sample sizes are indicated above each histogram. From Whitten (1956, 1959) and Marsden and Bronson (1964).

Females appeared to be equally vulnerable on each of the first 4 days *post coitum*, but became less so on the fifth day, by which time implantation is proceeding. The reaction virtually disappeared by the sixth day. As with the stimulus required for shortening the oestrous cycle, an exposure of 48 hours was required to produce the maximum number of blocked pregnancies. However, some females returned to oestrus after an exposure of only 12 hours (Bruce, 1961). Successive pregnancies could be blocked without subsequent impairment of fertility (Bruce, 1962). The pregnancy block did not occur in lactating mice mated on the post-partum oestrus (Bruce and Parkes, 1961b).

The induction of pregnancy block is determined by the female's ability to perceive a difference between the stud and the strange (or alien) male. No block occurred when the mice were made anosmic (Bruce and Parrott, 1960). If the male was from a different strain (alien) from the stud, the pregnancy was blocked in about 80% of the animals, and this percentage could not be increased by using several males together. With a male from the same strain (strange), the incidence was constant at about 30% if the strain was randomly bred. When both males were from the same inbred strain the incidence was lower, 16%, which does not appear to be significantly higher than for control animals (Parkes and Bruce, 1961). This can be interpreted to mean that even to the discriminating nose of a female mouse, male inbred mice smell alike. Bruce (personal communication) also has some evidence that related inbred strains of mice (CBA, C3H) may not block each other effectively.

Female mice remained pregnant if the stud male was removed but returned 24 hours later. Further, his presence largely eliminated her reaction to alien males surrounding the pair. On the other hand some confusion occurred if the female was exposed to the alien male before mating with the stud (Parkes and Bruce, 1961). The presence of other females reduced the incidence of pregnancy block in proportion to their number (Bruce, 1963).

Recent experiments (Bruce, personal communication) have failed to confirm earlier results which indicated that pregnancy block occurred after exposure to castrate strange males (Bruce, 1960). It has now been clearly shown that the ability to block pregnancy develops at puberty, does not appear in animals castrated before puberty and is abolished by castration during adulthood (Bruce, 1965).

Bruce and Parkes (1960) postulated that the immediate cause of pregnancy block was a failure of corpora lutea to become functional, and reasoned that the administration of appropriate hormones should prevent it. Injection of 10 I.U. of luteotrophin (prolactin) on the first, second or third day after mating prevented block to pregnancy by alien males. Administration of progesterone was far less effective but did preserve a proportion of pregnancies. Perhaps long acting oral progestogens would have been better. Confirmation of the role of luteotrophin was obtained when it was shown that pregnancy block did not occur in lactating mice, mated at the post-partum oestrus, when it can be assumed that luteotrophin was circulating. The reason for the failure of the secretion of luteotrophin was not determined. The possibility that the failure was due to antagonistic actions of follicle-stimulating or corticotrophic hormones was tested but with negative results, even though there is evidence that the secretion of both these hormones may be increased during exposure to alien males.

Again, Everett's (1956, 1964) concept of a reciprocal relationship between the secretion of FSH and luteotrophin provides the best explanation of the phenomenon of pregnancy block. Normal mating provides a stimulus for the secretion of luteotrophin and this is accompanied by a decrease in the secretion of FSH. However, when an alien male is present the female responds to his pheromone with the production of FSH, and this response prevents the secretion of luteotrophin, the penultimate cause of the block to pregnancy. In the case of post-partum mating of lactating females, the additional stimulus from suckling ensures the secretion of luteotrophin (prolactin) and thus prevents a response to the pheromone.

If this interpretation is correct, then the block to pregnancy is an example of the action of the same male pheromone which prevents ① CYCLE
pseudopregnancy and shortens cycles, but acting in the special cir- ② PSPG
cumstances of early pregnancy. It then remains to be determined ③ PGX
whether it is the detection of 'strangeness' of the males which initiates the sequence of events leading up to pregnancy block, or whether it is the recognition of 'sameness' of the stud male which blocks the follicle-stimulating action of the pheromone.

C. PROPERTIES OF MOUSE PRIMER PHEROMONES

1. How many primer pheromones in mice

Two effects which may be produced by primer pheromones from female mice have been described, and arguments have been put forward to indicate that these two effects could be produced by a single pheromone acting at two different dose levels. Evidence has also been presented of four effects produced by primer pheromones from male mice. All four have in common the development, earlier than would have been expected, of follicles, oestrus and ovulation. Again it has been argued that these may all be expressions of the action of a single pheromone in different contexts.

To explain pregnancy block by strange males, it is necessary to postulate the existence of an additional factor, an 'identifier'. This may be a pheromone or it may be non-specific, resembling the olfactory 'signature' by which animals identify each other. An alternative and equally plausible suggestion has been made by Parkes (1960), that the pheromone from males is in fact a spectrum of odours, and that the 'identifier' function is determined by a difference in intensity of various compounds.

2. Origin and nature of mouse primer pheromones

Discussion in this and the subsequent section will be based on the assumption that female mice produce only one pheromone, and that males produce another, together with an 'identifier'.

If the male pheromone is produced only by adult entire males, it must be secreted by the testes or under their control. The product is clearly produced to the exterior because it persists in soiled cages. Recently Marsden and Bronson (1964) have provided strong evidence that the pheromone is present in urine. It has long been recognized that male mouse urine has a musk-like odour lost after castration, which suggests that the pheromone may be an odoriferous steroid. However, Δ^{16}-androstenol, which according to Prelog, Ruzicka and Wieland (1944) possesses a strong musk-like odour and appears in the urine of some species, could not be detected in male mouse urine by Brooksbank (personal communication). The pheromone may, however, be a similar compound, and it is perhaps significant that there is sufficient β-glucuronidase in male mouse urine (Riotton and Fishman, 1953) to ensure that any steroid is excreted free and odoriferous and not rendered odourless by conjugation. The molecular weights of many free steroids fall within the limits set by Wilson and Bossert (1963) for chemicals suitable for pheromones.

Nothing is known of the nature of the female pheromone since all the evidence for its existence is indirect. However, the findings of Marsden and Bronson (1964) indicate that it too could be in the urine.

There are many possible sites of production and pathways of excretion for pheromones and odoriferous substances which may function as 'identifiers'. The special glands on the soles of the feet of mice (Ortman, 1956) and the sebaceous glands, which Kandutsch (1958) has shown are influenced by testosterone, may be involved. Excretion in the expired air may also be important for such volatile substances: Dziuk (personal communication) has pointed out that the breath of the boar apparently attracts sows.

3. Which receptors do they stimulate?

Though the experimental evidence suggests that the mouse primer pheromones act through the olfactory sense, it is not possible to exclude with certainty ingestion, inhalation, taste and the receptors of the vomeronasal organ. If the action is dependent on absorption following ingestion or inhalation, then one would expect that frequent injections of male urine would also be effective, but this is not so (Whitten, unpublished). Evidence from animals after removal of the olfactory bulbs should be interpreted with caution, since Sawyer (1955) has observed that intrinsic activity in the olfactory bulbs is an essential prelude to the release of gonadotrophin following instillation of histamine into the third ventricle. Further, the olfactory bulbs contain the accessory olfactory bulbs, which are the secondary connections of the vomeronasal organs (Allison, 1953). These organs appear to be chemical receptors and are particularly well developed in mice. As mentioned above, experiments designed to test the hypothesis that the vomeronasal organs were pheromone receptors were inconclusive, and the search for mice in which these structures were congenitally absent was unsuccessful (Whitten, 1963). Whether the receptors are olfactory or accessory olfactory, pathways exist from these rhinencephalic structures to the hypothalamus via the median forebrain bundle, or the amygdala and the stria terminalis (Sawyer, 1957).

One may speculate on whether both mouse pheromones act through the same receptor, even though no receptor has yet been positively identified. Since the male pheromone stimulates the release of FSH while the female one depresses its release, there is the intriguing possibility that both act by stimulating or depressing a single type of receptor. An analogous effect has been observed by Boeckh (1962) with single receptors of Necrophorus. These react with depolarization and generation of impulses to stimuli from homologous fatty acids containing 6 to 10 carbon atoms, but with hyperpolarization and inhibition of impulses when exposed to fatty acids with 3 or 4 carbon atoms. To speculate further, do the spontaneous intrinsic oscillations of potential or the discharges associated with non-specific olfactory stimulation (Adrian, 1950) serve in part to maintain the basal rate of pituitary secretion in isolated females? Is the male pheromone an androgen metabolite which increases this activity, and the female pheromone a product of the ovary which reduces the activity? Are

FSH
♂ ↑
♀ ↓

the two pheromones sufficiently similar to act on the same receptor site? (Amoore, 1964).

Theoretically, a female mouse could respond to her own pheromone. Stimulation of the receptors could occur either while the substance was still circulating in the body fluids, or after excretion. The pheromone, particularly if it were a steroid of ovarian origin, might play a role in the negative feedback from the ovary to the hypothalamic-hypophyseal system.

It has been suggested above that the block to pregnancy is produced by the primer pheromone from males, acting together with 'identifier' signals. Prevention of the block to pregnancy by removal of the olfactory bulbs indicates that at least one of the factors acts through olfaction or accessory olfaction. Other evidence suggests that this is the pathway for the primer pheromone, so that it is still possible for the 'identifier' to stimulate another chemical receptor, for example taste. The licking activity which occurs when an alien male is introduced supports this possibility.

D. OBSERVATIONS IN OTHER MAMMALS

Evidence is accumulating to show that primer pheromones modifying reproduction in mammals are not limited to the laboratory mouse which has been subjected for so long to artificial selection and environments. It now appears probable that deermice (*Peromyscus maniculatus bairdii*) produce a female pheromone which depresses cycles and a male one which stimulates FSH secretion. Bronson and Marsden (1964) have obtained evidence of cycle shortening and of oestrous synchrony, following a similar time sequence to synchrony in laboratory mice. Pregnancy block has also been demonstrated (Eleftheriou, Bronson and Zarrow, 1962; Bronson and Eleftheriou, 1963).

In contrast, attempts to demonstrate primer pheromones in rats have been unrewarding (Rosen, Shelesnyak and Zackarias, 1940; Hughes, 1964; Bruce, personal communication; Whitten, unpublished). Nevertheless, Everett (1963) considers that olfactory stimuli may play a part in the development of pseudopregnancy following progesterone injection. Perhaps related are the findings of Takewaki (1949) and Takewaki and Miyamoto (1949), who observed that pseudopregnancy in rats may follow instillation of ammonia or other chemicals into the nasal cavity. Though ammonia cannot be regarded as a pheromone, it accumulates in crowded cages and may thus complicate experiments.

Steinach (1936) claimed to have demonstrated that odours from females were essential for the normal development of the testes in male rats. However, Poynter (1939) was unable to confirm this with male rats reared in isolation.

Schinckel (1954 a,b) observed synchronization of lambing in merino sheep and related it to a shortening of oestrous cycles as the result of the introduction of rams into the previously segregated flock of ewes. This was the first real evidence that mammalian oestrous cycles could be modified by factors from males. Watson and Radford (1960) have since shown that the shortening of the cycles was produced by either chemical or vocal communication, and similar results have been obtained with goats (Shelton, 1960). However, removal of the olfactory bulbs did not induce changes in oestrous cycles in ewes (Signoret, 1964), any more than in rats (Rosen *et al.* 1940) or rabbits (Brooks, 1937). This operation caused anoestrus in guinea-pigs (Magnotti, 1936), mice (Whitten, 1956b) and pigs (Signoret and Mauleon, 1962). In pigs, the accumulation of gonadotrophin in the anterior pituitary was clearly demonstrated.

E. RELEASER PHEROMONES

Unquestionably olfactory signals play important roles in the reproduction of many mammals. They may, for instance, be involved in the establishment of dominance by the successful male, the location of a mate, the recognition of sexually receptive states and the identification of offspring. However, the precise nature of these pheromones has not been determined. Much of this deficiency is no doubt due to the difficulties of recording impulses from sensory receptors in non-anaesthetized animals and of quantitating behavioural patterns. In addition, the field has perhaps been neglected because of man's micro-osmatic outlook. Mykytowycz (1962), for instance, has shown that the chin gland of the rabbit is used extensively for territory marking: this function had previously been overlooked because the secretion is odourless to man.

In view of the limitations both of our human sensory equipment and of present chemical techniques, some study of the theory of mammalian releaser pheromones may be rewarding. Marler (1961) has suggested that Morris' (1946) theory of linguistics may be applied to animal communication. It is, however, too early to decide which categories of signals, locators, appraisors, prescriptors and so on are applicable to mammalian pheromones, because we know very little of the olfactory signals or of their information content. Meanwhile, parameters of olfactory communication have been derived by Bossert and Wilson (1963) for the range, rate of spread, and persistence of chemical signals.

Schaeffer (1940) has reviewed the morphology of scent glands, and Lederer (1950) and Kingston (1964) have discussed the chemistry of their secretions and of the odoriferous substances in urine and faeces. Amoore (1964) has developed a stereochemical theory of olfaction, and recent developments in olfactory physiology have been reported (Zotterman, 1963). No studies have yet been made of impulses generated by possible mammalian pheromones. We still do not know if Jacobson (1811) was correct when he ascribed the function of sex chemoreception to the vomeronasal organs (Adrian, 1955). However, Planel (1953) has reported that section of the nerves from these receptors did not prevent the male guinea-pig from searching out an oestrous female.

The use of scent glands, urine and faeces to mark trails and territories has been discussed at length (Hediger, 1951; Bourlière, 1955; Wynne-Edwards, 1962), but very few studies have been made of behavioural response to odours. Beach and Gilmore (1949) reported that dogs were more interested in urine from a receptive bitch than from a non-receptive one. Carr and Pender (1958) reported that male rats can distinguish between the urine of oestrous and dioestrous females. Carr and Caul (1962) demonstrated that normal and ovariectomized females can discriminate between entire and castrate males, while normal and castrate males can distinguish between oestrous and dioestrous females. Le Magnen (1952b) had previously arrived at similar conclusions.

It may be assumed that odours are in general genetically determined, but that some modification can be superimposed by disease, diet, and other environmental factors. Although it is not known whether the simple recognition of releaser pheromones in mammals is innate or learned, the information content of signals can probably be increased by additional learning, so that signals may be released more judiciously or interpreted with greater subtlety.

Le Magnen (1952a) has reported that olfactory sensitivity in women varies with ovarian function. Conversely, Kloek (1961) has presented evidence that each stage of the cycle has a distinctive odour for police dogs. These findings may provide a physiological basis for the age-old trade in perfumes prepared from the odoriferous glands of animals such as civet, beaver and deer. However, their method of use suggests that the appraisor and prescriptor functions of chemical communications have been confused with the desire for self-adornment, while the recent advertising phrase 'your perfume should be changed as often as your mood' indicates that olfactory signals may be further exploited by man.

F. EVOLUTIONARY IMPLICATIONS OF PHEROMONES

Efficient sex attractants, and primer pheromones which cause earlier puberty, early seasonable breeding and more regular oestrous cycles, would all result in evolutionary advantages. Under natural conditions female rodents would be unlikely to congregate away from males in sufficient numbers to depress each other's cycles; so this effect may be an artefact resulting from unnatural housing. However, in some species females remain in herds during the non-breeding season, while the males are solitary; mutual depression of ovarian activity may then facilitate subsequent synchronization of breeding.

Howard (1949) observed a high degree of inbreeding in a natural population of small rodents. Any factor which reduces this inbreeding should confer an advantage, and Bruce and Parrott (1960) have suggested that the block to pregnancy might favour exogamy. This may be even more significant if, as the experiments of Mainardi (1963a) indicate, alien males are unusually attractive to females.

The evidence from insects (Wilson and Bossert, 1963) does not support the suggestion by Sibley (personal communication) that pheromones may function as isolating mechanisms. Further experiments reported by Mainardi (1963b) using two subspecies of *Mus musculus* indicate that female mice are imprinted by their fathers, and that their sexual preferences are a consequence of this imprinting. Perhaps the imprinting is through the olfactory sense.

G. SUMMARY

In two species of rodents (house mouse and deermouse), FSH secretion in the female is depressed by a primer pheromone originating from other females, and stimulated by one from males. There has been no confirmed report of any similar phenomenon acting on males.

174   W. K. WHITTEN

The pheromone from males appears in the urine of non-castrated animals, but its origin and nature is unknown. There is strong evidence that it produces its effect by stimulating olfactory receptors. The scanty literature on possible mammalian releaser pheromones is reviewed. Before further advances can be made, it will be necessary to quantitate behavioural reactions and to devise methods of study which differentiate between innate and learned reactions.

Marsden and Bronson (1965) have recently shown that oestrous synchrony occurs on the night after pairing if the females had been isolated for two days but had previously been held in groups. This demonstrates that the synchrony of oestrus in grouped females can result from a release from the oestrus-suppressing effects of crowding even in the absence of the male pheromone.

ACKNOWLEDGEMENTS

I am grateful to Mrs. Jan Starkey and to Miss Liew Nyok Kheng for expert assistance in the preparation of this manuscript.

REFERENCES

Adrian, E. D. (1950) The electrical activity of the mammalian olfactory bulb. *Electroenceph. clin. Neurophysiol.*, **2**, 377–88.
Adrian, E. D. (1955) Synchronized activity in the vomeronasal nerves with a note on the function of the organ of Jacobsen. *Pflügers Arch.ges. Physiol.*, **260**, 188–92.
Allison, A. C. (1953) The morphology of the olfactory system in vertebrates. *Biol. Rev.*, **28**, 195–244.
Amoore, J. E. (1964) Current status of the steric theory of odor. *Ann. N.Y. Acad. Sci.*, **116**, 457–76.
Astwood, E. B. (1939) An assay method for progesterone based upon the decidual reaction in the rat. *J. Endocr.*, **1**, 49–55.
Beach, F. A. and Gilmore, J. (1949) Response of male dogs to urine from females in heat. *J. Mammal.*, **30**, 391–2.
Boeckh, J. (1962) Elektrophysiologische Untersuchungen an einzelnen Geruchsrezeptoren auf den Antennen des Totengräbers (*Necrophorus*, Coleoptera). *Z. vergl. Physiol.*, **46**, 212–48.
Bossert, W. H. and Wilson, E. D. (1963) The analysis of olfactory communication among animals. *J. theoret. Biol.*, **5**, 443–69.
Bourlière, F. (1955) *The Natural History of Mammals*. Harrap & Co., London.
Bronson, F. H. and Eleftheriou, B. E. (1963) Influence of strange males on implantation in the deermouse. *Gen. comp. Endocr.*, **3**, 515–18.
Bronson, F. H. and Marsden, H. M. (1964) Male-induced synchrony of estrus in deermice. *Gen. comp. Endocr.*, **4**, 634–7.
Brooks, C. McC. (1937) The role of the cerebral cortex and of various sense organs in the excitation and execution of mating activity in the rabbit. *Am. J. Physiol.*, **120**, 544–53.

Bruce, H. M. (1959) An exteroceptive block to pregnancy in the mouse. *Nature, Lond.*, **184**, 105.

Bruce, H. M. (1960) A block to pregnancy in mice caused by the proximity of strange males. *J. Reprod. Fert.*, **1**, 96–103.

Bruce, H. M. (1961) Time relations in the pregnancy-block induced in mice by strange males. *J. Reprod. Fert.*, **2**, 138–42.

Bruce, H. M. (1962) Continued suppression of pituitary luteotrophic activity and fertility in the female mouse. *J. Reprod. Fert.*, **4**, 313–18.

Bruce, H. M. (1963) Olfactory block to pregnancy among grouped mice. *J. Reprod. Fert.*, **6**, 451–60.

Bruce, H. M. (1965) The effect of castration on the reproductive pheromones of male mice. *J. Reprod. Fert.*, **10**, 141–3.

Bruce, H. M. and Parkes, A. S. (1960) Hormonal factors in exteroceptive block to pregnancy in mice. *J. Endocr.*, **20**, xxix–xxx.

Bruce, H. M. and Parkes, A. S. (1961a) An olfactory block to implantation in mice. *J. Reprod. Fert.*, **2**, 195–6.

Bruce, H. M. and Parkes, A. S. (1961b) The effect of concurrent lactation on the olfactory block to pregnancy in the mouse. *J. Endocr.*, **22**, vi–vii.

Bruce, H. M. and Parrott, D.M.V. (1960) Role of olfactory sense in pregnancy block by strange males. *Science*, **131**, 1526.

Butler, C. G. (1964) Pheromones in sexual processes in insects. In *Insect Reproduction*, ed. K. C. Highnam, Symposium No. 2 Royal Entomological Society, London.

Carr, W. J. and Caul, W. F. (1962) The effect of castration in the rat upon discrimination of sex odours. *Anim. Behav.*, **10**, 20–7.

Carr, W. J. and Pender, B. (1958) The effect of castration of the male rat upon olfactory sensitivity to oestrous female urine. Paper read at East Psychol. Assoc., Philadelphia.

Dewar, A. D. (1959) Observations on pseudopregnancy in the mouse. *J. Endocr.*, **18**, 186–90.

Eleftheriou, B. E., Bronson, F. H. and Zarrow, M. X. (1962) Interaction of olfactory and other environmental stimuli on implantation in the deermouse. *Science*, **137**, 764.

Everett, J. W. (1956) Functional corpora lutea maintained for months by autografts of rat hypophysis. *Endocrinology*, **58**, 786–96.

Everett, J. W. (1963) Pseudopregnancy in the rat from brief treatment with progesterone. *Nature, London*, **198**, 695–6.

Everett, J. W. (1964) Neural control of reproductive function of the adenohypophysis. *Physiol. Rev.*, **44**, 373–431.

Hediger, H. (1951) Observations sur la psychologie animale dans les Parcs Nationaux du Congo Belge. Institut des Parcs Nationaux du Congo Belge, Brussels.

Howard, W. E. (1949) Dispersal, amount of inbreeding, and longevity in a local population of prairie deermice on the George Reserve Southern Michigan. *Contr. Lab. vert. Biol.*, **43**, 1–50.

Hughes, R. L. (1964) Effect of changing cages, introduction of the male, and other procedures on the oestrous cycle of the rat. *C.S.I.R.O. Wildl. Res.*, **9**, 115–21.

Jacobson, L. (1811) Cited Allison (1953).

Kalmus, H. (1964) Some potentialities and constraints of chemical telecommunication. *Proc. 2nd Int. Congr. Endocrin.*, London.

Kandutsch, A. A. (1958) Physiological factors that alter the concentration of skin sterols: Δ^7—cholestenol as an indicator of sebaceous gland activity. *Archs. Biochem. Biophys.*, **75**, 148–62.

Karlson, P. and Butenandt, A. (1959) Pheromones (ectohormones) in insects. *Ann. Rev. Ent.*, **4**, 39–58.

Kingston, B. H. (1964) The chemistry and olfactory properties of musk, civet and castoreum. *Proc. 2nd Int. Congr. Endocrin.*, London.

Kloek, J. (1961) The smell of some steroid sex-hormones and their metabolites. *Psychiat. Neurol. Neurochir.*, **64**, 309–44.

Lamond, D. R. (1959) Effect of stimulation derived from other animals of the same species on oestrous cycles in mice. *J. Endocr.*, **18**, 343–9.

Lederer, E. (1950) Odeurs et parfums des animaux. *Fortschr. Chem. org. Nat-Stoffe*, **4**, 88–153.

Lee, S. van der and Boot, L. M. (1955) Spontaneous pseudopregnancy in mice. *Acta physiol. pharmac. neerl.*, **4**, 442–3.

Lee, S. van der and Boot, L. M. (1956) Spontaneous pseudopregnancy in mice II. *Acta physiol. pharmac. neerl.*, **5**, 213–14.

Le Magnen, J. (1952a) Les phénomènes olfacto-sexuels chez l'homme. *Archs. Sci. physiol.*, **6**, 125–60.

Le Magnen, J. (1952b) Les phénomènes olfacto-sexuels chez le rat blanc. *Archs. Sci. physiol.*, **6**, 295–332.

Magnotti, T. (1936) L'importanza dell'olfatto sullo sviluppo e funzione degli organi genitali. *Boll. Mal. Orecch. Gola Naso*, **54**, 281. Cited Poynter (1939).

Mainardi, D. (1963a) Un esperimento nella parte attiva svolta dalla femmina nella selezione sessuale in *Mus musculus*. *Archs. Sci. biol.*, **47**, 227–37.

Mainardi, D. (1963b) Speciazione nel topo. *Istituto Lombardo (Rend. Sc.) B*, **97**, 135–42 and 291–9.

Marler, P. (1961) The logical analysis of animal communication. *J. theoret. Biol.*, **1**, 295–337.

Marsden, H. M. and Bronson, F. H. (1964) Estrous synchrony in mice: alteration by exposure to male urine. *Science*, **144**, 1469.

Marsden, H. M. and Bronson, F. H. (1965) The synchrony of oestrus in mice: Relative roles of the male and female environments. *J. Endocr.*, **32**, 313–9.

Merton, H. (1938) VII. Studies on reproduction in the albino mouse. *Proc. R. Soc. Edinb.*, **58**, 80–96.

Morris, C. W. (1946) *Signs, Language and Behaviour*. Prentice-Hall, Englewood Cliffs, New Jersey.

Mykytowycz, R. (1962) Territorial function of chin gland secretion in the rabbit. *Oryctolagus cuniculus* (L.) *Nature, Lond.*, **193**, 799.

Ortman, R. (1956) *Z. Säugetierk.*, **21**, 138. Cited Parkes and Bruce (1961).

Parkes, A. S. (1960) The role of odorous substances in mammalian reproduction. *J. Reprod. Fert.*, **3**, 312–14.

Parkes, A. S. and Bruce, H. M. (1961) Olfactory stimuli in mammalian reproduction. *Science*, **134**, 1049–54.

Parkes, A. S. and Bruce, H. M. (1962) Pregnancy block in female mice placed in boxes soiled by males. *J. Reprod. Fert.*, **4**, 303–8.

Planel, H. (1953) Etude sur la physiologie de l'organ de Jacobson. *Archs. Anat. Histol. Embryol.*, **36**, 198–206.

Poynter, H. (1939) Testes hormone secretion in the rat under conditions of vasectomy and isolation. *Anat. Rec.*, **74**, 355–79.

Prelog, V., Ruzicka, L. and Wieland, P. (1944) Steroïde und Sexualhormone. *Helv. chim. Acta*, **27**, 66–8.

Riotton, G. and Fishman, W. H. (1953) β-glucuronidase studies in inbred mice: androgenic hormones and kidney and urinary β-glucuronidase activity. *Endocrinology*, **52**, 692–9.

Robson, J. M. and Wiesner, B. P. (1932) The causation of mucification and cornification in the vagina of the mouse. *Quart. J. exp. Physiol.*, **21**, 217–25.

Rosen, S., Shelesnyak, M. C. and Zackarias, L. R. (1940) Naso-genital relationship. Pseudopregnancy following extirpation of the sphenopalatine ganglion in the rat. *Endocrinology*, **27**, 463–8.

Sawyer, C. H. (1955) Rhinencephalic involvement in pituitary activation by intraventricular histamine in the rabbit under Nembutal anaesthesia. *Am. J. Physiol.*, **180**, 37–46.

Sawyer, C. H. (1957) Triggering of the pituitary by the central nervous system. In *Physiological Triggers*, ed. B. H. Bullock, Waverley Press, Baltimore.

Schaeffer, J. (1940) *Die Hautdrüsenorgane der Säugetiere*, Urban and Schwarzenberg, Berlin.

Schinckel, P. G. (1954a) The effect of the ram on the incidence and occurrence of oestrus in ewes. *Aust. vet. J.*, **30**, 189–95.

Schinckel, P. G. (1954b) The effect of the presence of the ram on the ovarian activity of the ewe. *Aust. J. agric. Res.*, **5**, 465–9.

Selye, H., Collip, L. S. B. and Thompson, D. L. (1934) Nervous and hormonal factors in lactation. *Endocrinology*, **18**, 237–48.

Shelton, M. (1960) Influence of the presence of a male goat on the initiation of oestrous cycling and ovulation of angora does. *J. Anim. Sci.*, **19**, 368–75.

Signoret, J. P. (1964) Action de l'ablation des bulbes olfactifs sur les mécanismes de la reproduction. *Proc. 2nd Int. Cong. of Endocrin., London.*

Signoret, J. P. and Mauleon, P. (1962) Action de l'ablation des bulbes olfactifs sur les mécanismes de la reproduction chez la truie. *Annls. Biol. anim. Biochem. Biophys.*, **2**, 167–74.

Steinach, E. (1936) Zur Geschichte des mannlichen Sexualhormons und seiner Wirkung am Säugetier und beim Menschen. *Wien. klin. Wschr.*, **49**, 164–72, 196–205. Cited Poynter (1939).

Takewaki, K. (1949) Occurrence of pseudopregnancy in rats placed in vapor of ammonia. *Proc. Japan Acad.*, **25**, 38–9.

Takewaki, K. and Miyamoto, Y. (1949) Induction of pseudopregnancy in rats by applying various substances to nasal mucosa. *Proc. Japan Acad.*, **25**, 31–7.

Watson, R. H. and Radford, H. M. (1960) Influence of rams on the onset of oestrus in merino ewes in the spring. *Aust. J. agric. Res.*, **11**, 65–71.

Whitten, W. K. (1956a) Modification of the oestrous cycle of the mouse by external stimuli associated with the male. *J. Endocr.*, **13**, 399–404.

Whitten, W. K. (1956b) The effect of removal of the olfactory bulbs on the gonads of mice. *J. Endocr.*, **14**, 160–3.

Whitten, W. K. (1957) Effect of exteroceptive factors on the oestrous cycle of mice. *Nature, Lond.*, **180**, 1436.

Whitten, W. K. (1958) Modification of the oestrous cycle of the mouse by external stimuli associated with the male. Changes in the oestrous cycle determined by vaginal smears. *J. Endocr.*, **17**, 307–13.

Whitten, W. K. (1959) Occurrence of anoestrus in mice caged in groups. *J. Endocr.*, **18**, 102–7.

Whitten, W. K. (1963) Is the vomeronasal organ a sex chemoreceptor in mice ? *Second Asia and Oceania Congress of Endocrinology, Sydney.*

Whitten, W. K. and Dagg, C. P. (1961) Influence of spermatozoa on the cleavage rate of mouse eggs. *J. exp. Zool.*, **148**, 173–82.

Wilson, E. O. and Bossert, W. H. (1963) Chemical communication among animals. *Recent Progr. Hormone Res.*, **19**, 673–710.

Wynne-Edwards, V. C. (1962) *Animal Dispersion in Relation to Social Behaviour.* Hapner, New York.

Zotterman, Y. ed. (1963) *Olfaction and Taste.* Pergamon Press, Oxford.

THE UTERUS AND THE CONTROL OF
OVARIAN FUNCTION

K. P. BLAND AND B. T. DONOVAN

*Department of Neuroendocrinology, Institute of Psychiatry,
Denmark Hill, London, S.E.5, England*

A. INTRODUCTION

The effect of a foreign body in the uterus in causing infertility is currently a topic of intense interest, although it is but a modern variant of a very old technique. Guttmacher (1964) relates that for many centuries Arab and Turkish camel owners have inserted small round stones into the uterus of their animals in order to prevent pregnancy, whilst for several centuries, at least, natives in the Dutch East Indies have introduced an elastic filament-like object into the uterus of maidens with a similar end in view. European experience in this field is of more recent date and mainly concerns the use of the ring of silver or gold wire introduced by Gräfenberg, and its modern variants (Tietze, 1962). Before Gräfenberg, physicians had inserted various devices into the cervical canal to prevent pregnancy, but these protruded into the vagina and provided an opportunity for infective organisms to ascend from the vagina into the uterus. Gräfenberg eliminated this possibility by placing his pessaries entirely within the uterus. The Gräfenberg ring was initially made from silkworm gut, but pliable spiral rings of coiled silver or gold wire, finally about 17.5 mm. in diameter, were developed. In the hands of the innovator such devices proved eminently successful and a failure rate of 1.6% in 600 patients fitted with silver rings was reported. However, 'the great majority of gynecologists did not wait until they had gained experience with the Gräfenberg ring but condemned the new method out of hand. This rejection was based partly upon theoretical considerations, partly upon a perhaps unavoidable confusion of the intra-uterine pessary with other, intracervical, devices and partly upon a series of unfavorable case reports involving the Gräfenberg ring itself' (Tietze, 1962). The Editors of the *American Journal of Obstetrics and Gynecology*, in introducing a revaluation of the effectiveness of the Gräfenberg ring by Oppenheimer (1959), wrote: 'At the seventh International Congress for Birth Control (1930), Pankow, Hammerschlag, Kuster, Adler and Frei all expressed opposition to the innovation—although not one of these distinguished gentlemen had ever had any experience of his own with the ring!' Nevertheless, the opposition won the day and as a result the ring fell out of use as a contraceptive device except in Japan, where a modification of the Gräfenberg ring was adopted (Ishihama, 1959), and Israel, where a series of 329 cases described in 1959 by Oppenheimer renewed interest in this method of contraception. Since that time a variety of Intra-Uterine Contraceptive Devices (IUCD's) have been made, tested and proven effective. But their mode of action remains obscure, particularly as the length of the menstrual cycle remains unchanged and uterine biopsies indicate that the endometrium stays essentially normal.

Lack of understanding is also apparent when another aspect of the function of the uterus is considered. Loss of the uterus is associated with profound changes in ovarian function in many species, but the factors underlying them have not been elucidated. Does the uterus secrete a hormone that modifies ovarian activity, or does the uterus act as an important afferent organ, exerting its control through the brain and pituitary gland? In recent years these topics have attracted increasing attention and it seems an appropriate time to review current knowledge in this area and to assess the validity of some of the theories that have been advanced. To this end, the effects of hysterectomy in various species will first be described in order to illustrate the type of effect observed. Next, the changes induced in the oestrous cycle by foreign bodies inserted into the uterus will be examined, and finally the possible modes of interaction between the uterus and ovaries will be discussed.

B. THE EFFECT OF HYSTERECTOMY UPON OVARIAN FUNCTION

The clinical effects of removal of the uterus have been studied for many years (Reynolds, 1949), but it has proved difficult to reach agreement over the changes following the operation. Some investigators considered that ovarian function quickly ceased and that an early menopause ensued. Others failed to find evidence of depressed gonadal activity and believed that any resulting abnormalities were due to inadvertent interference with the blood vessels or nerves of the ovary. Quite recently, Whitelaw (1958) followed ovarian function *PRIMATES* in hysterectomized, hysterectomized-ovariectomized, and normal women by means of basal temperature records, urinary pregnanediol estimations, vaginal smears, and measurement of gonadotrophin excretion. He concluded that the evidence obtained by vaginal smear and gonadotrophin assay demonstrated that the oestrogenic activity of ovaries conserved at the time of surgery persisted for years. There was no indication that hysterectomy hastened the onset of the menopause, as had been suggested by earlier workers (e.g. Sessums and Murphy, 1932). The menses naturally cease in women after removal of the uterus unless a small quantity of endometrium is conserved, but cyclic ovarian function continues. Fresh corpora have been observed in human ovaries long after ablation of the uterus (Rock, 1955) and, to judge from the changes in oestrogen and pregnanediol excretion, ovulation occurred regularly in several cases of congenital absence of the uterus studied by Brown and Matthew (1962). In women, then, the consequences of hysterectomy provide no sound foundation for the conclusion that the uterus is of significance in the control of gonadal function, though psychic changes following the cessation of menstruation may be important. Hysterectomy of the monkey also appears to be without effect on ovarian function as indicated by the occurrence of rhythmic changes in the sex skin and in the quantity of vaginal sediment (Burford and Diddle, 1936; van Wagenen and Catchpole, 1941).

In non-primate species, by contrast, the situation is quite different. *NON-PRIMATE* After hysterectomy, well-defined changes in ovarian function occur, which mainly concern the activity of the corpus luteum. Unfortun-

182   K. P. BLAND AND B. T. DONOVAN

ately, species differences exist and make it advisable to outline the kind of information available from a range of animals with differing sexual cycles.

Removal of the uterus from the oestrous *rabbit* (when corpora lutea are absent from the ovaries) does not affect ovarian function (Robbins and Shepherd, 1963), but if hysterectomy is performed after a sterile mating then the life span of the corpora lutea induced in the ovaries is extended from an expected time of 16 days to a period very close to that of pregnancy (30 days). Subsequent pseudo-pregnancies are also lengthened (Gillard, 1937; Greep, 1941; Heckel, 1942; Chu, Lee and You, 1946).

In the *rat*, ovulation occurs regularly at 4- or 5-day intervals, but the corpora lutea so formed secrete little progesterone and survive for a very short time unless mating occurs, when their life becomes extended to approximately 12 days. Hysterectomy does not affect the periodicity of oestrus, or the life span of the cyclic corpora lutea, but when carried out in the pseudopregnant animal the activity of the corpora lutea becomes prolonged and pseudopregnancy lasts about 20 days, which is close to the 23-day duration of normal pregnancy (Bradbury, 1937a; Hechter, Fraenkel, Lev and Soskin, 1940; Bradbury, Brown and Gray, 1950; Perry and Rowlands, 1961). After this period normal oestrous cycles are resumed, but mating

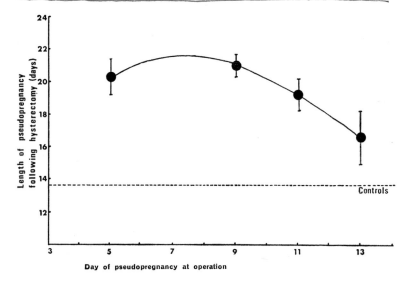

Fig. 1. The effect of hysterectomy, at different stages of pseudopregnancy, on the length of pseudopregnancy in the rat. Data from Melampy, Anderson & Kragt, 1964.

again induces a lengthened pseudopregnancy of approximately 18 days. It seems that the age of the corpora lutea at hysterectomy is of importance in determining the final length of the pseudopregnant period (Silbiger and Rothchild, 1963; Melampy, Anderson and Kragt, 1964; Fig. 1), and that the greatest effect is exerted on the 9th day. Melampy and his colleagues have also established that there is a relationship between the quantity of tissue removed and the degree of extension of pseudopregnancy. If both horns of the uterus are removed on the 5th day of pseudopregnancy, then this progestational phase lasts approximately 20 days. Removal of one horn lengthens pseudopregnancy to 17 days only.

Effects akin to those induced by hysterectomy in the rat can be brought about in other ways. When the endometrium of the uterus is irritated the affected area shows growth and transformation of the mucosal cells to decidual tissue. It is now known that conversion of the endometrium to decidual tissue in this way produces an effect

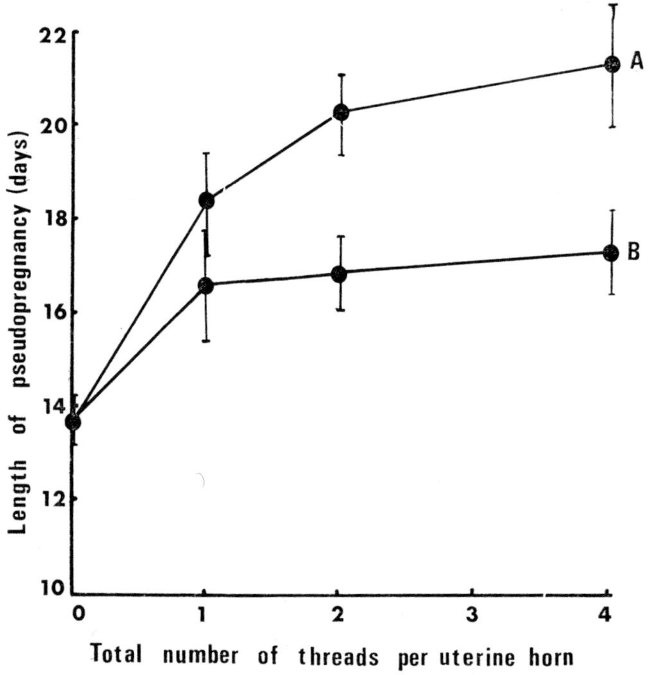

Fig. 2. The effect of traumatization of the uterus on the length of pseudopregnancy in the rat. The degree of traumatization increases with the number of threads inserted; the effect of damage to both horns (Curve A) is greater than that provoked by interference with a single horn (Curve B), even though the total number of threads inserted is the same.
Data from Melampy, Anderson & Kragt, 1964.

equivalent to that of hysterectomy, so that when decidua are induced down the length of both horns of the uterus on the 5th day of pseudopregnancy this state persists for a further 16 days (Velardo, Olsen, Hisaw and Dawson, 1953; Melampy et al., 1964). Removal of successively smaller quantities of endometrium by decidualization exerts a diminishing effect on the life span of the corpora lutea (Fig. 2). The parallel between hysterectomy and decidualization of the uterus can be extended. If one horn of the uterus is traumatized to induce deciduomata, then the secretion of progesterone by the corpora lutea is manifest for about 17 days, which is the same period as that observed to follow surgical removal of one horn of the uterus. Traumatization of one horn on day 4 with ablation of the second on day 9, after deciduomata have formed in the first horn, produces a pseudopregnancy of 22 days (Melampy et al., 1964). Somewhat surprisingly, the production of deciduomata in mice does not seem to delay the recurrence of oestrus (Kamell and Atkinson, 1948).

The oestrous cycle of the *guinea-pig*, like that of many other polyoestrous animals, is longer than the cycle of the rat and mouse. It lasts 16 days as compared with 4 or 5 in the latter species. This is because the corpora lutea secrete more progesterone and for a longer time during each cycle and, in effect, produce a pseudopregnancy on each occasion. Appropriately, the stimulus of copulation, in the absence of fertilization, does not alter the oestrous rhythm. On the other hand, the removal of the uterus greatly extends the luteal phase of the cycle. This effect was first studied by Loeb (1923, 1927) and has been confirmed on many occasions. Hysterectomy on the 5th day of the cycle, that is 5 days after ovulation, causes the corpora lutea to secrete progesterone for more than 8 months (Rowlands, 1961). Postponement of the operation to day 10 reduces the effect, for the corpora persist for a period equivalent to gestation only (65–70 days), with enlargement of the luteal bodies to the size seen during pregnancy. Removal of the uterus late in the cycle and up to the 15th day, when regression of the corpora lutea is in progress, exerts a less consistent action. In most animals the impending ovulation is suppressed and the regressive changes in the corpora lutea arrested. The bodies remain in the ovaries for some time but increase little in size. Other animals hysterectomized late in the oestrous cycle experience normal oestrus and ovulation, but the newly formed corpora lutea then persist for several months. The detailed work of Rowlands (1961) has been largely confirmed by Butcher, Chu and Melampy (1962b) who, in addition, found that 10 of 16 guinea-pigs hysterectomized on days 5 or 6 came into heat after 63–98 days, whilst the remainder failed to display oestrus up to the time they were killed, some 4 months after the operation. It would thus seem that the reaction of the corpus luteum to ablation of the uterus changes abruptly about the 6th day after formation, which, interestingly, coincides with the expected time of implantation. A relationship between the life span of the corpora lutea and the amount of endometrium remaining after partial hysterectomy exists in the guinea-pig, as in the rat (Loeb, 1927; Butcher et al., 1962b). The effect, however, is more variable in the larger animal. Destruction of the mucosa by chemical means causes changes equivalent to those seen after hysterectomy (Butcher et al., 1962b), but extensive traumatization of the uterus in the early part of the cycle to induce deciduomata lengthens the cycle by 3 to 7 days only (Loeb, 1923).

The reproductive pattern of *farm animals* is broadly similar to that of the guinea-pig, and the effect of hysterectomy is comparable. In the *sheep*, loss of the uterus at any time up to the 15th day of the 16-day oestrous cycle results in continued luteal function, provided the corpora retain some activity at the time of operation (Wiltbank and Casida, 1956; Moor and Rowson, 1964). Following the removal of increasing proportions of the uterus in a series of animals, the number of oestrous cycles extended roughly matches the amount of uterus removed (Rowson and Moor, 1964). However, the ablation of one entire horn prolongs luteal function only by some 5 days. Hysterectomy of the *heifer* during the mid-luteal phase of the cycle causes maintenance of the corpora lutea for at least the equivalent of the gestation period, 280 days (Wiltbank and Casida, 1956; Anderson, Neal and Melampy, 1962). A subtotal hysterectomy sparing the cervix and a very small amount of endometrium prolongs the cycle from a normal length of 19 days to 28 days. With larger amounts of residual endometrium the effect wanes (Anderson et al., 1962). It thus appears that much less endometrium is necessary for normal luteal function in the ewe and cow than in the guinea-pig, which in turn requires less than the rat.

The *pig* seems to show certain peculiarities in its response to hysterectomy. The normal oestrous cycle lasts 22 days and hysterectomy up to 16 days after ovulation results in persistence of the corpora lutea for about 115 days, the span of pregnancy (Du Mesnil du Buisson and Dauzier, 1959; Spies, Zimmerman, Self and Casida, 1960; Anderson, Butcher and Melampy, 1961). When the operation is carried out between days 16–18, ovulation occurs as expected, but the newly formed luteal bodies persist. Partial hysterectomy does not greatly affect the oestrous cycle (normal or slightly prolonged (25–30 day) cycles are observed), but removal of more than three-quarters of the uterus abolishes oestrus for several months (Du Mesnil du Buisson, 1961a; Anderson *et al.*, 1961). These findings in the pig correspond to those derived from the sheep and cow, but in addition the existence of a local mechanism through which one horn of the uterus may control the function of the ipsilateral ovary is indicated by the work of Du Mesnil du Buisson (1961b) and Rathmacher and Anderson (1963). In cases of partial hysterectomy which leave intact the tubal end of one uterine horn, the corpora lutea in the ovary on that side regress earlier than those in the ovary further removed from the uterine remnant. Also, it is difficult to maintain unilateral pregnancy in sows with one horn rendered sterile by ligation or transection of the oviduct, for the corpora in the ovary close to the sterile horn regress and progesterone secretion by the corpora in the other ovary is insufficient to support gestation. Thus it seems that the normal endometrium can produce a luteolytic factor which inhibits luteal function in the sow. If this be so, then it is likely that the corpora lutea vary in susceptibility to the agent at different ages. Neill and Day (1964) find that the corpora lutea induced in the ovaries of gilts that already possess a full complement survive normally for the span of a cycle, despite regression of the pre-existing set. After hysterectomy the lives of both old and new corpora lutea are extended. If an endometrial luteolysin is always effective, both collections should regress together: it is only by postulating a variation in susceptibility that theory and observation can be reconciled. In the ewe, on the other hand, spontaneously formed and induced corpora lutea regress simultaneously (Inskeep, Oloufa, Pope and Casida, 1963).

From the information just presented it is evident that the life of the corpus luteum is closely associated with the changes taking place in the uterus. In the absence of luteal bodies hysterectomy does not appear to modify ovarian function. The facts available are consistent in showing that the life span of corpora lutea is limited in the presence of a normal endometrium. Removal of the endometrium by hysterectomy, by chemical means, or (in some species) by the induction of deciduomata favours the secretion of progesterone by the corpora lutea for a much longer period than normal. Species differences are apparent in the amount of endometrium required to maintain the normal oestrous rhythm; this becomes progressively less as one moves from the rabbit and rat to the guinea-pig, sheep and cow. Primates stand at the extreme end of the scale in that cyclic ovarian function continues in the absence of any endometrial tissue. This is perhaps to be expected, for loss of part of the wall of the uterus occurs during each menstrual cycle, and if this were associated with loss of a factor ⃰ necessary for terminating the life of the corpora lutea then there would be no series of cycles: the corpora would function indefinitely. The implication may also be drawn that the mechanism controlling luteal function in the primate differs in emphasis from that of other species.   PRIMATE VS NON-PRIMATE

C. THE EFFECT OF FOREIGN BODIES IN THE UTERUS

Despite longstanding clinical interest in the action of intra-uterine contraceptive devices, few experimental studies were undertaken before the commencement of the present decade. The effect of distension of the uterus on the initiation of lactation was examined by Selye (1934), but the findings proved controversial (Bradbury, 1941; Greene, 1941) and were not followed up. Much later, in 1953, Moore and Nalbandov published their observations on the effects of uterine distension on the oestrous cycle of the sheep. Most of the subsequent work on the sheep, guinea-pig, cow and sow, now to be described, has grown from this seed.

It is well established that the oestrous cycle of the *sheep* is influenced by an inert body lying in the lumen of the uterus (Moore and Nalbandov, 1953; Nalbandov, Moore and Norton, 1955). The introduction of an 8 mm. diameter glass bead into one horn of the uterus of ewes on the 3rd day of the oestrous cycle reduces the length of that cycle from a mean of 16.3 days to 11.5 days (Fig. 3). Subsequent cycles are also shortened, but to a lesser extent. According to Nalbandov et al. (1955), if a bead is inserted on the 8th day the cycle is prolonged to a mean of 21.6 days, and the ensuing cycles are similarly extended. Reduction of the diameter of the inserted bead to 2 mm. is followed by loss of the shortening effect on the cycle although lengthening is still observed when the bead is introduced on the 8th day. Subsequent cycles are normal. The change in effectiveness with varying bead diameter implies the participation of a neural mechanism in this response, probably activated by the distension caused by the foreign body, and this view is supported by the finding that denervation of the dilated segment of the uterus, by ablation and replacement, causes loss of action of the stimulus. However, another explanation

DAY 3

DAY 8

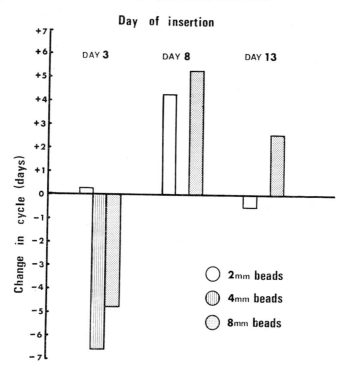

Fig. 3. The effect of different sizes of beads in altering the oestrous cycle of the sheep. Three sizes of bead were used and introduced on day 3, 8 or 13 of the cycle. Note the change in response between day 3 and 8. Data from Moore & Nalbandov, 1953, and Nalbandov, Moore & Norton, 1955.

can be advanced (p. 206). Some of these findings in the sheep have been confirmed by Inskeep, Oloufa, Howland, Pope and Casida (1962), who observed that distension of the uterus on the 3rd day shortened the cycle, while the presence of beads inserted on the 8th day did not extend it.

Distension of the uterus also modifies the periodicity of oestrus in the *guinea-pig* (Donovan and Traczyk, 1960, 1962). When two cylindrical glass beads (7 × 3 mm.) are inserted into each horn of the uterus at any time during the first 3 days, the cycle is shortened by 3 to 4 days. With progressively delayed introduction of the beads the effect on the cycle diminishes and is lost by the 9th or 10th day (Fig. 4). Bead insertion later in the cycle tends to prolong the current cycle by a day or so but in all cases subsequent oestrous cycles are either shortened or unchanged, but not lengthened. Moore (1961) found that when a 1.5 mm. diameter glass bead was sutured into one

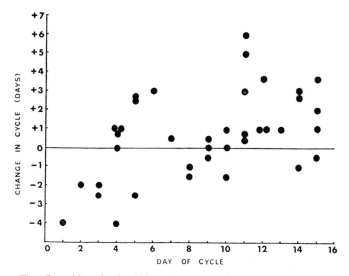

Fig. 4. The effect of inserting beads into the uterus of the guinea pig, at different stages of the oestrous cycle, on the length of that cycle. Note the trend towards a change in response. Data from Donovan & Traczyk, 1962.

horn of the uterus on the 3rd day, that cycle was shortened to 11.7 days; but when the operation was carried out on the 8th day, the cycle was prolonged to 22.4 days. Here the response to a thread passing through the wall of the uterus may be important. The shortening effect observed by Donovan and Traczyk (1960, 1962) following bead insertion during the first 4 days of the cycle has since been examined in more detail (Bland and Donovan, 1965b). Two beads in each horn shorten the cycle by 3 days, but if only one bead distends each horn the cycle is shortened by 1.75 days (Fig. 5). Unilateral application of the stimulus is less efficient than bilateral: 4 beads inserted into the right horn shorten the cycle by 1.7 days, whilst two beads in the right horn do not modify the cycle. The spatial relationships, and the apparent need for stimuli that affect both horns of the uterus, could imply that a neural mechanism is involved; and Moore (1961) reports that denervation of a segment of uterus containing the beads restores the cycle to normality. However, as in the sheep, other possibilities remain (p. 206).

Dilatation of the uterus of the cow during the early luteal phase of the cycle (days 1–7) by means of an indwelling inflated catheter shortens the rhythm from 20 days to 12–13 days (Hansel and Wagner, 1960). Abbreviation of the cycle is also observed after suturing plastic

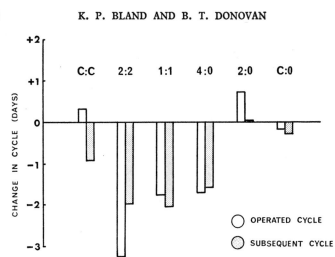

Fig. 5. The mean change in length of the first two cycles following the introduction of various numbers of beads into the uterus of guinea-pigs. C:C=Bilateral control bead insertion with beads inserted into both horns and removed immediately. C:O=Unilateral control bead insertion. 2:2=2 beads inserted into each horn. 1:1=1 bead inserted into each horn. 4:0=4 beads inserted into right horn only. 2:0=2 beads inserted into right horn only. Data from Bland & Donovan 1965b.

or vitallium cylinders into the uterine horns, but the response is not consistent (Anderson, Bowerman and Melampy, 1963).

Unlike that of the sheep, guinea-pig and cow, the oestrous cycle of the *pig* does not appear to be influenced by the presence in the uterus of foreign bodies as varied as tantalum cylinders (24 mm. × 16 mm., weighing 74 g.), vitallium cylinders (24 mm. × 16 mm., weighing 32 g.), plastic cylinders of similar or larger size, or glass marbles of 16.5 mm. diameter (Anderson, 1962). In this respect sows and women act alike, for intra-uterine contraceptive devices do not appear to modify the menstrual cycle to any significant degree, though there may be a very slight tendency for the cycle to be lengthened and made more regular (Oppenheimer, 1959).

D. THE MODE OF INTERACTION BETWEEN UTERUS AND OVARIES

In considering the means by which the uterus could influence ovarian function, four alternatives may be examined (Fig. 6). There is the possibility that the endometrium secretes a factor which possesses luteolytic properties and so could destroy corpora lutea. Elimination of this factor would allow the corpora lutea to remain active for longer than normal. This possibility is somewhat akin to to a second suggestion, that a stimulus arising from the uterus could cause the release of a hormone from the hypophysis which destroys ②2 the corpora lutea. In the absence of a signal from the uterus the

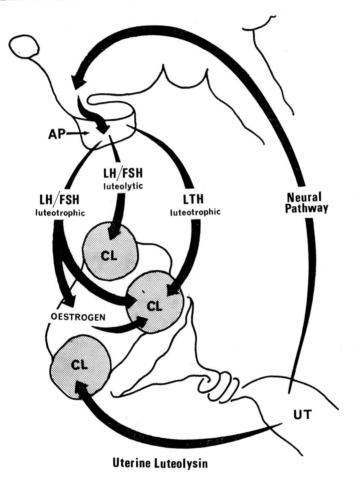

Fig. 6. Schematic diagram of possible factors governing the function of the corpora lutea. AP=Anterior pituitary; CL=Corpus luteum; FSH=Follicle-stimulating hormone; LH=Luteinizing hormone; LTH=Luteotrophic hormone; UT=Uterus.

hormone would not be discharged and the luteal bodies would remain active. The hypophysis could also be involved in a different manner, for the uterus might act as an afferent organ which provides

③ information controlling the secretion of a luteotrophic hormone from the pituitary. Unlike a luteolytic hormone, a luteotrophic factor would actively promote the secretion of progesterone by the corpora lutea and so extend their functional life. Lastly, there is the possible ④ role of the uterus in the metabolism of ovarian steroid hormones. It has been suggested that oestrogen and progesterone might be taken up and inactivated by the endometrium. In this way the metabolic activity of the uterus could operate to alter the blood level of these steroids and so modify the setting of the feed-back mechanism between the ovaries and hypophysis. Supportive evidence from work in at least one species is available for each suggestion.

E. AN ENDOMETRIAL LUTEOLYSIN

The relationship between the amount of endometrium removed during a partial hysterectomy and the prolongation of luteal function in the rat (Melampy et al., 1964), rabbit (Heckel, 1942) and guinea-pig (Loeb, 1927; Butcher et al., 1962b) has proved important in promoting the idea that the uterus elaborates a luteolytic substance, especially as the particular part of the uterus removed is unimportant except in the pig. Indeed the localized effect of partial hysterectomy in the pig (p. 186) provides a strong argument for the control by each uterine horn of luteal function in the ovary closely associated with it. It has been found that hysterectomy followed by replacement of uterine tissue does not result in prolonged luteal function. Pseudopregnancy is of normal length in rats (Hechter et al., 1940; Bradbury et al., 1950) and rabbits (Chu et al., 1946), and the grafts permit the continuation of near normal oestrous cycles in the pig (Du Mesnil du Buisson and Rombauts, 1963; Anderson, Butcher and Melampy, 1963) and guinea pig (Butcher, Chu and Melampy, 1962a). Thus, extension of luteal function is associated with loss of uterine tissue and not with the destruction of the nerve and blood supply of the organ. The fact that chemical destruction of the endometrium brings about the same ovarian response as removal of the entire organ in the pig (Anderson et al., 1961) and guinea-pig (Butcher et al., 1962b) underlines the physiological importance of the lining of the uterus. Appropriately, the replacement of endometrial tissue alone can maintain oestrous cycles in the hysterectomized guinea-pig (Butcher

Special Case of Pig

Replacement of Ut. Tissue

et al., 1962a), although a relationship between the presence of glands and the life span of the corpora lutea is not apparent in experiments involving partial hysterectomy in which the glands in the endometrium degenerated (Butcher *et al.*, 1962b). A similar observation has been made by Donovan (unpublished). Ligation of the base of the uterine horns in the guinea pig caused hydrometria and resulted in degeneration of the endometrial glands and reduction in the amount of endometrium, but despite these changes the oestrous cycle remained normal.

The nature of the factor believed to be produced in the endometrium is unknown. In the hysterectomized rat the implantation of uterine tissue from an oestrous donor restores the extended pseudopregnancy to a normal length of 11–13 days, but uterine tissue taken from dioestrous rats is not effective in this way. If the tissue from oestrous animals is frozen in solid carbon dioxide before implantation, the corpora lutea are maintained for the 21-day interval characteristic of hysterectomy alone (Hechter *et al.*, 1940; Bradbury *et al.*, 1950). It thus appears that the uterine factor is inactivated by freezing or that the activity of viable uterine cells is required. In either case it would seem that the release and action of any steroid hormone stored in the uterus can be excluded. Some information derived from work with isolated tissues may also be cited. Filtrates prepared from pig endometrium collected during the late luteal phase of the cycle (days 16–18) have been reported to exert an inhibitory effect on the synthesis of progesterone by incubated luteal tissue, whilst preparations made from the uterus at days 12–13 of the cycle were found to increase the production of progesterone (Duncan, Bowerman, Anderson, Hearn and Melampy, 1961). However, human chorionic gonadotrophin (HCG) is known to increase the synthesis of progesterone by bovine luteal tissue *in vitro*, but is unable to exert the same effect *in vivo* (Short, 1964). The results of biochemical work of this kind need not always apply to the *in vivo* situation.

It is not clear whether the uterine luteolytic factor, if it exists, acts directly upon the corpora lutea or through the pituitary gland. As yet few hysterectomized-hypophysectomized animals have been used to test this point. Hypophysectomy is known to curtail luteal function following hysterectomy in the sheep (Denamur and Mauléon, 1963b) and pig (Du Mesnil du Buisson and Léglise, 1963), so that the pituitary appears to be involved in some way. However, hypophysectomy does not depress luteal function in the guinea pig (Rowlands, 1962), and other information derived from the pig (p. 186)

13

indicates that a uterine luteolytic factor may act directly on the corpus luteum. The action of the hypophysis may be general and not specific.

F. THE SIGNIFICANCE OF AFFERENT STIMULI FROM THE UTERUS

Since transplantation of the uterus is without effect on the oestrous rhythm and ovulation in all species so far studied (pp. 192–193), it would seem unlikely that afferent stimuli arising from the uterus are of much importance in the physiological control of ovarian function. However, it has been claimed that denervation of the uterus or the ovaries of the guinea-pig brings about the same changes as follow hysterectomy, although very slight or sub-threshold changes of an oestrogenic nature may occur in the vagina (Hill, 1962). Also, the effects of distension of the uterus (p. 187) are now well established, and suggest that neural mechanisms involving the uterus may be of importance in controlling luteal function. Foreign bodies in the uterus may increase the activity of the sensory innervation of the organ, although direct information on this point is limited. Distension of the uterus of the rabbit increases the electrical activity recorded from the uterine sensory nerves (Bower, 1959), and electrical stimulation of the uterus of cats has been shown to evoke potentials in restricted areas of the hypothalamus (Abrahams, Langworth, and Theobald, 1964). Mechanical stimulation of the vagina or cervix of the oestrous rat will induce pseudopregnancy (Long and Evans, 1922), and denervation of the region, or stimulation under deep anaesthesia, blocks the occurrence of pseudopregnancy (Meyer, Leonard and Hisaw, 1929; Haterius, 1933), so that the participation of the nervous system in this response is clear. Distension of the uterus of the pseudopregnant rabbit is said to favour the persistence of the corpora lutea and enhance the excretion of pregnanediol; the output of pregnanediol is depressed by section of the spinal cord in the thoracic region (Andreoli, 1960). Yet it remains possible that some substance affecting corpus luteum function is released from the endometrium by mechanical means, as well as in response to the contractions caused by oxytocin (p. 199).

On the assumption that pituitary function is affected by stimuli derived from the uterus, two processes require consideration: a possible luteotrophic action on the part of pituitary hormones, or a possible luteolytic effect. These will be discussed next.

G. POSSIBLE LUTEOTROPHIC ACTION BY THE HYPOPHYSIS

It is now certain that the pituitary gland of the rat contains a luteotrophic hormone and that this can be equated with the lactogenic hormone, prolactin. In recent work administration of prolactin to the rat has been shown to induce pseudopregnancy (von Berswordt-Wallrabe and Turner, 1961), and stimulation of the cervix to induce pseudopregnancy is associated with a fall in the pituitary content of this hormone (Herlyn, Geller, von Berswordt-Wallrabe and von Berswordt-Wallrabe, 1965). Nevertheless, it has proved difficult to extend this conclusion to other species. In a review in 1955 Cowie and Folley wrote: 'There is no unequivocal evidence that prolactin is capable of exerting a luteotrophic function in species other than the rat; even yet it may be premature to conclude that prolactin is the specific luteotrophic hormone.' The caution of these workers is justified.

The degenerative changes observed in the corpora lutea after hypophysectomy in the rat (Smith, 1930), rabbit (Smith and White, 1931) and ferret (Donovan, 1963) indicate that the pituitary gland is producing some substance with a trophic action on the luteal bodies, but the identity of the active material has not been fully established. Exogenous prolactin maintains luteal function in the hypophysec-tomized ferret (Donovan, 1965) and intact mouse (Dresel, 1935), but is ineffective in the rabbit (Hilliard, Endröczi and Sawyer, 1961; Kilpatrick, Armstrong and Greep, 1964; Rennie, Davies and Friedrich, 1964), guinea pig (Aldred, Sammelwitz and Nalbandov, 1961; Rowlands, 1962), sheep (Moore and Nalbandov, 1955; Denamur and Mauléon, 1963b; Short, McDonald and Rowson, 1963; Short, 1964), pig (Sammelwitz and Nalbandov, 1958; Duncan et al., 1961), cow (Smith, McShan and Casida, 1957; Armstrong and Hansel, 1959; Simmons and Hansel, 1964), monkey (Bryans, 1951) and woman (Bradbury et al., 1950; Cowie and Folley, 1955). Homogenates of pituitary glands taken from gilts at different stages of the oestrous cycle or of gestation fail to modify the secretion of progesterone by gilt luteal tissue maintained under in vitro conditions. Among other substances, oxytocin and prolactin are also ineffective, but extracts of the endometrium alter the secretion of progesterone (Duncan et al., 1961). It is surprising that prolactin does not possess any luteotrophic action in the rabbit, for the reproductive mechanisms of the rat, rabbit and ferret possess several features in common. Luteinizing hormone stimulates luteal function in the rabbit (Kilpatrick et al., 1964) and rat (Armstrong, O'Brien and Greep, 1964), but it is without effect in the sheep (Denamur and Maulson, 1964) and cow (Simmons and Hansel, 1964). However, the progesterone content of the corpora lutea of the cow is raised by the administration of crude extracts of anterior pituitary tissue; and progesterone synthesis by slices of corpora lutea is increased by luteinizing hormone or follicle-stimulating hormone under conditions when prolactin is ineffective (Mason, Marsh and Savard, 1962). The stimulatory action of follicle-stimulating hormone is about one-hundredth that of luteinizing hormone, and has been attributed to contamination of the preparation with the luteinizing principle (Mason and Savard, 1964). Thus the evidence for the existence of a separate luteotrophic factor in species other than the rat, mouse and ferret is marginal, although the finding that hypophysectomy interferes with the extension of luteal function after hysterectomy in the sheep and pig is indicative of a need for some pituitary factor (Denamur and Mauléon, 1963b; Du Mesnil du Buisson and Léglise, 1963).

The need for a continuous secretion of a luteotrophic substance during the luteal phase of the oestrous cycle in some species is minimized by the results of studies employing hypophysectomized animals, for removal of the pituitary during the first two days of the cycle of the guinea-pig (Perry and Rowlands, 1962), pig (Du Mesnil du Buisson and Léglise, 1963) and sheep (Denamur and Mauléon, 1963a; Short, 1964) is without effect on the normal activity of the corpora lutea. This suggests either that luteinizing hormone, released at oestrus to cause ovulation, exerts a sufficiently prolonged action upon luteal function, or that discharge of a luteotrophin occurs at or immediately after ovulation. Similar conclusions were reached by Nalbandov and his colleagues, who found that blockade of pituitary gonadotrophin secretion in pigs (Brinkley, Norton and Nalbandov, 1964a, b) and guinea-pigs (Aldred et al., 1961) by the daily administration of progesterone or a progestational compound from the day before ovulation onwards failed to prevent the formation of corpora lutea or their normal survival. If ovulation is provoked by the injection of HCG during blockade of the hypophysis with progesterone, corpus luteum formation and maintenance is normal. However, the corpora lutea of the guinea-pig are reduced in size if systemic treatment with progesterone is started within 48 hours of ovulation. In the sheep, ovulation can be prevented by progesterone blockade of the pituitary; while if ovulation is caused during such blockade by the injection of HCG (non-luteotrophic in sheep (Short, 1964)) or ovine pituitary extract, the ensuing oestrous cycle lasts for a mean of only 8.8 days instead of 17.5 days (Inskeep, Howland, Pope and Casida, 1964). Again, it seems that some trophic factor is required for normal luteal function.

Changes in luteal function become evident during pregnancy. At this time hypophysectomy causes regression of the corpora lutea in the sheep (Denamur and Martinet, 1961). Progesterone or a progestational compound is able to cause regression of the corpora lutea in the pregnant pig which cannot be reversed by HCG (Sammelwitz, Aldred and Nalbandov, 1961; Brinkley et al., 1964b), although daily treatment with HCG can maintain the weight but not the function of the luteal bodies. Similar blockade of the hypophysis in pregnant sheep by daily treatment with progesterone depresses the weight of the corpora lutea as early as the 13th day after mating (Inskeep et al., 1964). Thus it seems that during pregnancy in the sheep and pig luteal function is maintained by the constant secretion of a pituitary luteotrophin—a conclusion which is supported by the finding that the maintenance of luteal function seen after hysterectomy is prevented by hypophysectomy (Denamur and Mauléon, 1963b; Du Mesnil du Buisson and Léglise, 1963). However, the evidence for the existence of a pituitary luteotrophin in the guinea-pig is less clear cut, for hypophysectomy of the hysterectomized animal fails to modify luteal function (Rowlands, 1962). On the other hand progesterone-blockade of the hypophysis during pregnancy reduces the size of the luteal bodies (Aldred et al., 1961), and hypophysectomy between days 30 and 40 causes luteal regression (Pencharz and Lyons, 1934).

H. POSSIBLE LUTEOLYTIC ACTION BY THE HYPOPHYSIS

Several authors have suggested that the luteinizing hormone of the pituitary gland, which initially causes ovulation and the formation of corpora lutea, may also destroy mature luteal bodies (Bunde and Greep, 1936; Greep, 1938; Desclin, 1958; Everett, 1961; Rothchild, 1962). The shortening of the cycle observed to follow distension of the uterus in the guinea pig corresponds very closely to that brought about by removal of the corpora lutea soon after ovulation (Loeb, 1911; Dempsey, 1937). On this basis it may be presumed that the stimulus from the uterus causes destruction of the corpora lutea, shortens the luteal phase and accelerates the appearance of the next oestrus (Donovan and Traczyk, 1962). This result could be achieved by the release of a luteolytic hormone from the hypophysis; distension may thus activate an afferent arm of the reflex outlined on p. 191. After hypophysectomy the corpora lutea persist in the ovaries of rats beyond the usual term (Smith, 1930), and some hypophysial factor is presumably necessary for their destruction. Autografts of pituitary tissue can support the existence of secretory corpora lutea in the ovaries of rats almost indefinitely, presumably by the secretion of prolactin (Everett, 1956), but when grafts of pituitary tissue are made in otherwise intact mice (Mühlbock and Boot, 1956) and rats (Quilligan and Rothchild, 1960), a series of pseudopregnancies ensues. In some way the existing crop of corpora lutea is destroyed to allow a fresh ovulation.

This problem was approached from a different direction by Silbiger and Rothchild (1963), who were concerned to determine the means by which hysterectomy increased the duration of pseudopregnancy in the rat. Since their findings led them to conclude that a luteolytic hormone was present in the hypophysis their results are of considerable interest. With the idea in mind that the extension of pseudopregnancy might be associated with an increased secretion of pituitary luteotrophic hormone, homografts of pituitary tissue—known to release the factor—were inserted beneath the capsule of the kidney of hysterectomized rats. However, the incidence of prolonged pseudopregnancies was not raised by this means, although the pseudopregnancies were slightly longer. In other experiments it was observed that after unilateral ovariectomy the growth of the remaining ovary was slower in cyclic hysterectomized rats than in those in which the uterus remained intact. With otherwise intact pseudopregnant rats compensatory hypertrophy of the ovary began on the 9th day, but was delayed to the 15th day in hysterectomized animals. In order to analyse the change in pituitary function responsible for this difference, the 'folliculotrophic' potency of the hypophysis—probably a mixture of follicle-stimulating hormone and luteinizing hormone—was also measured at intervals in normal and hysterectomized pseudopregnant rats and found to be reduced after hysterectomy. The increase expected as pseudopregnancy progressed was delayed in hysterectomized animals.

Two aspects of pituitary function loomed large in the discussion of these results: whether a pituitary luteotrophic hormone was important in extending pseudopregnancy in the rat, and whether a pituitary luteolytic factor—tentatively identified with luteinizing hormone—brought pseudopregnancy to an end. For if hysterectomy promoted the secretion of a luteotrophic agent, then the effects of hysterectomy should match those seen in the presence of a pituitary homograft, but they did not. Hysterectomy lengthened pseudopregnancy in the rat, whilst the pseudopregnancies studied in animals carrying additional pituitary tissue were of normal span. Hysterectomy should have raised the incidence of pseudopregnancies in otherwise cyclic rats, as occurred with pituitary homografts, but the procedure was ineffective. When cyclic rats were subjected to hysterectomy, the incidence of pseudopregnancies was even less than that observed in rats with intact uteri plus pituitary transplants. As an alternative, Silbiger and Rothchild (1963) suggested that hysterectomy reduced the secretion of folliculotrophin, and so interfered with destruction of the corpora lutea by a luteolytic mechanism. With prolongation of the life of the corpora lutea after hysterectomy, pseudopregnancy would naturally be extended and ovulation delayed. This concept takes into account the delay in increase of folliculotrophic potency after hysterectomy, which is held to imply that less luteinizing hormone was released and less luteolytic action exerted, but does not explain the change in luteinizing hormone secretion. *OR NATURE!* Also, it is hard to reconcile this viewpoint with the fact that the frequency of ovulation is unaltered by hysterectomy in the rat. If hysterectomy retards the secretion of luteinizing hormone then ovulation should be delayed and some change in the oestrous cycle noted. Perhaps the most important conclusion to be drawn from the work of Silbiger and Rothchild (1963) is that the extension of pseudopregnancy after hysterectomy in the rat is not to be attributed to the action of a pituitary luteotrophic factor. The elimination of this misconception may be of great value in subsequent considerations of luteal function.

Luteolysis can be brought about in cattle by the administration of oxytocin (Armstrong and Hansel, 1959; Hansel and Wagner, 1960; Black and Duby, 1965). Daily treatment with this polypeptide from the neurohypophysis advances oestrus in heifers so that the cycle length is reduced from 21 days to 8–12 days. Interference with luteal function is indicated by histological changes in the corpora and by a fall in the content of progesterone (Staples and Hansel, 1961; Staples, McEntee and Hansel, 1961). Since the effect is abolished by hysterectomy, a direct action of oxytocin upon the hypophysis to release a luteolytic factor appears unlikely, although the factor could be discharged in response to afferent stimuli initiated in the uterus. Attempts have been made by Simmons and Hansel (1964) to block the luteolytic effect of oxytocin by the concurrent administration of luteinizing hormone, growth hormone, ovine prolactin, human chorionic gonadotrophin or a crude aqueous extract of bovine anterior pituitary tissue, but only the last two raise the content of progesterone in the corpora lutea. Both atropine and adrenaline are able to block the action of oxytocin but the mode of action of these drugs is not known (Black and Duby, 1965). A luteolytic effect of oxytocin has not been observed in the pig (Duncan *et al.*, 1961) or guinea-pig (Donovan, 1961), but it is of particular interest to note that vasopressin and oxytocin exert a luteolytic effect in rats bearing autografts of anterior pituitary tissue (Faulkner and Hansel, 1962). Newly-formed corpora lutea produced in the ovaries of sheep on days 5, 9 or 13 of the cycle, with or without removal of the pre-existing natural corpora lutea, do not function for their normal life span and instead, the cycle lasts for the usual period of 16–18 days (Inskeep *et al.*, 1963). This suggests that some factor or factors act on the luteal bodies to determine their survival time.

I. THE UTERUS AND STEROID METABOLISM

There seems to be a close connection between oestrogen action and corpus luteum function, for oestrogen can maintain the secretion of progesterone by the corpora lutea of the hypophysectomized pseudopregnant rabbit (Robson, 1937; Greep, 1941), as well as those of the intact animal (Heckel and Allen, 1939; Greep, 1941; Chu *et al.*, 1946; Gagnière and Klein, 1956). Implantation of solid oestrogen into the corpora lutea of pseudopregnant rabbits causes persistence of the treated luteal bodies beyond the life span of control bodies (Hammond and Robson, 1951). Alongside this evidence for a direct action of oestrogen on the corpora lutea it is known that hypophysectomy of the pseudopregnant rabbit is rapidly followed by luteal regression (Smith and White, 1931; Greep, 1941); it has therefore been postulated that the pituitary secretes small amounts of follicle-stimulating and luteinizing hormone during pseudopregnancy, which cause the secretion of oestrogen by the ovary to act within the organ upon the corpora lutea (Everett, 1961). Oestrogen is luteotrophic in the rat (Merckel and Nelson, 1940; Desclin, 1949; Everett, 1956), pig

(Gardner, First and Casida, 1963) and sheep (Short, 1964), although *ESTROGEN ↗LTH* it is not so in the ferret (Donovan, unpublished), cow (Kaltenbach, *FERRET* Niswender, Zimmerman and Wiltbank, 1964) or woman (Fluhmann *COW* and Hoffman, 1935; Brown, Bradbury and Jennings, 1948). (Argu- *WOMAN* ments in favour of a clinical luteotrophic action of oestrogen have been presented by Westman (1940)). The pituitary gland is generally considered to be concerned in this luteotrophic action, for removal of the hypophysis of the rat (Desclin, 1949) and sheep (Denamur and Mauléon, 1963b) prevents the response to the steroid. Oestrogen given to rats raises the pituitary content and enhances the secretion *PROLACTION* of prolactin (Reece and Turner, 1937; Wolthuis, 1963), thus implica- ting the luteotrophic properties of prolactin in the mediation of the effect. The functional corpora lutea maintained in the ovaries of rats in which the hypophysis has been autotransplanted to the kidney increase in size when oestrogen is given, and histological changes in the grafted pituitary tissue ensue (Everett, 1956). A similar increase in the size of the corpora occurs with the administration of oestrogen to intact pseudopregnant rats but does not follow prolactin injection (Weichert and Schurgast, 1942).

Another suggestion is that removal of the uterus takes away a major *HYSTERX* participant in the metabolism of sex hormone, leading to the accumul- ation of unmetabolized hormone or of abnormal end-products which would favour the secretion of pituitary luteotrophic hormone, or could act directly upon the corpus luteum. At the time this view was put forward (Bradbury, 1937b), it seemed clear that the injection of oestrone into hysterectomized rabbits was not followed by its con- *ESTROGEN T HYSTERX* version to oestriol as in normal animals (Pincus and Zahl, 1937); and this theory was further supported by the finding of Heckel (1942), that in the rabbit an amount of oestrogen insufficient to prolong the life of the corpora lutea in intact pseudopregnant animals could maintain luteal function after removal of part of the uterus. However, the effect of hysterectomy alone in prolonging the life of the corpora *✳* lutea must also be taken into consideration, so that the interpretation of experiments of this nature becomes hazardous.

Rowlands (1961) has more recently attributed the extension of luteal function in the guinea-pig to the action of oestrogen. He considers that a supply of oestrogenic hormone could be provided by the follicles that continue to mature throughout the post-operative period, and that because of a possible sparing effect of hysterectomy much larger amounts of this hormone might become available after removal of the uterus. Exogenous oestrogens given to cycling, hysterectomized or pregnant heifers cause a fall in the weight and progesterone content of the corpora lutea (Kaltenbach et al., 1964). Follicular activity is also depressed. It is difficult to interpret this finding on the basis of any one mechanism, although it supports the conclusion that oestrogen is not luteotrophic in this species. Oestrogen is also luteolytic when given to hamsters during the first 3 days of pregnancy (Greenwald, 1964), probably owing to a direct effect either on pituitary gonadotrophin secretion which affects luteal development, or on the developing corpus luteum itself. The fate of labelled oestrogen given subcutaneously to immature rats has been followed by Jensen and Jacobson (1962), without any indication of an especially high concentration in the uterus. Although the concentration of oestradiol in the uterus increases rapidly after injection, and is maintained at an elevated level when compared to the liver and kidney, the fraction picked up never exceeds 0.1 to 0.2%. Confirmatory findings have been made in the mouse by Stone, Baggett and Donnelly (1963). The proportion seems too low to be of importance in modifying or controlling the blood concentration of circulating oestrogen. It is also of interest that inactivation of oestrogens in the uterus appears to be carried out by eosinophils and not by the organ itself (Klebanoff, 1965). Kimura (1958, 1961) refers to several investigations which indicate that the uterus is concerned in the metabolism of oestrogen, but his studies on the response of vaginal grafts to oestrogen in spayed and spayed-hysterectomized rats, or on the oestrogen-inactivating potency of the uterus, fail to support them. Similarly, metabolites of oestrogen are rare in uterine tissue after the administration of labelled oestradiol (King, Gordon and Inman, 1965). Only oestradiol and oestrone were present in the uterus, but at least six compounds could be found in the liver.

Comparison of the action of oestrogen in hysterectomized, and non-hysterectomized, spayed rats (de Jongh and Wolthuis, 1964) further supports the view that the uterus does not metabolize oestrogen to any appreciable extent, but indicates that the organ might be important in the disposal of progesterone. On this basis, loss of the endometrium might favour an increase in the blood level of progesterone, although similar rates of excretion of pregnanediol by normal and hysterectomized women follow progesterone treatment, and there appears to be no obvious change in the metabolism of progesterone (Guterman, 1953). Progesterone treatment increases the output of the luteotrophic factor from the hypophysis of the rat (Rothchild, 1960; Wolthuis, 1963) and inhibits the release of the follicle-stimulating and luteinizing hormones (van Rees, 1959; Rothchild, 1962), although Sammelwitz, Aldred and Nalbandov (1961) found in rats that progesterone administration throughout pregnancy or pseudopregnancy has no detectable effect on the corpora lutea. Progesterone exerts distinct luteolytic activity and reduces luteal weight when supplied in large doses (ranging from 0.4–1 mg./lb. body weight) to pregnant guinea-pigs (Aldred, Sammelwitz and Nalbandov, 1961), pregnant sheep (Zimbelman, Pope and Casida, 1959) and hysterectomized (Spies, Zimmerman, Self and Casida, 1958, 1960) or pregnant (Sammelwitz and Nalbandov, 1958; Sammelwitz et al., 1961; Spies et al., 1958, 1959, 1960) pigs. In pigs the hypophysis is probably involved, since direct injection into the corpora lutea has no effect upon their weight or hormone content (Spies et al., 1960).

The view that the uterus may be of significance in controlling the blood level of sex hormones fails to take into account the activities of the liver in this regard. There is no doubt that the liver is responsible for the inactivation of large amounts of steroids by conjugation or transformation, and it can be argued with equal validity that hepatectomy may exert beneficial effects in extending luteal function. It thus appears that, apart from some information concerning the rabbit, there is little evidence in favour of the ovarian hormones operating either directly or through the hypophysis to maintain luteal function.

J. THE PLACENTA AND OVARIAN FUNCTION

A constant supply of progesterone is required to support pregnancy in all mammals. In many species this is provided by the corpora lutea, whose secretory function is often prolonged to last throughout gestation. Possible ways in which this may be achieved have already been discussed when dealing with the changes following hysterectomy. The role of the placenta now merits attention, as the maternal portion of this organ is composed entirely of modified uterine endometrium.

The placenta is a highly active endocrine organ during gestation (Diczfalusy and Troen, 1961), but for present purposes two products only need be mentioned: placental luteotrophin and progesterone. In women the excretion of placental or chorionic gonadotrophin in the urine forms the basis of sensitive tests for pregnancy. The hormone acts on the corpora lutea in the ovaries to promote the secretion of progesterone and so extend the luteal phase of the cycle. Gonadotrophins are secreted by the placenta of the woman (Jones, Gey and Gey, 1943; Stewart, Sano and Montgomery, 1948; Diczfalusy, 1953), monkey (Hamlett, 1937), chimpanzee (Zuckerman, 1935; Schultz and Snyder, 1935), horse (Cole and Saunders, 1935), mouse (Newton and Beck, 1939; Gardner and Allen, 1942) and rat (Astwood and Greep, 1938; Ray, Averill, Lyons and Johnson, 1955), but the evidence is strongest, just as for pituitary luteotrophin, for the last species mentioned. The situation is complicated in some animals by the simultaneous secretion of large quantities of progesterone, which override the activities of the corpora lutea. For this reason the corpora lutea (and the ovaries) can be dispensed with early in pregnancy in women (Melinkoff, 1950; Tulsky and Koff, 1957), monkeys (Hartman, 1941; Hartman and Corner, 1947), sheep (Neher and Zarrow, 1954) and guinea-pigs (Deanesly, 1963). The adrenals may also act as an important source of progesterone during pregnancy in the cow and sheep (Balfour, Comline and Short, 1957). Little progesterone is elaborated by the placenta of rats, mice, hamsters or rabbits; loss of the ovaries is therefore followed by abortion in these species (Zarrow, 1961). It also appears that placental gonadotrophin has not replaced the pituitary supply in the dog, rabbit and ferret, for in these species hypophysectomy terminates pregnancy at any stage (Aschner, 1912; Smith and White, 1931; McPhail, 1935).

Until the placenta can take over full responsibility for the maintenance of pregnancy by the production of progesterone, there must exist an intervening period during which the presence of a fertilized egg in the uterus has to be signalled to the rest of the endocrine system. In women the oncoming menstrual period must be prevented; otherwise the conceptus would be shed with the unwanted endometrial fragments. Clinical studies (Hertig, 1964) indicate that the secretion of chorionic gonadotrophin begins within 2 or 3 days after implantation, or during the 21st to 22nd days of the cycle in which conception has occurred. The hormone can be detected in the urine within a few days, and there appears to be sufficient time available for luteal activity to be extended and the expected menstrual period inhibited. However, this mechanism is not of general application, for it is difficult to demonstrate the production of gonadotrophin by placental structures in lower forms in sufficient amount to interrupt the sexual cycle. For example, placental tissue grown outside the

uterus of the mouse (Kirby, 1965) or guinea pig (Bland and Donovan, *implanted placenta*
1965a) does not interrupt the periodicity of oestrus, although the
menstrual cycle stops in clinical cases of ectopic pregnancy. It is
difficult to argue that insufficient placental tissue is present in the
mouse or guinea-pig, for the quantity available matches that seen at
the equivalent stages of normal pregnancy. Of more importance
would seem to be the occurrence of a decidual reaction.

The changes in the oestrous cycle of the rat and guinea-pig following the induction of deciduomata in the uterus were described on *DCR & cycle*
p. 183. Implantation is also associated with deciduoma formation in
the rabbit, rat, guinea-pig and primate, and it may be this change that
disturbs normal cyclic function. Functional removal of the endometrium by this means could act like hysterectomy in prolonging luteal
activity for a time long enough to allow the placental elaboration of
gonadotrophin to get under way, or for the provocation of release of
a pituitary luteotrophin. Nevertheless some reservations must still
be made: the extent of decidual formation in the endometrium with
implantation is relatively limited and, in the guinea-pig for example,
does not approximate to that which must be removed by surgical
means to prolong luteal function. Similarly, decidualization in the *DCR rabbit mouse*
rabbit (Hammond, 1917) and mouse (Kamell and Atkinson, 1948) *C. L.*
does not influence the life span of the corpora lutea. Present uncertainty concerning the existence of a pituitary luteotrophic hormone
in all species, or, indeed, of a placental gonadotrophin, makes further *★*
elaboration of this hypothesis hazardous. Note may also be taken of
the recent observation of Kirby (unpublished) that neither the *mouse*
decidua nor the placental trophoblast of the mouse can produce a
luteotrophic principle in isolation, but an association of these two *★ culture*
tissues is capable of causing enlargement of the corpora lutea to
pregnancy size and the persistence of these organs. Work carried out *GP*
in the guinea pig by Bland and Donovan (1965a and unpublished)
tends to support this conclusion, for it has proved extremely difficult
to induce ectopic pregnancy in this species. Trophoblastic tissue
develops, but the embryo fails to differentiate and there is no alteration of the oestrous cycle. It may be of importance that ectopic
implantation in the guinea pig and mouse is not associated with the
occurrence of a decidual reaction at the point of embedding, whilst *species*
a decidual reaction is commonly found in clinical cases of ectopic
pregnancy. This difference in reaction between the tissues of the
human and of other species was commented upon many years ago
by Loeb (1915).

K. CONCLUDING REMARKS

The material presented in the preceding pages establishes the importance of the uterus in the control of ovarian function. However, the means by which the control is exerted remains obscure and seems to vary from species to species. Few conclusions seem possible at the present time although several general principles seem to be emerging. Thus it is reasonable to presume that a luteotrophic action on the part of the hypophysis is less important for ovarian function than considered hitherto. A luteotrophic hormone separable from other pituitary factors apparently exists in the hypophysis of the rat but comparable information is not available for other species. On the other hand, luteinizing hormone causes the formation of corpora lutea and could provide sufficient stimulus for the continued secretion of progesterone. It is known to exert luteotrophic activity in the rabbit, although stimulatory effects on the corpora lutea of the sheep and cow have been observed only with isolated tissues. Nevertheless, luteolytic effects are probably of major significance in the economy of the ovary, and there is good reason for supposing that the uterus itself exercises a prime luteolytic influence, although luteolysis by a pituitary factor cannot be ignored. The existence of a luteolytic substance in the endometrium is implied by the work described on pages 192–194; it is very difficult to explain the unilateral responses observed in the pig upon any other basis. The changes wrought by distension of the uterus of the sheep and guinea-pig can also be accounted for in this manner. Although it has been suggested that the nervous system is involved in the response, the evidence for this point is not entirely satisfying. 'Denervation' of a segment of uterus, said to abolish the reaction to distension, was achieved by dissecting the piece away from the body of the uterus, and suturing it back into position. This procedure must inevitably interfere with the normal activities of the endometrium by disruption of its blood supply; to attribute the loss of effectiveness of distension to interference with the nerve supply to the mucosa is to present only one side of the coin. One theory discussed, that concerning the part played by the uterus in steroid metabolism, can be rejected, but the remaining possibilities still merit careful evaluation.

ADDENDUM

Since this chapter was written it has become clear that the uterus exerts a local control of luteal function in the guinea-pig. This has been shown in two ways. Distension of one horn of the uterus by two glass beads brings about an accelerated regression of the corpora lutea in the ovary on the operated side, as demonstrated by comparison of the volumes of the corpora lutea in each ovary (Bland and Donovan, *Nature*, 1965, **207**, 867-9). Further, removal of one horn of the uterus favours the maintenance of the corpora lutea on the side lacking uterine tissue, when comparison is made with those in the ovary on the opposite side of the body (Bland and Donovan, unpublished). Such responses, which are restricted to the ipsilateral ovary, imply the existence of a locally acting hormone produced by the uterus, and are in accord with the information derived from the pig.

REFERENCES

Abrahams, V. C., Langworth, E. P. and Theobald, G. W. (1964) Potentials evoked in the hypothalamus and cerebral cortex by electrical stimulation of the uterus. *Nature, Lond.* **203**, 654–6.

Aldred, J. P., Sammelwitz, P. H. and Nalbandov, A. V. (1961) Mechanism of formation of corpora lutea in guinea-pigs. *J. Reprod. Fert.*, **2**, 394–9.

Anderson, L. L. (1962) Effect of uterine distention on the estrous cycle of the gilt. *J. Anim. Sci.*, **21**, 597–601.

Anderson, L. L., Bowerman, A. M. and Melampy, R. M. (1963) *Neuro-utero-ovarian relationships.* In Advances in Neuroendocrinology, ed. A. V. Nalbandov. University of Illinois Press, Urbana.

Anderson, L. L., Butcher, R. L. and Melampy, R. M. (1961) Sub-total hysterectomy and ovarian function in gilts. *Endocrinology*, **69**, 571–80.

Anderson, L. L., Butcher, R. L. and Melampy, R. M. (1963) Uterus and occurrence of oestrus in pigs. *Nature, Lond.*, **198**, 311–12.

Anderson, L. L., Neal, F. C. and Melampy, R. M. (1962) Hysterectomy and ovarian function in beef heifers. *Am. J. vet. Res.*, **23**, 794–801.

Andreoli, C. (1960) Azione luteotrofica esplicata nella coniglia dalla distensione uterina. *Minerva Ginec.*, **12**, 727–9.

Armstrong, D. T. and Hansel, W. (1959) Alteration of the bovine estrous cycle with oxytocin. *J. Dairy Sci.*, **42**, 533–42.

Armstrong, D. T., O'Brien, J. and Greep, R. O. (1964) Effects of luteinizing hormone on progestin biosynthesis in the luteinized rat ovary. *Endocrinology*, **75**, 488–500.

Aschner, B. (1912) Uber die Funktion der Hypophyse. *Pflüger's Arch. ges. Physiol.*, **146**, 1–146.

Asdell, S. A. and Hammond, J. (1933) The effects of prolonging the life of the corpus luteum in the rabbit by hysterectomy. *Am. J. Physiol.*, **103**, 600–5.

Astwood, E. B. and Greep, R. O. (1938) A corpus luteum-stimulating substance in the rat placenta. *Proc. Soc. exp. Biol. Med.*, **38**, 713–6.

Balfour, W. E., Comline, R. S. and Short, R. V. (1957) Secretion of progesterone by the adrenal gland. *Nature, Lond.*, **180**, 1480–1.

von Berswordt-Wallrabe, R. and Turner, C. W. (1961) Influence of lactogenic hormone and estradiol benzoate upon placentoma formation in intact rats measured by total DNA. *Proc. Soc. exp. Biol. Med.*, **108**, 212–4.

Black, D. L. and Duby, R. T. (1965) Effect of oxytocin, epinephrine and atropine on the oestrous cycle of the cow. *J. Reprod. Fert.*, **9**, 3–8.

Bland, K. P. and Donovan, B. T. (1965a) Experimental ectopic implantation of eggs and early embryos in guinea pigs. *J. Reprod. Fert.*, **10**, 189–96.

Bland, K. P. and Donovan, B. T. (1965b) A quantitative study of the effect of uterine distension on the oestrous cycle of the guinea pig. *J. Physiol., Lond.* **179**, 34P-35P.

Bower, E. A. (1959) Action potentials from uterine sensory nerves. *J. Physiol., Lond.*, **148**, 2P–3P.

Bradbury, J. T. (1937a) Prolongation of the life of the corpus luteum by hysterectomy in the rat. *Anat. Rec.*, **70**, Supplement 1, 51.

Bradbury, J. T. (1937b) in discussion. *Cold Spring Harb. Symp. quant. Biol.*, **5**, 56.

Bradbury, J. T. (1941) Uterine distention and lactation. *Endocrinology*, **29**, 393–6.

Bradbury, J. T., Brown, W. E. and Gray, L. A. (1950) Maintenance of the corpus luteum and physiologic actions of progesterone. *Recent Progr. Hormone Res.*, **5**, 151–90.

Brinkley, H. J., Norton, H. W. and Nalbandov, A. V. (1964a) Role of a hypophysial luteotrophic substance in the function of porcine corpora lutea. *Endocrinology*, **74**, 9–13.

Brinkley, H. J., Norton, H. W. and Nalbandov, A. V. (1964b) Is ovulation alone sufficient to cause formation of corpora lutea? *Endocrinology*, **74**, 14–20.

Brown, J. B. and Matthew, G. D. (1962) The application of urinary estrogen measurements to problems in gynecology. *Recent Progr. Hormone Res.*, **18**, 337–73.

Brown, W. E., Bradbury, J. T. and Jennings, A. F. (1948) Experimental alteration of the human ovarian cycle by estrogen. *J. clin. Endocr. Metab.*, **8**, 453–60.

Bryans, F. E. (1951) Progesterone of the blood in the menstrual cycle of the monkey. *Endocrinology*, **48**, 733–40.

Bunde, C. A. and Greep, R. O. (1936) Suppression of persisting corpora lutea in hypophysectomized rats. *Proc. Soc. exp. Biol. Med.*, **35**, 235–7.

Burford, T. H. and Diddle, A. W. (1936) Effect of total hysterectomy upon the ovary of the Macacus rhesus. *Surg. Gynec. Obstet.*, **62**, 701–7.

Butcher, R. L., Chu, K. Y. and Melampy, R. M. (1962a) Effect of uterine autotransplants on the oestrous cycle in the guinea pig. *Endocrinology*, **70**, 442–3.

Butcher, R. L., Chu, K. Y. and Melampy, R. M. (1962b) Utero-ovarian relationships in the guinea pig. *Endocrinology*, **71**, 810–15.

Chu, J. P., Lee, C. C. and You, S. S. (1946) Functional relation between the uterus and the corpus luteum. *J. Endocr.*, **4**, 392–8.

Cole, H. H. and Saunders, F. J. (1935) The concentration of gonad-stimulating hormone in blood serum and of oestrin in the urine throughout pregnancy in the mare. *Endocrinology*, **19**, 199–208.

Cowie, A. T. and Folley, S. J. (1955) Physiology of the gonadotropins and the lactogenic hormone. In *The Hormones*, Vol. 3, 309–87, ed. G. Pincus and K. U. Thimann. Academic Press, New York.

Deanesly, R. (1963) Early embryonic growth and progestagen function in ovariectomized guinea-pigs. *J. Reprod. Fert.*, **6**, 143–52.

Dempsey, E. W. (1937) Follicular growth rate and ovulation after various experimental procedures in the guinea pig. *Am. J. Physiol.*, **120**, 126–32.

Denamur, R. and Martinet, J. (1961) Effets de l'hypophysectomie et de la section de la tige pituitaire sur la gestation de la brebis. *Annls. Endocr.*, **22**, 755–9.

Denamur, R. and Mauléon, P. (1963a) Effets de l'hypophysectomie sur la morphologie et l'histologie du corps jaune chez les brebis. *C. r. hebd. Séanc. Acad. Sci., Paris*, **257**, 264–8.

Denamur, R. and Mauléon, P. (1963b) Contrôle endocrinien de la persistance du corps jaune chez les ovins. *C. r. hebd. Séanc. Acad. Sci., Paris,* **257**, 527–30.

Denamur, R. and Mauléon, P. (1964) quoted by Short (1964).

Desclin, L. (1949) Action des oestrogènes sur l'ovaire chez le rat normal et hypophysectomisé. *C. r. Séanc. Soc. Biol.,* **143**, 1004–6.

Desclin, L. (1958) A propos des facteurs qui déterminent la longueur de vie des corps jaunes chez le rat. *Annls. Endocr.,* **19**, 890–4.

Diczfalusy, E. (1953) Chorionic gonadotrophin and oestrogens in the human placenta. *Acta Endocr., Copenh. Supplement* 12, 1–175.

Diczfalusy, E. and Troen, P. (1961) Endocrine functions of the human placenta. *Vitam. and Horm.,* **19**, 229–311.

Donovan, B. T. (1961) The role of the uterus in the regulation of the oestrous cycle. *J. Reprod. Fert.,* **2**, 508–9.

Donovan, B. T. (1963) The effect of pituitary stalk-section on luteal function in the ferret. *J. Endocr.,* **27**, 201–11.

Donovan, B. T. (1965) Hormonal control of corpus luteum function in the ferret. *Abst. XXIIIrd Internat. Congress Physiol. Sci., Tokyo, Japan.* 1965, 284.

Donovan, B. T. and Traczyk, W. (1960) Uterine distension and the vaginal cycle in the guinea-pig. *J. Physiol., Lond.,* **154**, 50P–51P.

Donovan, B. T. and Traczyk, W. (1962) The effect of uterine distension on the oestrous cycle of the guinea-pig. *J. Physiol., Lond.,* **161**, 227–36.

Dresel, I. (1935) The effect of prolactin on the estrus cycle of non-parous mice. *Science,* **82**, 173.

Duncan, G. W., Bowerman, A. M., Anderson, L. L., Hearn, W. R. and Melampy, R. M. (1961) Factors influencing *in vitro* synthesis of progesterone. *Endocrinology,* **68**, 199–207.

Everett, J. W. (1956) Functional corpora lutea maintained for months by autografts of rat hypophyses. *Endocrinology,* **58**, 786–96.

Everett, J. W. (1961) The Mammalian Female Reproductive Cycle and its Controlling Mechanisms. In *Sex and Internal Secretions.* Vol. I., ed. W. C. Young. Williams & Wilkins Co., Baltimore.

Faulkner, L. C. and Hansel, W. (1962) Hypothalamic substances in adenohypophyseal function. *The Physiologist,* **5**, 138.

Fluhmann, C. F. and Hoffman, P. E. (1935) Effect of large doses of estrin on the human menstrual cycle. *Am. J. Obstet. Gynec.,* **29**, 308.

Gagnière, E. and Klein, M. (1956) Réactions utérines sous l'effet lutéotrophique des oestrogènes chez la lapine. *C. r. Séanc. Soc. Biol.,* **150**, 1266–8.

Gardner, M. L., First, N. L. and Casida, L. E. (1963) Effect of exogenous estrogens on corpus luteum maintenance in gilts. *J. Anim. Sci.,* **22**, 132–4.

Gardner, W. U. and Allen, E. (1942) Effects of hypophysectomy at mid-pregnancy in the mouse. *Anat. Rec.,* **83**, 75–97.

Gillard, J. L. (1937) The effects of hysterectomy on mammary gland development in a rabbit. *Am. J. Physiol.,* **120**, 300–3.

Greene, R. R. (1941) Uterine distention and lactation in the rat. *Endocrinology,* **29**, 1026.

Greenwald, G. (1964) Luteolytic activity of oestrogen on the corpus luteum of pregnancy of the hamster. *Amer. Zool.,* **4**, 281.

Greep, R. O. (1938) The effect of gonadotropic hormones on the persisting corpora lutea in hypophysectomized rats. *Endocrinology,* **23**, 154–63.

Greep, R. O. (1941) Effects of hysterectomy and of oestrogen treatment on volume changes in the corpora lutea of pregnant rabbits. *Anat. Rec.,* **80**, 465–76.

Guterman, H. S. (1953) Progesterone metabolism in the human female: its significance in relation to reproduction. *Recent Progr. Hormone Res.,* **8**, 293–326.

Guttmacher, A. F. (1964) *The Intra-uterine Contraceptive Device (I.U.C.D.)* The Eighth Oliver Bird Lecture, 23 Nov. 1964, London.

Hamlett, G. W. D. (1937) Positive Friedman tests in the pregnant rhesus monkey, *Macaca mulatta. Am. J. Physiol.*, **118**, 664–6.

Hammond, J. (1917) On the causes responsible for the developmental progress of the mammary glands in the rabbit during the latter part of pregnancy. *Proc. roy. Soc. B.*, **89**, 534–46.

Hammond, J. Jr., and Robson, J. M. (1951) Local maintenance of the rabbit corpus luteum with oestrogen. *Endocrinology*, **49**, 384–9.

Hansel, W. and Wagner, W. C. (1960) Luteal inhibition in the bovine as a result of oxytocin injections, uterine dilatation, and intrauterine infusions of seminal and preputial fluids. *J. Dairy Sci.*, **43**, 796–805.

Hartman, C. G. (1941) Non-effect of ovariectomy on the twenty fifth day of pregnancy in the rhesus monkey. *Proc. Soc. exp. Biol. Med.*, **48**, 221–3.

Hartman, C. G. and Corner, G. W. (1947) Removal of the corpus luteum and of the ovaries of the rhesus monkey during pregnancy: Observations and cautions. *Anat. Rec.*, **98**, 539–46.

Haterius, H. O. (1933) Partial sympathectomy and induction of pseudopregnancy. *Am. J. Physiol.*, **103**, 97–103.

Hechter, O., Fraenkel, M., Lev, M. and Soskin, S. (1940) Influence of the uterus on the corpus luteum. *Endocrinology*, **26**, 680–3.

Heckel, G. P. (1942) The estrogen-sparing effect of hysterectomy. *Surg. Gynec. Obstet.*, **75**, 379–90.

Heckel, G. P. and Allen, W. M. (1939) Maintenance of the corpus luteum and inhibition of parturition in the rabbit by injection of estrogenic hormone. *Endocrinology*, **24**, 137–48.

Herlyn, U., Geller, H–F., von Berswordt-Wallrabe, I. and von Berswordt-Wallrabe R. (1965) Pituitary lactogenic hormone release during onset of pseudopregnancy in intact rats. *Acta Endocr., Copenh.*, **48**, 220–4.

Hertig, A. T. (1964) Gestational hyperplasia of endometrium. A morphologic correlation of ova, endometrium and corpora lutea during early pregnancy. *Lab. Invest.*, **13**, 1153–91.

Hill, R. T. (1962) *Paradoxical Effects of Ovarian Secretions.* In The Ovary, Vol.2, ed. S. Zuckerman. Academic Press, N. York and London.

Hilliard, J., Endröczi, E. and Sawyer, C. H. (1961) Stimulation of progestin release from rabbit ovary *in vivo. Proc. Soc. exp. Biol. Med.*, **108**, 154–6.

Inskeep, E. K., Howland, B. E., Pope, A. L. and Casida, L. E. (1964) Ability of corpora lutea induced experimentally in progesterone-treated ewes to prevent subsequent ovulation. *J. Anim. Sci.*, **23**, 1172–5.

Inskeep, E. K., Oloufa, M. M., Howland, B. E., Pope, A. L., and Casida, L. E. (1962) Effect of experimental uterine distention on estrual cycle lengths in ewes. *J. Anim. Sci.*, **21**, 331–2.

Inskeep, E. K., Oloufa, M. M., Pope, A. L. and Casida, L. E. (1963) Functional capabilities of experimentally induced corpora lutea in ewes. *J. Anim. Sci.*, **22**, 159–161.

Ishihama, A. (1959) Clinical studies on intrauterine rings especially the present state of contraception in Japan and the experiences in the use of intrauterine rings. *Yokohama Med. Bull.*, **10**, 89–105.

Jensen, E. V. and Jacobson, H. I. (1962) Basic guides to the mechanism of estrogen action. *Recent Progr. Hormone Res.*, **18**, 387–408.

Jones, G. E. S., Gey, G. O. and Gey, M. K. (1943) Hormone production by placental cells maintained in continuous culture. *Bull. Johns Hopkins Hosp.*, **72**, 26–38.

de Jongh, S. E. and Wolthuis, O. L. (1964) Factors determining cessation of corpus luteum function; the possible role of oestradiol and progesterone. *Acta Endocr., Copenh., Supplement* 90, 125–32.

Kaltenbach, C. C., Niswender, G. D., Zimmerman, D. R. and Wiltbank, J. N. (1964) Alteration of ovarian activity in cycling, pregnant and hysterectomized heifers with exogenous estrogens. *J. Anim. Sci.*, 23, 995–1001.

Kamell, S. A. and Atkinson, W. B. (1948) Absence of prolongation of pseudo-pregnancy by induction of deciduomata in the mouse. *Proc. Soc. exp. Biol. Med.*, 67, 415–6.

Kilpatrick, R., Armstrong, D. T. and Greep, R. O. (1964) Maintenance of the corpus luteum by gonadotrophins in the hypophysectomized rabbit. *Endocrinology*, 74, 453–61.

Kimura, T. (1958) Response of vaginal grafts to injected estrogen in rats with or without uterus. *Annotnes. zool. jap.*, 31, 194–7.

Kimura, T. (1961) Estrogen-inactivating potency of the uterus in the rat. *Annotnes. zool. jap.*, 34, 180–4.

King, R. J. B., Gordon, J. and Inman, D. R. (1965) The intracellular localization of oestrogen in rat tissue. *J. Endocr.*, 32, 9–15.

Kirby, D. R. S. (1965) The endocrinological effects of experimentally induced extrauterine pregnancy in virgin mice. *J. Reprod. Fert.* (in press).

Klebanoff, S. J. (1965) Inactivation of estrogen by rat uterine preparations. *Endocrinology*, 76, 301–11.

Loeb, L. (1911) Ueber die Bedeutung des Corpus Luteum für die Periodizität des sexuellen Zyklus beim weiblichen Säugetierorganismus. *Dtsch. med. Wschr.*, 37, 17–21.

Loeb, L. (1915) An early stage of an experimentally produced extauterine pregnancy and the spontaneous parthenogenesis of the eggs in the ovary of the guinea pig. *Biol. Bull. Mar. biol. Lab., Woods Hole*, 28, 59–76.

Loeb, L. (1923) The effect of extirpation of the uterus on the life and function of the corpus luteum in the guinea pig. *Proc. Soc. exp. Biol. Med.*, 20, 441–3.

Loeb, L. (1927) The effects of hysterectomy on the system of sex organs and on the periodicity of the sexual cycle in the guinea pig. *Am. J. Physiol.*, 83, 202–24.

Long, J. A. and Evans, H. M. (1922) The oestrous cycle in the rat and its associated phenomena. *Mem. Univ. Calif.*, 6, 1–148.

Mason, N. R., Marsh, J. M. and Savard, K. (1962) An action of gonadotropin *in vitro. J. biol. Chem.*, 237, 1801–6.

Mason, N. R. and Savard, K. (1964) Specificity of gonadotrophin stimulation of progesterone synthesis in bovine corpus luteum *in vitro. Endocrinology*, 74, 664–8.

McPhail, M. K. (1935) Studies on the hypophysectomized ferret. IX. The effect of hypophysectomy on pregnancy and lactation. *Proc. roy. Soc. B.*, 117, 34–45.

Melampy, R. M., Anderson, L. L. and Kragt, C. L. (1964) Uterus and lifespan of rat corpora lutea. *Endocrinology*, 74, 501–4.

Melinkoff, E. (1950) Questionable necessity of the corpus luteum. *Am. J. Obstet. Gynec.*, 60, 437–9.

Merckel, C. and Nelson, W. O. (1940) The relation of the estrogenic hormone to the formation and maintenance of corpora lutea in mature and immature rats. *Anat. Rec.*, 76, 391–409.

du Mesnil du Buisson, F. (1961a) Regression unilatérale des corps jaunes après hystérectomie partielle chez la truie. *Annls. Biol. anim. Biochim. Biophys.*, 1, 105–12.

du Mesnil du Buisson, F. (1961b) Possibilité d'un fonctionnement dissemblable des ovaires pendant la gestation chez la truie. *C. r. hebd. Séanc. Acad. Sci., Paris*, 253, 727–9.

du Mesnil du Buisson, F. and Dauzier, L. (1959) Contrôle mutuel de l'utérus et de l'ovaire chez la truie. *Annls. Zootech.*, Supplement 1959, 147–59.

du Mesnil du Buisson, F. and Léglise, P–C. (1963) Effet de l'hypophysectomie sur les corps jaunes de la truie. Résultats préliminaires. *C. r. hebd. Séanc. Acad. Sci., Paris*, **257**, 261–3.

du Mesnil du Buisson, F. and Rombauts, P. (1963) Effet d'autotransplants utérins sur le cycle oestrien de la truie. *C. r. hebd. Séanc. Acad. Sci., Paris*, **256**, 4984–6.

Meyer, R. K., Leonard, S. L. and Hisaw, F. L. (1929) Effect of anesthesia on artificial production of pseudopregnancy in the rat. *Proc. Soc. exp. Biol. Med.*, **27**, 340–2.

Moor, R. M. and Rowson, L. E. A. (1964) Influence of the embryo and uterus on luteal function in the sheep. *Nature, Lond.*, **201**, 522–3.

Moore, W. W. (1961) Effect of uterine distention on the estrous cycle of the guinea pig. *The Physiologist*, **4**, 76.

Moore, W. W. and Nalbandov, A. V. (1953) Neurogenic effects of uterine distention on the estrous cycle of the ewe. *Endocrinology*, **53**, 1–11.

Moore, W. W. and Nalbandov, A. V. (1955) Maintenance of corpora lutea in sheep with lactogenic hormone. *J. Endocr.*, **13**, 18.

Mühlbock, O. and Boot, L. M. (1956) La fonction hormonale d'ovaires, testicules et hypophyses transplantés chez des souches de souris génétiquement pures. *Annls. Endocr.*, **17**, 338–43.

Nalbandov, A. V., Moore, W. W. and Norton, H. W. (1955) Further studies on the neurogenic control of the estrous cycle by uterine distention. *Endocrinology*, **56**, 225–331.

Neher, G. M. and Zarrow, M. X. (1954) Concentration of progestin in the serum of the non-pregnant, pregnant and post partum ewe. *J. Endocr.*, **11**, 323–30.

Neill, J. D. and Day, B. N. (1964) Relationship of developmental stage to regression of the corpus luteum in swine. *Endocrinology*, **74**, 355–60.

Newton, W. H. and Beck, N. (1939) Placental activity in the mouse in the absence of the pituitary gland. *J. Endocr.*, **1**, 65–75.

Oppenheimer, W. (1959) Prevention of pregnancy by the Gräefenberg ring method. *Am. J. Obstet. Gynec.*, **78**, 446–54.

Pencharz, R. I. and Lyons, W. R. (1934) Hypophysectomy in the pregnant guinea-pig. *Proc. Soc. exp. Biol. Med.*, **31**, 1131–2.

Perry, J. S. and Rowlands, I. W. (1961) Effect of hysterectomy on the ovarian cycle of the rat. *J. Reprod. Fert.*, **2**, 332–40.

Perry, J. S. and Rowlands, I. W. (1962) The effect of hypophysectomy on the ovarian cycle of the guinea-pig. *J. Endocr.*, **25**, V–VI.

Pincus, G. and Zahl, P. A. (1937) The biogenesis of primary sex hormones. I. The fate of estrins injected into the rabbit. *J. gen. Physiol.*, **20**, 879–93.

Quilligan, E. J. and Rothchild, I. (1960) The corpus luteum-pituitary relationship; the luteotrophic activity of homotransplanted pituitaries in intact rats. *Endocrinology*, **67**, 48–53.

Rathmacher, R. P. and Anderson, L. L. (1963) Sterile uterine horn and embryonic survival in pigs. *J. Anim. Sci.*, **22**, 1139.

Ray, E. W., Averill, S. C., Lyons, W. R. and Johnson, R. E. (1955) Rat placental hormonal activities corresponding to those of pituitary mammotropin. *Endocrinology*, **56**, 359–73.

Reece, R. P. and Turner, C. W. (1937) Experimentally altering galactin content of the rat pituitary. *Proc. Soc. exp. Biol. Med.*, **36**, 283–5.

van Rees, G. P. (1959) The effect of progesterone on the ICSH- and FSH-content of anterior pituitary and blood serum. I. Survey of the literature; ICSH. *Acta physiol. pharmac. néerl.*, **8**, 180–94.

Rennie, P., Davies, J. and Friedrich, E. (1964) Failure of ovine prolactin to show luteotrophic or luteolytic effects in the rabbit. *Endocrinology*, 75, 622–6.

Reynolds, S. R. M. (1949) *Physiology of the Uterus*, 2nd ed. Paul B. Hoeber, Inc., New York.

Robbins, S. L. and Shepherd, J. (1963) Effect of hysterectomy on the rabbit ovary. *Am. J. Obstet. Gynec.*, 86, 367–73.

Robson, J. M. (1937) Maintenance by oestrin of the luteal function in hypophysectomised rabbits. *J. Physiol., Lond.*, 90, 435–9.

Rock, J. (1955) In discussion in Tenny, Parker and Robbins (1955).

Rothchild, I. (1960) The corpus luteum-pituitary relationship: the lack of an inhibiting effect of progesterone on the secretion of pituitary luteotrophin. *Endocrinology*, 67, 54–61.

Rothchild, I. (1962) The corpus luteum-pituitary relationship: the effect of progesterone on the folliculotropic potency of the pituitary of the rat. *Endocrinology*, 70, 303–13.

Rowlands, I. W. (1961) Effect of hysterectomy at different stages in the life cycle of the corpus luteum in the guinea-pig. *J. Reprod. Fert.*, 2, 341–50.

Rowlands, I. W. (1962) The effect of oestrogens, prolactin, and hypophysectomy on the corpora lutea of hysterectomized guinea-pigs. *J. Endocr.*, 24, 105–12.

Rowson, L. E. A. and Moor, R. (1964) Effect of partial hysterectomy on the length of the dioestrous interval in sheep. *Proc. V Congr. Internaz. Riprod. Anim. Fecond., Artif.*, 2, 393–8.

Sammelwitz, P. H., Aldred, J. P. and Nalbandov, A. V. (1961) Mechanisms of maintenance of corpora lutea in pigs and rats. *J. Reprod. Fert.*, 2, 387–93.

Sammelwitz, P. H. and Nalbandov, A. V. (1958) Progesterone-induced regression of corpora lutea in pregnant and cycling gilts. *J. Anim. Sci.*, 17, 1233–4.

Schultz, A. H. and Snyder, F. F. (1935) Observations on reproduction in the chimpanzee. *Bull. Johns Hopkins Hosp.*, 57, 193–205.

Selye, H. (1934) Influence of the uterus on ovary and mammary gland. *Proc. Soc. exp. Biol. Med.*, 31, 488–90.

Sessums, J. V. and Murphy, D. P. (1932) Hysterectomy and the artificial menopause. *Surg. Gynec. Obstet.*, 55, 286–9.

Short, R. V. (1964) Ovarian steroid synthesis and secretion *in vivo*. *Recent Progr. Hormone Res.*, 20, 303–40.

Short, R. V., McDonald, M. F. and Rowson, L. E. A. (1963) Steroids in the ovarian venous blood of ewes before and after gonadotrophic stimulation. *J. Endocr.*, 26, 155–69.

Silbiger, M. and Rothchild, I. (1963) The influence of the uterus on the corpus luteum-pituitary relationship in the rat. *Acta Endocr., Copenh.*, 43, 521–38.

Simmons, K. R. and Hansel, W. (1964) Nature of the luteotropic hormone in the bovine. *J. Anim. Sci.*, 23, 136–41.

Smith, P. E. (1930) Hypophysectomy and a replacement therapy in the rat. *Am. J. Anat.*, 45, 205–73.

Smith, P. E. and White, W. E. (1931) The effect of hypophysectomy on ovulation and corpus luteum formation in the rabbit. *J. Am. Med. Ass.*, 97, 1861-3.

Smith, V. R., McShan, W. H. and Casida, L. E. (1957) On maintenance of the corpora lutea of the bovine with lactogen. *J. Dairy Sci.*, 40, 443–0.

Spies, H. G., Zimmerman, D. R., Self, H. L. and Casida, L. E. (1958) Influence of hysterectomy and exogenous progesterone on the size and progesterone content of the corpora lutea in gilts. *J. Anim. Sci.*, 17, 1234.

Spies, H. G., Zimmerman, D. R., Self, H. L. and Casida, L. E. (1959) The effect of exogenous progesterone on formation and maintenance of the corpora lutea and on early embryo survival in pregnant swine. *J. Anim. Sci.*, 18, 163–72.

Spies, H. G., Zimmerman, D. R., Self, H. L. and Casida, L. E. (1960) Effect of exogenous progesterone on the corpora lutea of hysterectomised gilts. *J. Anim. Sci.*, **19**, 101-108.

Staples, R. E. and Hansel, W. (1961) Luteal function and embryo survival in the bovine. *J. Dairy Sci.*, **44**, 2040-8.

Staples, R. E., McEntee, K. and Hansel, W. (1961) Luteal function as related to pituitary and ovarian cytology and embryo development in the bovine. *J. Dairy Sci.*, **44**, 2049-57.

Stewart, H. L., Sano, M. E. and Montgomery, T. L. (1948) Hormone secretion by human placenta grown in tissue culture. *J. clin. Endocr. Metab.*, **8**, 175-88.

Stone, G. M., Baggett, B. and Donnelly, R. B. (1963) The uptake of tritiated oestrogens by various organs of the ovariectomized mouse following intravenous administration. *J. Endocr.*, **27**, 271-80.

Tenny, B., Parker, F., Jr., and Robbins, S. L. (1955) The effect of hysterectomy on ovarian function in the rabbit. *Am. J. Obstet. Gynec.*, **70**, 889-91.

Tietze, C. (1962) Intra-uterine contraceptive rings: history and statistical appraisal. In *Intra-Uterine Contraceptive Devices*, ed. C. Tietze and S. Lewit. Excerpta Medica. Internat. Congr. Series No. 54, 9-20.

Tulsky, A. S. and Koff, A. K. (1957) Some observations on the role of the corpus luteum in early human pregnancy. *Fert. Steril.*, **8**, 118-30.

Velardo, J. T., Olsen, A. G., Hisaw, F. L. and Dawson, A. B. (1953) The influence of decidual tissue upon pseudopregnancy. *Endocrinology*, **53**, 216-20.

Van Wagenen, G. and Catchpole, H. R. (1941) Hysterectomy at parturition and ovarian function in the monkey (M. mulatta). *Proc. Soc. exp. Biol. Med.*, **46**, 580-2.

Weichert, C. K. and Schurgast, A. W. (1942) Variations in size of corpora lutea in the albino rat under normal and experimental conditions. *Anat. Rec.*, **83**, 321-34.

Westman, A. (1940) Maintenance of the corpus luteum function in women by estrogenic substances. *Endocrinology*, **26**, 774-8.

Whitelaw, R. G. (1958) Ovarian activity following hysterectomy. *J. Obstet. Gynaec., Br. Commonw.*, **65**, 917-32.

Wiltbank, J. N. and Casida, L. E. (1956) Alteration of ovarian activity by hysterectomy. *J. Anim. Sci.*, **15**, 134-40.

Wolthuis, O. L. (1963) The effects of sex steroids on the prolactin content of hypophyses and serum in rats. *Acta Endocr., Copenh.*, **43**, 137-46.

Zarrow, M. X. (1961) Gestation. In *Sex and Internal Secretions*. Vol. 2, ed. W. C. Young, Williams & Wilkins Co., Baltimore.

Zimbelman, R. G., Pope, A. L. and Casida, L. E. (1959) Effect of exogenous progesterone on the corpus luteum of the bred ewe. *J. Anim. Sci.*, **18**, 1327-32.

Zuckerman, S. (1935) The Aschheim-Zondek diagnosis of pregnancy in the chimpanzee. *Am. J. Physiol.*, **110**, 597-601.

OBITUARY

M. J. R. DAWKINS, M.D., M.R.C.P.

Dr. M. J. R. Dawkins, senior lecturer in paediatric pathology at the Neonatal Department of the Institute of Child Health and pathologist to the Hammersmith Hospital, died on 27 June after a brief illness. He was 34.

Michael John Ransford Dawkins was born in London, the son of C. J. Massey Dawkins, M.D., F.F.A.R.C.S., senior consultant anaesthetist at University College Hospital, and Dr. Sylvia Dawkins. From Epsom College he went to Cambridge, gaining a senior scholarship at Emmanuel College, and he obtained a first-class in both parts of the natural sciences tripos. He entered University College Hospital Medical School with a Filliter Entrance Scholarship and was awarded the Trotter and Puke medals and the Atchison scholarship for the best student of the year. He qualified M.B., B.Chir. in 1955, and became M.R.C.P. in 1959; the Cambridge M.D. was conferred on him in 1962. In 1957 he was appointed Stothert Research Fellow of the Royal Society, working at the Graham Research Laboratory, University College Hospital Medical School; in 1959 he became lecturer in morbid anatomy. In 1960 he joined the Nuffield Institute for Medical Research, University of Oxford, as a research officer, and in 1961 spent six months as a visiting professor of pathology in the University of Chicago. He became senior lecturer in paediatric pathology at the Hammersmith Hospital in 1964. In 1954 he married Julia Smith, the daughter of Dr. Annis Gillie, now President of the College of General Practitioners; they had two sons, William and Guy.

Michael Dawkins was a man of exceptional qualities, very learned and brimming over with ideas. His early training was in morbid anatomy, where he first acquired an interest in perinatal pathology and a determination to solve the problems of this field by any available method. Thus he quickly became a very competent biochemist and physiologist; and this training, added to a wide clinical and pathological experience, gave him an exceptional range of knowledge and skills. In the past few years he produced a wealth of original work on the effects of birth asphyxia and chronic foetal deprivation, on the activation of hepatic enzymes in the new-born and the role of brown adipose tissue in heat production. The latter work, in collaboration with Dr. David Hull, was probably his most important contribution. As his brilliance as a speaker became known he was in increasing demand for international meetings of many kinds. He played a valuable part in the Perinatal Mortality Survey of the National Birthday Trust, and at his death was engaged in editing a new number of the *British Medical Bulletin* on the foetus and newborn.

This is reprinted with the kind permission of the *British Medical Journal.*

8

THE HAZARDS OF BIRTH

THE LATE M. J. R. DAWKINS

Institute of Child Health, Hammersmith Hospital, London, W.12

A. INTRODUCTION

More deaths in this country occur at or near birth than between one week of age and forty years. Although abortion in early pregnancy is probably about three times commoner than death in the perinatal period, a large proportion of abortions are grossly abnormal (Hertig, Rock, Adams and Menkin, 1959; Carr, 1963). Since most perinatal deaths are not malformed there is very considerable perinatal wastage of potentially normal children. Death in the perinatal period can therefore be considered a major factor in reproductive failure.

The establishment of separate existence at birth involves an abrupt change in environment, and calls for considerable anatomical, physiological and biochemical adaptations on the part of the newly born animal. The onset of respiration with expansion of the lungs is the first essential, but the circulation also must soon be altered from foetal to adult pathways. This involves closure of the ductus arteriosus and the foramen ovale, so that the ventricles no longer act in parallel, but in series (Dawes, 1961). Nutrition becomes intermittent instead of continuous, and a co-operative relationship with the mother is necessary for the establishment of suckling. This requires complex reflex behaviour which must be appropriate on both sides. Light, cold, colonization by micro-organisms, gravity and many cutaneous sensations are all experienced for the first time, and all these may pose considerable challenges. The numerous regulatory functions of the placenta *in utero* become the sole responsibility of such organs as lungs, liver and kidneys. The problems of the transition from intra-uterine to extra-uterine existence have in recent years been the subject of much investigation, most of it stemming from the pioneer work of Barcroft (1946). Several symposia, review articles and books devoted to the physiology and pathology of the newborn have been published in the last few years. Further impetus has been given to studies of the perinatal period by the recent publication of the results of a unique survey of perinatal mortality undertaken in this country in 1958 (Butler and Bonham, 1963). The present review is an attempt to interpret perinatal mortality in the light of recent advances in understanding of foetal and neonatal physiology, and to see to what extent death can be regarded as a failure in adaptation at birth. It has become clear that the maternal and perinatal factors associated with mortality are also associated with serious handicaps in surviving babies (Drillien, 1965), so that the same underlying problems are probably involved here also.

B. PERINATAL MORTALITY

In the 1958 perinatal mortality survey (Butler and Bonham, 1963), all stillbirths after 28 weeks of gestation and liveborn babies dying in the first week of life were studied. The perinatal mortality was 33 per 1,000 deliveries: at that time there had been very little improvement in the mortality rate for a decade, although in the five years after 1958 it fell to about 29 per 1,000 (Registrar General, 1964). This represents an annual loss of about 25,000 lives on the basis of the current birth rate. Statistics for perinatal mortality in animals are not available, but in the sheep and pig, mortality is substantially higher than in man and constitutes a serious economic loss to farmers. Perinatal mortality shows considerable variations from one country to another: the lowest rates where records are reliable are from the Scandinavian countries. The minimum perinatal mortality, the so-called 'unavoidable loss', is probably about 20 per 1,000, given the social class structure of our present society. Considerable improvements in perinatal mortality are possible in this country, and should be accompanied by a reduction also in the number of handicapped survivors.

Analysis of the cause of perinatal death is often not possible at autopsy, although the mode of death is obvious. Assessment of the factors involved requires knowledge of the mother's health before and during pregnancy and a detailed history of labour, delivery and the post-natal course. For this reason the material of the 1958 Perinatal Mortality Survey was initially tabulated according to the relatively simple anatomical classification shown in Table I. The largest single

TABLE I

ANATOMICAL CAUSE OF DEATH IN THE PERINATAL PERIOD

Data derived from the 1958 Perinatal Mortality Survey (Butler and Bonham, 1963).

Cause of death	Rate/1000 deliveries	Percentage of all perinatal deaths
Intrapartum anoxia and/or Cerebral birth trauma	10.2	30.7
Antepartum stillbirth	6.8	20.5
Lethal congenital malformation	5.8	17.6
Hyaline membrane with atelectasis	1.6	4.8
Pneumonia	1.5	4.5
Rhesus incompatibility	1.3	3.9
Neonatal deaths—no anatomical lesion	1.0	3.0
Intraventricular haemorrhage	0.7	2.1
Massive pulmonary haemorrhage	0.6	1.8
Miscellaneous	1.3	3.9
No autopsy	2.4	7.2
TOTAL	33.2	100.0

group are those babies dying as a result of anoxia or trauma during labour (10.2 per 1,000). Anoxia and trauma have been classified together since cerebral birth trauma is mostly inflicted during attempts to deliver a baby already showing signs of anoxia. Most of the babies in this anoxia/trauma group die during labour or within minutes of delivery. It is here that improvements in obstetric management can most easily reduce perinatal mortality.

The second largest group are the antepartum stillbirths (6.8 per 1,000). These can mostly be attributed to placental failure, although the reasons for failure are usually not obvious. Premature separation of the placenta with accompanying haemorrhage from maternal vessels to the placental site is the cause of stillbirth in about 10% of cases. Hypertension in the mother is also frequent, and this is known to be associated with obliterative lesions in the maternal arterioles supplying the placental bed (Dixon and Robertson, 1958) and a reduced uterine blood flow (Dixon, Browne and Davey, 1963). Prolongation of pregnancy 14 days beyond the expected date of delivery is also associated with an increased rate of antepartum still-births and a reduced uterine blood flow (Dixon et al., 1963). Ante-partum stillbirths and lethal congenital malformations (5.8 per 1,000) cannot be considered as failures in adaptation at birth and will not be further considered.

Hyaline membrane with atelectasis is only found in babies born several weeks before the expected date of delivery. These babies die in the first 48 hours with respiratory distress. Hyaline membrane is never seen in stillborn infants. The membrane, which lines the alveolar ducts, is composed of structureless eosinophilic material. There is always accompanying atelectasis and pulmonary oedema; these, rather than the membrane itself, are the cause of death from respiratory failure. These babies constitute a major problem in paediatric management and this syndrome of 'respiratory distress' has been the subject of much research. The fundamental abnormality seems to be an inability to establish stable lung expansion; this will be discussed in a later section.

Pneumonia (1.5 per 1,000) in the first week of life is numerically very nearly as important as hyaline membrane, although it has received much less attention. Asphyxia in labour is usually the pre-disposing cause; pneumonia will be discussed in this context. In addition, the ability of the newborn to react appropriately to bacterial or viral invasion will be considered.

Rhesus incompatibility (1.3 per 1,000), due to maternal sensitiza-tion of rhesus-negative mothers to their rhesus-positive offspring, is outside the scope of this review.

Neonatal deaths with no anatomical lesion (1.0 per 1,000) and intraventricular haemorrhage (0.7 per 1,000) are confined to the very premature baby who is on the borderline of viability (about 28 weeks' gestation). Neonatal deaths with no anatomical lesion have very primitive lungs which, for reasons discussed later, are structurally inadequate for normal gas exchange. Intraventricular haemorrhage occurs from a branch of the great cerebral vein, the vena terminalis, into the lateral ventricles of the brain. The vena terminalis is very thin-walled and easily ruptured. Rupture has been attributed to anoxia, but intraventricular haemorrhage may occur suddenly in well oxygenated babies, although it is most common in babies with the respiratory distress syndrome.

Massive pulmonary haemorrhage (0.6 per 1,000) is found only in babies which are small in relation to their supposed chronological age. It seems to be related to prolonged neonatal hypoglycaemia, and is often associated with a low body temperature (the so-called 'cold injury'). This is clearly a failure in adaptation. More rarely failures in metabolic homeostasis may lead to death from accumulation of some toxic product such as bilirubin or such drugs as chloramphenicol. In both cases this is related to a slow rate of detoxication of these compounds by the liver.

We are therefore concerned with the reasons for failure to survive in the normally formed baby who is alive at the start of labour. Babies dying of anoxia and/or trauma in labour, pneumonia, hyaline membrane with atelectasis, intraventricular haemorrhage and massive pulmonary haemorrhage can be regarded as failures in physiological adaptation to the changes in environment at birth. The physiological mechanisms involved and the underlying reasons for these failures will now be considered in detail.

C. ANOXIA IN LABOUR

Most newborn babies show evidence of acidaemia at birth (James, 1960), and their arterial O_2 saturation may be very low (Karlberg and Celander, 1965). Before labour, the average oxygen saturation in foetal arteries is probably about 60% (Dawes, 1961), but because of the shape of the dissociation curve for foetal haemoglobin (Darling, Smith, Asmussen and Cohen, 1941), and the very large blood flow through the placenta (Dawes and Mott, 1964), the tissues are fully supplied with oxygen. In fact foetal oxygen consumption may be considerably higher than maternal oxygen consumption when expressed relative to body weight. During labour, uterine contractions cause temporary reduction in uterine blood flow (Assali, Holm and

Parker, 1961) and, therefore, intermittent tissue hypoxia (Misrahy, Behran, Spradley and Garwood, 1960). The foetus may be able to compensate for this to some extent by increasing umbilical blood flow (Assali, Holm and Sehgal, 1962). This is probably effected by pulmonary vaso-constriction, mediated by hypoxia. The small pulmonary arteries of the foetal lung have a thick muscular coat (Wagenvoort, Neufeldt and Edwards, 1961) which constricts actively when exposed to a low oxygen tension, a low pH or a high carbon dioxide tension (Cassin, Dawes, Mott, Ross and Strang, 1964). As a result, blood flow is diverted from the lungs via the ductus arteriosus to the umbilical arteries, and blood flow to the placenta is increased. A secondary consequence of this may also be an increase in oxygen saturation of the blood going to the brain, since there will be less mixture of pulmonary vein blood with blood coming through the foramen ovale. During the passage through the birth canal the umbilical cord is occluded, so that a short period of total anoxia is produced. However, the human foetus, like other foetal animals, can easily tolerate this degree of anoxia. Death in labour occurs either when labour is abnormal, or when foetal tolerance is so reduced that the anoxia of normal labour becomes lethal.

The well-known prolonged survival of newborn animals during anoxia has been the subject of much investigation and speculation (Mott, 1961). The behaviour of newborn mammals subjected to anoxia follows a remarkably stereotyped pattern, illustrated in Fig. 1. After an initial period of struggling during which there is a rise in blood pressure and a profound bradycardia, there is a period of primary apnoea. The initial bradycardia is probably vagal, since it is abolished by atropine or vagotomy (Barcroft, 1946). This is shortly followed by a phase of strong regular gasping, during which heart rate and blood pressure gradually decline. Gasping seems to be the result of stimulation of the arterial chemoreceptors since it is abolished by denervation of these structures (Davis, J. A., personal communication). The last few gasps are weaker and after the last gasp the heart continues to beat very slowly and weakly for a few minutes, sometimes with an irregular rhythm. This phase has been called terminal apnoea. The fundamental difference between newborn and adult animals seems to be related to the capacity of the myocardium to maintain an effective circulation during anoxia.

Although the pattern of response is stereotyped, considerable differences in timing exist between newborn animals of different species (Fazekas, Alexander and Himwich, 1941). The newborn rat will continue to gasp for 50 minutes in an atmosphere of nitrogen at room temperature. Newborn rabbits gasp for 17 minutes, newborn monkeys for $8\frac{1}{2}$ minutes and the newborn guinea-pig gasps for only 6 minutes in an atmosphere of nitrogen (Dawes, 1965). Adult animals of all species survive only a few minutes under these circumstances. In general, the more immature the animal at birth, the longer is the period of gasping in nitrogen. Animals of all species, if removed from nitrogen at any time before the last gasp, recover immediately and thereafter appear entirely normal. After the last gasp, newborn animals can be resuscitated by artificial ventilation with 100% oxygen, in extreme cases with the addition of external cardiac massage. However, in newborn monkeys resuscitated after the last gasp, some residual damage to subcortical neurones in the midbrain and brain stem is found when the monkey is later killed (Dawes, Hibberd and Windle, 1964). This is increasingly severe with longer intervals between the last gasp and resuscitation. Once the heart beat has ceased for more than a few minutes, resuscitation is no longer possible. Experience with postmortem caesarean sections, after the death of the mother, has shown that the human foetus can survive up to 25 minutes of foetal anoxia (Vitsky, 1964). This is slightly longer than the newborn rhesus monkey. The time to the last gasp in the human foetus is not known, but is probably about ten minutes.

Analysis of the physiological mechanisms in this anoxic survival has shown that anaerobic breakdown of glycogen to lactic acid is the underlying process supplying the energy necessary for survival (Dawes, 1965). In fact, the acidaemia present at birth in many normal babies is largely due to production of lactic acid. Poisoning with iodoacetate, which inhibits anaerobic glycolysis, reduces survival of newborn rats in nitrogen to adult levels (Himwich, Bernstein, Herrlich, Chester and Fazekas, 1942).

Tissue analysis of glycogen levels of foetal and newborn animals revealed that the levels of glycogen were very high in the myocardium, liver and skeletal muscle (Shelley, 1961). Myocardial glycogen disappeared rapidly during anoxia (Dawes, Mott and Shelley, 1959). There is, in fact, a very good correlation between initial level of cardiac glycogen and length of survival in nitrogen of newborn animals (Mott, 1961). Liver glycogen falls during anoxia but skeletal muscle glycogen is unaffected (Dawes et al., 1959). Frequent repeated sub-lethal episodes of anoxia lead to progressive depletion of glycogen in the myocardium and a greatly shortened survival time (Stafford and Weatherall, 1960). The restoration of the cardiac glycogen reserve after an episode of anoxia takes several hours, so that the effects of intermittent anoxia on subsequent survival during anoxia are cumulative over a few hours. Thus survival of the anoxic newborn animal depends chiefly on the maintenance of an effective circulation; the necessary energy for cardiac contraction is supplied by the anaerobic breakdown of glycogen in the myocardium. Since hypoglycaemia shortens the gasping time in anoxic newborn rats (Stafford and Weatherall, 1960) and the brain has virtually no glycogen reserve (Shelley, 1961), the respiratory centre depends on the anaerobic breakdown of glucose brought to it by the bloodstream after mobilization from the liver. Anoxia leads to the release of catecholamines from the newborn adrenal medulla (Comline and Silver, 1958). Catecholamines are known to mobilize liver glycogen (Sutherland and Rall, 1960). However, anoxia has little or no effect on blood glucose levels in the newborn rhesus monkey (Adamsons, Behrman, Dawes, Dawkins, James and Ross, 1963), and hyperglycaemic agents such as glucagon and adrenaline are relatively ineffective in producing hyperglycaemia in the foetal and newborn lamb (Dawkins, 1964b). It is possible, therefore, that gasping during anoxia might, under certain conditions, be compromised by low blood glucose levels.

During anoxia in newborn animals there is also a rapid fall in the pH of arterial blood, largely owing to the production of lactic acid by the myocardium. However, the rate of production of lactic acid slows down considerably as the pH falls (Adamsons et al., 1963). The heart beat ceases at a pH of about 6.6, while substantial amounts of glycogen are still present in the myocardium (Dawes, Mott, Shelley and Stafford, 1963). The anaerobic breakdown of glycogen appears to be progressively inhibited by the fall in pH. Correction of the acidaemia during anoxia by infusion of an alkali allows the heart to go on beating for much longer, until all the glycogen is used up (Dawes, Mott et al., 1963); under these conditions the production of lactic acid is linear with time. Infusion with an alkali, especially when combined with glucose, also prolongs gasping in lambs and monkeys (Dawes, Jacobson, Mott, Shelley and Stafford, 1963), which provides further evidence that the respiratory centre depends on the maintenance of an adequate circulation for survival during anoxia. Glucose alone is not effective in prolonging activity of the respiratory centre during anoxia.

At autopsy, babies which have died of anoxia show characteristic petechial haemorrhages on pleura and pericardium, a dilated heart

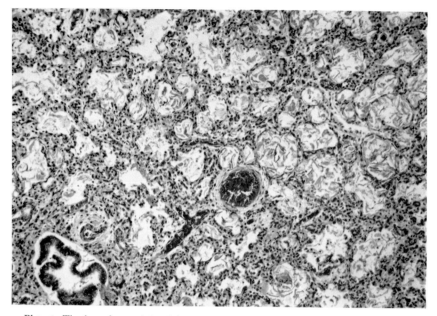

Plate 1. The lung from a baby dying six hours after birth as a result of aspiration of meconium during delivery. Magnification x 100.

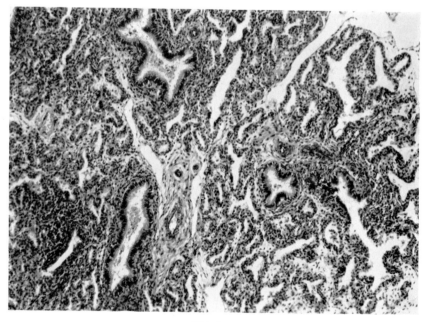

Plate 2a.

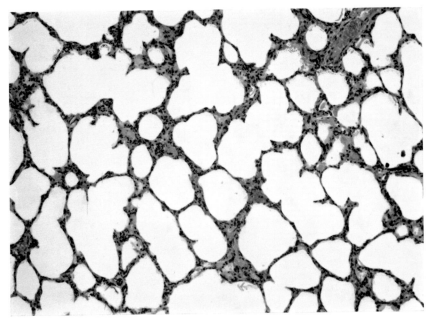

Plate 2b.

Plates 2a and b. The lung from newborn babies of (a) 27 weeks' gestation and (b) 40 weeks' gestation. At 27 weeks the alveoli are poorly developed and lined with cubical epithelium, and blood vessels in the alveolar walls are scanty. Magnification x 100.

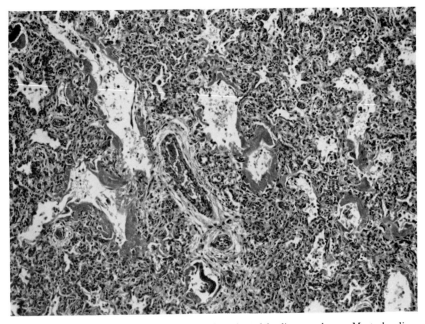

Plate 3. The lung from a baby dying of atelectasis and hyaline membrane. Most alveoli are collapsed and the alveolar ducts leading to them are lined with a thick amorphous membrane. Magnification x 100.

and generalized venous congestion. Analysis of the time of death in labour reveals that nearly 50% of babies die in the first stage of labour, that is before the cervix uteri is fully dilated (Fig. 2). A further 35% die during the second stage of labour. The remaining 15% die after birth from the delayed effects of intrapartum anoxia: this group will be considered later. Taken as a whole, more than three quarters of the intrapartum deaths are of sufficient maturity to have escaped the hazards of neonatal death from hyaline membrane or intraventricular haemorrhage if they had survived delivery.

TABLE II

AETIOLOGICAL FACTORS IN INTRAPARTUM ANOXIA (501 CASES)

Aetiological factor	% of deaths from anoxia in labour
Complication of labour (prolapsed cord, placental separation with bleeding or malpresentation of the foetus)	61
Complication of pregnancy (hypertension or prolonged pregnancy or both)	31
Neither of the above	8

Death from anoxia in labour is found to fall into one of two main aetiological categories (see Table II), although there is often an overlap between the two. In the first category anoxia is caused by a definite anatomical abnormality in labour. Examples are prolapse of the cord through the cervix, with compression and/or spasm of umbilical vessels, and premature detachment of the placenta from the uterine wall, with haemorrhage from maternal vessels and mal-presentations of the foetus, of which by far the commonest is the breech. Umbilical cord obstruction is the most probable cause of anoxia during breech delivery. In this category death occurs because the duration of anoxia is far greater than in normal labour and exceeds the tolerance of the normal foetus. The presence of foetal anoxia is indicated by bradycardia, irregularity of the foetal heart and the passage of meconium – the signs of 'foetal distress'.

The second category consists of those babies delivered either by women with hypertension in the last third of pregnancy, or after pro-longation of pregnancy beyond term. Both conditions are known to be

15

associated with reduced uterine blood flow (Dixon *et al.*, 1963), increased risk of foetal death in labour (Butler and Bonham, 1963) and evidence of prolonged foetal malnutrition (Gruenwald, 1964a). Foetal malnutrition is implicated when the baby is unexpectedly small for its gestational age. Its aetiology is discussed in a later section. In this group death occurs suddenly and unexpectedly in labour, without any obvious abnormality. Death may be due to the inadequacy of the myocardial and liver glycogen reserves to meet even trivial degrees of anoxia. Diminished glycogen reserves have been demonstrated in human babies with intra-uterine malnutrition (Shelley, 1964). Also, maternal blood flow to the placental site may be insufficient to correct the oxygen debt incurred during uterine contractions. The combination of diminished reserves and progressive hypoxia is obviously likely to be dangerous. The detection and management of these cases is a difficult problem, but clearly prolongation of pregnancy beyond term should be avoided.

Finally, there is a third very small category, consisting of women with entirely normal pregnancies and labours. Under such circumstances foetal death from anoxia is a very uncommon event.

D. THE FIRST BREATH

Under normal circumstances the foetus makes only a very occasional respiratory movement *in utero*, despite the fact that the arterial oxygen tension is low (Dawes, 1965). The low arterial oxygen tension is inevitable even when umbilical vein blood is 100% saturated because of the anatomy of the foetal circulation. However, the foetus is not in a state of acidaemia and the carbon dioxide tension is in the normal range (Dawes, 1965). The foetus is therefore not hypoxic and its oxygen consumption may be as high as after birth.

Gasping *in utero* can be elicited as a response to anoxia (see Fig. 1), in which there is a fall in oxygen tension to very low levels, a fall in pH and a rise in carbon dioxide tension. The factors which lead to a newborn baby taking its first gasp on delivery are complex (Karlberg and Celander, 1965), and certainly include the rising carbon dioxide tension resulting from the fall in pH, due in turn to anoxia. This has a stimulatory effect on the arterial chemoreceptors. Hypoxia itself also stimulates the chemoreceptors. By an ingenious technique in which arterial pH and oxygen and carbon dioxide tension could be measured continuously in the foetal lamb, it has recently been possible to examine the effects of changes in oxygen and carbon dioxide tension independently, while the pH was held constant (Harned, Rowshan, McKinney and Sugioka, 1964). Neither a fall in the first nor a rise in the second initiated gasping, although this always occurred immediately the umbilical cord was clamped.

The sudden enormous increase in cutaneous sensations at birth must also be very important in the initiation of breathing. Painful cutaneous stimuli, such as bottom smacking, have often been used in the past to stimulate gasping in the apnoeic newborn infant. The sensitivity of the respiratory centre is greatly enhanced by an increase in non-specific afferent impulses in the reticular formation of the brain stem (Burns, 1963), and this may be the means by which cutaneous stimulation can set off gasping in the infant during the phase of primary apnoea. Respiratory stimulants may also be effective in this way. The first breath is probably the result of summation of various stimuli none of which are effective by themselves. It may also be reinforced by Head's paradoxical reflex, in which a gasp is initiated by a small increase in intrathoracic pressure. This reflex is present in the newborn baby, but disappears after the first few days of life (Cross, Klaus, Tooley and Weisser, 1960).

95% of new-born babies take their first gasp within 60 seconds of birth; a series of irregular breaths is then quickly followed by regular breathing. The factors involved in the transition from the first gasp, with its large negative intrathoracic pressures, to quiet regular breathing are unknown.

Some 5% of newborn babies fail to take a gasp within one minute of birth. There are three main reasons for this, but, whatever the cause, prompt endotracheal intubation and inflation of the lungs is the only rational and effective treatment. The likely causes of apnoea are (i) preceding anoxia leading to depression of the respiratory centre, (ii) transplacental passage of respiratory depressant drugs given to the mother, and (iii) cerebral birth trauma.

1. Intrapartum anoxia

Apnoea due to anoxia is probably due to depression of the respiratory centre by a combination of high carbon dioxide and low oxygen tension. In assessing the response of anoxic newborn babies apnoeic at one minute it is fundamental to understand the distinction between primary and terminal apnoea (see Fig. 1). These phases of apnoea correspond roughly to the states of blue asphyxia and white asphyxia described in older textbooks. In primary apnoea, gasping will start

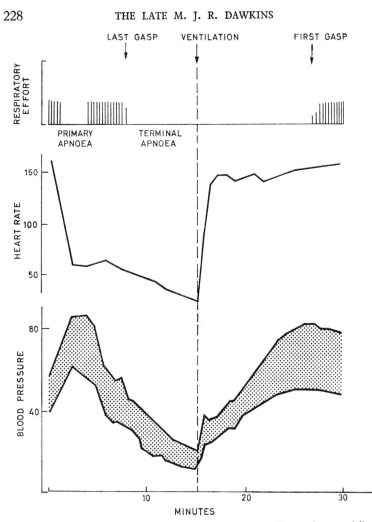

Fig. 1. Anoxia and resuscitation in a newborn Rhesus monkey. The monkey was delivered by Caesarean section under local anaesthesia, its head was placed in a bag of saline to prevent expansion of the lungs, and the cord was then clamped. Fifteen minutes later the lungs were inflated with oxygen.

whatever treatment is given, or even if nothing is done. In terminal apnoea death is imminent and brain damage is increasing in severity every minute (Dawes, Hibberd and Windle, 1964). Since most babies apnoeic from hypoxia are probably in the primary phase, many methods of resuscitation have been fallaciously believed to be effective. These include the intra-gastric administration of 100% oxygen, the use of various drugs which are respiratory stimulants, and, most recently, the hyperbaric oxygen chamber. The successes attributed to these methods have been merely the result of the natural onset of gasping after the phase of primary apnoea. Hyperbaric oxygen and intragastric oxygen have been unequivocally demonstrated to be totally ineffective in the terminal apnoea of the newborn animal with unexpanded lungs (James, Apgar, Moya, Kvisselgard, Burnard, Brady, Tuchman, Crawford and Holaday, 1963; Cross, Dawes, Hyman and Mott, 1964). In practice, it is not always easy to make the distinction between primary and terminal apnoea when presented with an apnoeic newborn baby. Therefore all apnoeic newborn babies with a heart which is still beating should be treated as if they were in a state of terminal apnoea, in which the only effective method of treatment is endotracheal intubation and artificial ventilation, usually with 100 % oxygen. An immediate large increase in heart rate indicates arrival of oxygenated blood at the myocardium. If there is no rise in heart rate, external cardiac massage should be given. Under these circumstances blood flow through the lungs is probably at a very low level, owing to the combination of intense pulmonary vasoconstriction from anoxia and its biochemical consequences (Cassin et al., 1964), and the low cardiac output. Cardiac massage improves the cardiac output sufficiently to allow oxygen to be absorbed from the lungs and the circulation can then recover. Once the heart rate has improved, gasping will soon begin, to be followed in a few minutes by spontaneous respiration. The longer the period of anoxia has been, the longer it takes for the establishment of spontaneous respiration (Dawes, 1965). Anoxic babies in which the heart has only just ceased beating may also occasionally be resuscitated by cardiac massage and endotracheal intubation, but serious brain damage is often detectable in such cases.

Failure to start breathing at birth because of immediately preceding anoxia makes only a small contribution to the large number of deaths from intrapartum anoxia (see Fig. 2). These are the babies which can be saved by the use of endotracheal intubation and intermittent positive pressure respiration. Although of course effective resuscitation is a necessary adjunct to the delivery of the anoxic foetus, the largest dividends in improved mortality statistics in the category of intrapartum anoxia and trauma will be from improvements in the recognition and treatment of foetal distress in utero, rather than from better facilities for resuscitation of anoxic babies at birth.

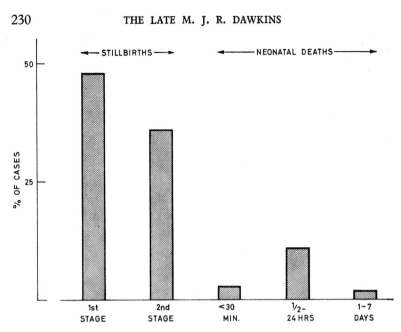

Fig. 2. Time of death in babies dying as the result of anoxia in labour.

2. Drugs which depress the respiratory centre

Almost every drug which has been tested has been found to pass freely and rapidly across the placenta (Baker, 1960; Cohen, 1962). Consequently, drugs used as analgesics or sedatives in labour will also be present in foetal tissues. Drugs such as morphine, pethidine and barbiturates given to the mother may all produce respiratory depression in the newborn. Similarly, general anaesthetics given to the mother for delivery with forceps or by caesarean section will also reach the foetus and may cause difficulties in the establishment of respiration after birth. There is some evidence that newborn animals are more sensitive to drugs such as morphia at a given blood level than adult animals (Kupferberg and Way, 1963). After administration of a drug, blood levels are higher and remain higher for longer in the newborn infant than in the adult (Vest and Salzberg, 1965). The reasons for this will be discussed in the section on metabolic homeostasis, but the consequences are that drugs given to the mother may exert profound and prolonged effects on the newborn after delivery.

Analysis of the mechanism of action of morphia and pethidine in newborn rabbits has shown that doses which have no effect on the respiration of the normal newborn rabbit cause profound depression of gasping in the anoxic newborn rabbit (Davis and Moore, 1965). The primary phase of apnoea is greatly prolonged at the expense of the gasping period. Larger doses may abolish gasping altogether. However, the biochemical changes secondary to anoxia are unaffected and the heart ceases to beat at the same time as in the undrugged controls. These results imply that depression of respiration by drugs like morphia is by itself unlikely to cause apnoea, but that the combination of anoxia plus a respiratory depressant will do so. This is very much in accord with clinical experience. The combination of severe anoxia with the use of drugs such as morphia is likely to occur in premature deliveries, especially when complicated by maternal antepartum haemorrhage. The specific antagonist n-allyl normorphine given to the baby on delivery or to the mother immediately before delivery will be effective when the baby's circulation is good. However, in a severely anoxic newborn baby with a failing heart, the first essential is endotracheal intubation and inflation of the lungs with 100% oxygen. Once the circulation has been restored and the biochemical effects of anoxia checked, then the morphine antagonist may be of value in initiating spontaneous respiration.

The extent to which respiratory depressants contribute towards perinatal mortality is extremely difficult to assess. In a personal analysis of 451 cases of death from asphyxia in labour (Dawkins, 1962), in no case was it likely that death was due solely to the administration of depressant drugs. In every death when depressants had been used in labour, there was also clinical and pathological evidence of severe anoxia *in utero*. This reinforces the experiments quoted above on the effects of morphia in anoxic newborn rabbits.

3. Cerebral birth trauma

Cerebral birth trauma refers to the subdural haemorrhage associated with lacerations of the falx cerebri or tentorium cerebelli. These folds of dura mater contain within them large venous sinuses which are easily torn. In addition, the vein of Galen, into which flows all the venous drainage from cerebral white matter and central grey matter, crosses the subarachnoid and subdural space to join the inferior sagittal sinus at the point of junction of the falx and tentorium. This large vein is also very liable to rupture when the falx or tentorium is torn. The injury is produced by distortion of the soft foetal skull in an upwards direction and is usually found after difficult forceps or breech delivery. In both circumstances, there is likely to have been accompanying foetal anoxia, leading to venous congestion and distension of these large veins. Once rupture has occurred, a large subdural haemorrhage develops and gross circulatory disturbances of the brain stem are inevitable. Death in most cases occurs at or very shortly after delivery, with the baby making little or no effort to breathe. A few cases may survive, apparently normal, for a day or two and then die suddenly. The reasons for this are not clear. Cerebral birth trauma is clearly not amenable to any form of treatment once it has occurred, but its incidence can be greatly reduced by good obstetrics. Its contribution to perinatal mortality is fortunately not large.

E. DELAYED EFFECTS OF INTRAPARTUM ANOXIA

About 13% of babies dying from intrapartum anoxia survive the immediate insult, establish respiration at birth and expand their lungs, but subsequently die from a complication of the anoxic insult (Fig. 2). In most instances this is related to inhalation of meconium. Anoxia causes contraction of the colon, with emptying of the meconium into the amniotic cavity. The foetus is at the same time gasping and sucking the contaminated amniotic fluid into its lungs. In about one in five stillborn babies dying from anoxia in labour, meconium is found in the trachea and main bronchi. Meconium is extremely sticky and difficult to extract or cough up. In surviving babies it is sucked into smaller airways and alveoli and may cause serious and progressive difficulties with respiration, ending in death within a few hours (Plate 1). Further complications associated with meconium aspiration are the development of pneumonia, which is considered in a later section, and the development of peri-vascular emphysema. This is probably due to the establishment of a valvular mechanism with a plug of meconium in an airway, so that air passes the obstruction during inspiration, but cannot pass back during expiration. There is local overdistension of the lung beyond the plug, with rupture into the loose perivascular lymphatic tissue. Air may then escape backwards towards the mediastinum, producing mediastinal emphysema which may seriously embarrass venous return to the heart. An alternative course is rupture into the pleural cavity, with the development of a rapidly fatal tension pneumothorax.

Further complications of intrapartum anoxia which may cause death in the neonatal period are related to the petechial haemorrhages which are the pathological hall-mark of intrapartum anoxia. When these occur under the capsule of the liver, quite large 'blood blisters' are formed, which are very fragile. These subcapsular haematomata may rupture; massive bleeding from the raw liver surface into the peritoneal cavity then occurs, causing death from exsanguination. Rarely, lethal massive subarachnoid bleeding may occur, from multiple small petechial haemorrhages in the meninges.

F. BRAIN DAMAGE AND INTRAPARTUM ANOXIA

The association between anoxia at birth and severe neurological disturbances in surviving infants was first recognized in the 19th century by Little and has subsequently been the subject of much research and speculation. It has recently been investigated in the newborn primate in a controlled and careful study by Dawes, Hibberd and Windle (1964). A reproducible and standardized method of inflicting anoxia on newborn monkeys was devised, and monkeys were resuscitated after varying intervals of total anoxia. Brain damage was assessed by clinical examination, and by psychometric testing. Finally, when the monkey was at least 6 weeks old, it was killed and the brain was subjected to very thorough histological examination. The earliest indication of damage was death of neurones in the inferior colliculus. This occurred in monkeys resuscitated after 7–8 minutes anoxia, i.e. at about the time of the last gasp. By 10 minutes there were signs of cell death in auditory and vestibular nuclei and by 12 minutes, most of the nuclei of the brain stem showed lesions. After 15 minutes brain damage was widespread, and monkeys died after about 18 minutes. These relationships are shown diagramatically in Fig. 3. Clinical examination of these monkeys only revealed abnormalities in those subsequently shown to have widespread damage, and in many of these cases neurological abnormalities were transient. Young monkeys are obviously able to compensate for quite serious degrees of brain damage, although of course no regeneration of dead neurones is possible. The relationship between anoxia at birth and neurological function in man is much more difficult to assess. Currently, many disorders in childhood and later life, from anti-social behaviour to failure to pass the 11 + examination, are being attributed to the residual effects of birth anoxia (Prechtl, 1960). The association between major neurological defects and severe birth anoxia is clear enough, but the problem is the minor defect which is difficult to recognize.

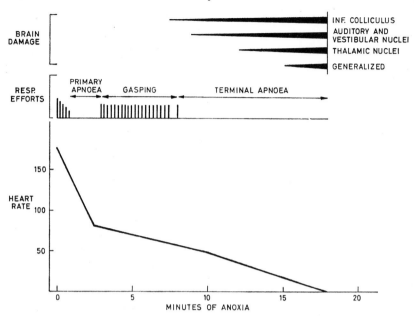

Fig. 3. Brain damage and duration of anoxia in the newborn Rhesus monkey. (Drawn from the data of Dawes, Hibberd and Windle, 1964).

G. EXPANSION OF THE LUNGS

In order to establish gas exchange, the lungs must first be expanded with air, and a certain amount of air must remain in the lungs at the end of expiration. This known as the residual capacity. Blood flow through the lungs is usually low in the foetal state (Dawes and Mott, 1962). After birth most of the cardiac output must now go through the lungs, where it is separated from alveolar gas only by the alveolar-capillary barrier. The morphological characteristics of this barrier in the human foetus at term have been examined in the electron microscope and found to be the same as in the adult lung (Campiche, Gautier, Hernandez and Reymond, 1963). The viability of the human foetus delivered prematurely is to some extent determined by the nature of the barrier between pulmonary capillaries and the gas in the alveoli. Before 28 weeks' gestation, the alveoli are lined by cubical epithelium, and pulmonary capillaries do not come very close to the basement membranes of these cells (Plates 2a and b). In addition, the special surface-active material necessary for maintenance of stable alveolar expansion with air (*vide infra*) may be absent. This material probably appears after about 26-28 weeks' gestation (Avery and Mead, 1959; Pattle, Claireaux, Davies and Cameron, 1962). Effective gas exchange is therefore not possible at this stage of gestation.

In utero, potential air spaces of the lungs contain fluid in continuity with the fluid of the amniotic cavity. This alveolar fluid is closely similar in composition to foetal plasma, except that it has a very low protein content (Adams, Fujiwara and Rowshan, 1963). It is widely different from amniotic fluid. Alveolar fluid is therefore probably a transudate of foetal plasma, formed in the pulmonary capillaries and contributing to amniotic fluid. During the passage through the birth canal there is considerable compression of the thorax (Karlberg, Adams, Geubelle and Wallgren, 1962) and quite large amounts of fluid can be seen coming out of the mouth. Elastic recoil after delivery results in replacement of this fluid with air. Consequently, the trachea and main bronchi usually contain air, even before the first breath is taken.

Initially, expansion of the lungs often requires quite high pressures. Negative intrathoracic pressures of up to —80 cms. of water have been recorded (Karlberg and Celander, 1965) and compliance (change in volume per unit change in pressure) of the lung is low (Karlberg and Koch, 1962). This means that the lung is difficult to expand. However, within a few breaths the lung is virtually completely expanded and the compliance has increased considerably (Karlberg and Koch, 1962). Consequently, much smaller changes in pressure are now sufficient to move gas in and out of the lung. At this stage expansion is often assisted by crying, during which positive pressures of up to 40 cms. of water may be generated on expiration. During expansion of the lung, there is a very large drop in pulmonary vascular resistance (Dawes, Mott, Widdicombe and Wyatt, 1953). This is in part mechanical, due to uncoiling of blood vessels, and in part due to changes in oxygen and carbon dioxide tension, which have a direct effect on pulmonary vascular tone (Cassin *et al.* 1964). The drop in pulmonary vascular resistance is accompanied by a fall in pulmonary artery pressure and a large increase in pulmonary blood flow, with a subsequent increase in left atrial pressure and functional closure of the foramen ovale (Dawes, 1961). The rise in arterial oxygen tension associated with lung expansion also causes constriction of the ductus arteriosus by a direct effect on its muscular wall (Born, Dawes, Mott and Rennick, 1956; Kovalcík, 1963), although closure may not be complete for several hours or even days (Moss, Emmanouilides, Adams and Chang, 1964). Clamping of the umbilical cord causes a rise in systemic arterial pressure (Dawes, 1961), so that after birth any flow through the ductus arteriosus is likely to be from left to right, that is, the reverse of the foetal situation. Thus the proper expansion of the lung at birth is closely linked with the changes in circulation necessary after birth. A further factor necessary for the expansion of the lungs is the removal of residual alveolar fluid. Because of its low protein content most of this fluid can pass back easily and rapidly into pulmonary capillaries (Chinard, Enns and Nolan, 1962), assisted by the large increase in pulmonary blood flow. Transient dilatation of perivascular lymphatics in the lungs immediately after delivery suggests that the lymphatic system also plays a part in removal of the fluid (Aherne and Dawkins, 1965).

Intrapartum anoxia may interfere in several ways with lung expansion and subsequent effective gas exchange. In the first place, intrauterine gasping may lead to the inhalation of considerable amounts of amniotic fluid, which may in some cases be contaminated with meconium. This in itself may block bronchioles and alveolar ducts and interfere with lung expansion. Anoxia can also cause intense pulmonary vasoconstriction (Cassin et al., 1964), so that the blood flow through the lungs may be greatly reduced. This will considerably impair effective gas exchange. If the arterial oxygen tension remains low, the ductus arteriosus will not constrict. Under these circumstances, with a high pulmonary vascular resistance and an open ductus arteriosus, a substantial R → L shunt could continue after delivery. It is easy to see how the effects of intrapartum anoxia can lead to a vicious spiral after birth, in which anoxia may be difficult to relieve even by endotracheal oxygen, because of pulmonary vasoconstriction and a large R → L shunt through the ductus arteriosus. Further, alveolar fluid interfering with gas exchange may not be removed because of the low pulmonary blood flow. Finally, the cardiac output will decline as a result of progressive hypoxia, and death will then be inevitable.

The physical problems involved in the maintenance of stable expansion of alveoli have attracted both physicists and physiologists (Avery, 1964). Alveolar stability at the end of expiration represents a balance between the slight negative intrathoracic pressure holding the alveoli open, and the surface tension of the thin layer of fluid lining the alveoli, tending to collapse the alveoli. If this fluid had the same surface tension as other biological fluids (50–70 dyne/cm.), then expansion of alveoli would require large negative pressures and the alveoli would collapse during expiration. Since this does not happen, the air-water interface of the alveolar lining film must have very unusual properties.

The presence in lung extracts of a material capable of producing substantial reduction in surface tension was first demonstrated by Pattle (1955), although its existence had been predicted on the basis of pressure-volume curves of lungs inflated with air or fluid (Gruenwald, 1947). This material has now been shown to be a phospholipid, dipalmityl phosphatidyl choline (Brown, 1965), which has the property of aligning itself as a mono-molecular film at air-water interfaces. This greatly reduces the surface tension at the interface. When the mono-molecular film is compressed laterally and reduced in surface area, the surface tension falls even further (Clements, Brown and Johnson, 1958). Clearly this property would be extremely appropriate for an alveolar lining film, since surface tension would be lowest at low alveolar volumes (the end of expiration). Surface-active material has been shown to be present in the alveolar fluid of the mature foetal lamb and guinea-pig (Adams and Fujiwara, 1963), but is absent from amniotic fluid (Adams et al., 1963). It appears in human foetal lung at about 26–28 weeks' gestation. Considerable interest has recently been aroused by the demonstration that the material is absent from the lungs of babies dying with atelectasis and hyaline membrane (Avery and Mead, 1959; Pattle et al., 1962).

Postnatal atelectasis, with or without hyaline membrane, is much the most frequent cause of death in the normally formed neonate who survives birth (Table III). These babies are born on average eight

TABLE III

CAUSES OF DEATH IN THE NORMALLY FORMED NEWBORN BABY IN THE FIRST WEEK OF LIFE

Cause of Death	% of neonatal deaths
Hyaline membrane with atelectasis	19
Pneumonia	17
Cerebral birth trauma with or without anoxia ..	14
Delayed intrapartum anoxia	11
Atelectasis only and/or primitive lung	11
Intraventricular haemorrhage	8
Massive pulmonary haemorrhage	8
Rhesus incompatibility	5
Miscellaneous	7

weeks before their expected date of delivery; the disease is only very rarely seen in babies delivered at term. Delivery itself is often complicated by antepartum haemorrhage, and at birth there are usually signs of very recent intrapartum hypoxia (James and Burnard, 1961). Respiratory difficulties are apparent within minutes of birth, but initially these may not be severe. The respiratory rate is increased and there is indrawing of the sternum. Arterial oxygen tension then starts to fall. This can be corrected at first by increasing the concentration of the oxygen, but later arterial blood is desaturated even in 100% oxygen. This indicates that most of the right ventricular output is bypassing the lungs and not coming into contact with alveolar oxygen. At this stage auscultation reveals very poor air entry, and X-ray shows total atelectasis of the lungs. Acidaemia becomes progressively more severe, owing partly to retention of carbon dioxide and partly to production of lactic acid as a result of tissue hypoxia. In the terminal stages the pH may be as low as 6.7. At this point respiration starts to fail and episodes of apnoea develop, which soon result in death. This clinical picture has been given the name 'respiratory distress syndrome'. It is seen in about 10% of babies weighing less than 2.5 Kg., and has an overall mortality of about 40% (Gairdner, 1965). Incidence and mortality are considerably higher in the lowest birth-weight group. More than 95% of the fatal cases die in the first 48 hours; complete recovery is usual in babies who survive beyond this time. Additional precipitating factors seem to be delivery by caesarean section (Usher, McLean and Maugham, 1964) and maternal diabetes mellitus (Farquhar, 1962).

The abnormalities of lung function underlying this clinical picture have been studied by many investigators, notably the Boston group associated with Dr. Clement Smith. Their extensive investigations have recently been summarized (Prod'hom, 1964). The major abnormalities are a lowered compliance, which greatly increases the work of respiration, and a decrease in the volume of air remaining in the lungs at the end of expiration. Physiological alveolar ventilation is decreased: mass spectrometer tracings of expired air indicate that the tidal volume may be smaller than the dead space in severe cases (Strang, 1963). As a result of all these abnormalities, ventilation is grossly inefficient. Coupled with this ventilatory inefficiency is a very considerable R → L shunt, which may be total as death approaches. This shunt can occur through the ductus arteriosus or the foramen ovale and may be due to pulmonary vasoconstriction from hypoxia, hypercapnia and acidaemia (Cassin et al., 1964). In determining the prognosis of the respiratory distress syndrome, the most important measurable abnormality seems to be the size of this R → L shunt (Prod'hom, 1964). Babies in whom a large shunt can be demonstrated usually die, though this may simply be an indication of the severity of hypoxia in fatal cases. Serial studies of lung function indicate that size of the shunt increases as hypoxia becomes more severe (Prod'hom, 1964), presumably because of progressive atelectasis.

In cases of respiratory distress, the lungs are found at autopsy to be airless, bulky and congested, and the ductus arteriosus is widely patent. Pressure-volume loops on the excised lung show low compliance and a small residual capacity, with the lungs tending to collapse at low pressures (Gribetz, Frank and Avery, 1959). These lungs have been described as showing 'poor stability'. Histological examination of the lungs shows that the alveolar spaces are collapsed and airless, and that there is over-dilatation of the alveolar ducts. Many of these dilated alveolar ducts may be lined with an eosinophilic structureless membrane, the so-called hyaline membrane (Plate 3). In addition there may be pulmonary oedema, with occasional areas of alveolar haemorrhage. The hyaline membrane was at first believed to be composed of aspirated amniotic material and was therefore called the vernix membrane. Subsequently, various components of plasma proteins, principally fibrin, were identified in the membrane by micro-chemical techniques (Gitlin and Craig, 1956), having presumably come from foetal capillary blood. Amniotic debris, fat and the remains of bronchial epithelium can also often be seen, and the membrane stains strongly for polysaccharide other than glycogen. This polysaccharide may be derived from bronchial mucus glands or from plasma polysaccharide-protein complexes. It was also believed that the membrane itself was obstructing alveolar ducts (Craig, Fenton and Gitlin, 1958), leading to distal collapse and impairment of gas exchange. However cases with an identical clinical picture often show only atelectasis and oedema at autopsy, while those dying in the first six hours rarely show hyaline membranes. We may conclude that the membrane is composed largely of foetal plasma proteins, and contains extraneous material trapped within it. It takes some time to develop, and its presence implies a gross increase in foetal pulmonary capillary permeability at some stage. Pulmonary oedema is a constant accompaniment of hyaline membrane.

Examination of the collapsed lungs has shown that the phospholipid surface-active material is absent from the areas of atelectasis (Avery and Mead, 1959). However, in cases with some areas of expansion (usually the anterior borders of the upper lobes), surface-active material can be detected in the expanded areas. Atelectasis is therefore unlikely to be due to primary deficiency of surface-active material. Considerable improvement in the stability of the excised lung during the measurement of a pressure-volume loop can be obtained by heating to 48 °C. (Gruenwald, 1964b), which also suggests that surface-active material is not primarily deficient, but is in some way inactivated. In any case, surface-active material appears in the human lung at 26–28 weeks' gestation, while most cases of respiratory distress have a gestation of about 32 weeks (Butler and Bonham, 1963). Without a quantitative method for measuring the surface-active material it is not possible to say whether there is too little present; but this is unlikely to be so, since by no means all babies born at this gestation develop respiratory distress. Nevertheless the progressive atelectasis, low compliance, low functional residual capacity and the resulting ventilatory inefficiency is probably due to the absence of surface-active material. Under experimental conditions such material can be made to disappear from the lung by embolisation or ligation of a pulmonary artery (Tooley, Gardner, Thing and Finlay, 1961), or after atelectasis from any cause (Sutnick and Soloff, 1964); it is therefore not surprising that it is absent from the premature atelectatic lung, through which, because of pulmonary vasoconstriction and a low cardiac output, there is probably very little blood flow. Clearly this is a situation which would be very difficult to reverse and which represents the terminal stage of the syndrome. What precise abnormalities initiate this chain of events remains unknown. The combination of intra-uterine hypoxia and premature delivery seems to be important, and leads to the development of respiratory distress in newborn monkeys (Adamsons, Behrman, Dawes, James and Koford, 1964) and lambs (Stahlman, LeQuire, Young, Merrill, Birmingham, Payne and Gray, 1964) also. At autopsy the histological picture of the lungs is very similar to the human disease.

There are many hypotheses concerning the nature of the funda-mental disturbance of cardio-pulmonary function in the respiratory-distress syndrome. The following is a speculative interpretation of the sequence of events. Intra-uterine hypoxia is known to lead to intra-uterine gasping, with the drawing of amniotic fluid into the lungs. This may lead to difficulties in lung expansion at birth, especially in the premature infant with its soft rib cage and less powerful inspiratory efforts. The presence of amniotic fluid in the alveoli may also lead to disappearance of surface-active material; such material can be inactivated *in vitro* by amniotic fluid. Neutral lipids present in amniotic fluid may be responsible for this by binding phospholipid (Fujiwara, Adams and Scudder, 1964). As a result of poor lung expansion, there is progressive hypoxia. Hypoxia either before or after birth causes an increase in capillary permeability in neonatal lungs, with leakage of plasma proteins into alveoli and alveolar ducts (Seller and Spector, 1964). Pulmonary oedema fluid will also inactivate surface-active material *in vitro* (Tierney and Johnson, 1961). Fibrin may then be deposited as a result of contact with thromboplastin or acidic mucopolysaccharides present in the amniotic fluid (Carone and Spector, 1960), leading to the appearance of hyaline membranes. Hypoxia could also cause extreme pulmonary vasoconstriction in the newborn lung, which would lead to the disappearance of any remaining surface-active material, a failing heart, a large R → L shunt, total atelectasis and death.

Therapy for the respiratory distress syndrome is aimed at correcting abnormalities of blood gases and pH before the irreversible stage of a large R → L shunt is reached. High environmental concentrations of oxygen given continuously for several days can cause blindness from retrolental fibroplasia in premature babies (Editorial, 1954). If, however, the arterial oxygen tension is measured frequently on blood samples taken from a catheter in the umbilical artery, high concentrations of oxygen can be used without danger since the concentration can be adjusted to give a normal oxygen tension in the blood. Acidaemia can be corrected by the infusion of alkali. Correction of acidaemia would also help to relieve any pulmonary vasoconstriction due to a high carbon dioxide tension. Infusions of glucose may be useful as a source of oxidizable substrate for the increased work of respiration. Artificial aids to ventilation have proved disappointing but have usually been tried only in the terminal stages. Close attention to environmental temperature is also important (Day, Caliguiri, Kamenski and Ehrlich, 1964; Buetow and Klein, 1964). As a result of all these measures the mortality of this syndrome has fallen considerably in the last few years. The real problem, however, lies in the prevention of premature labour, the cause of which is unknown in more than 50% of cases (Baird, 1964).

16

H. TEMPERATURE REGULATION IN THE NEWBORN

Body temperature in the newborn animal is unstable in the first day or two of life, and it has often been assumed that the newborn animal is to some extent poikilothermic. Heat production can be readily assessed by measuring oxygen consumption. The basal oxygen consumption at the neutral temperature is higher in newborn animals than in adults of the same species (Brück, 1961). The neutral temperature is defined as the temperature zone at which oxygen consumption is minimal, which in newborn animals is about 33–35 °C. In adult animals the neutral temperature range extends to much lower levels, largely because they are able to control heat loss more effectively than can newborns. When the temperature falls below the neutral range, most newborn animals can double or treble their oxygen consumption, increasing their heat production considerably. Even so, deep body temperature may fall at environmental temperatures as high as 25 °C., because of the much larger surface area relative to body mass in small animals. In addition, newborn animals have thin skin, little subcutaneous adipose tissue, and little or no hair; their heat conservation is therefore poor, and their skin temperature is much higher than in adults of the same species. One fascinating consequence of this is that the newborn seal, which has little or no blubber, when born on deep snow may actually drown in a pocket of melted snow (Laws, 1953). Adult seals do not melt the snow under them, since their skin temperature under these circumstances falls to 0 °C. (Hart and Fisher, 1964). The problems of the newborn animal in a cool environment are therefore those of heat conservation rather than any deficiency in heat production. Heat conservation is an even more acute problem in the premature than in the mature baby, because it has less subcutaneous adipose tissue, a very thin skin and a larger surface area relative to body mass.

When newborn animals of most species are exposed to cold, they show little or no evidence of shivering, despite a several-fold increase in oxygen consumption. This non-shivering heat production has recently been shown to take place in brown adipose tissue (Dawkins and Hull, 1963). This specialised form of adipose tissue has a very rich blood supply, and its oxidative metabolism *in vitro* is substantially higher than that of cardiac muscle (Dawkins and Hull, 1964a). Heat production is due to the local oxidation of stored triglycerides after they have been split into glycerol and free fatty acids. This hydrolysis is probably initiated by the local release of noradrenaline from sympathetic nerve endings, since stimulation of the sympathetic nerves to brown adipose tissue leads to a local increase in heat production (Hull and Segall, 1965a). Glycerol cannot be metabolized by adipose tissues and therefore appears in the blood stream in substantial amounts during thermogenesis. Brown adipose tissue is present in the newborn rabbit as a large interscapular deposit, with extensions around the neck to form a sort of collar, and totalling as much as 5–6% of the body weight; it thus forms a discrete organ bigger than the liver. Surgical removal of this tissue does not alter the basal oxygen consumption, but completely prevents the three to four fold increase which the newborn rabbit normally shows when exposed to cold (Hull and Segall, 1964).

Large interscapular deposits of brown adipose tissue are also found in the newborn guinea-pig and coypu (Dawkins and Hull, 1964b). Smaller interscapular deposits are present in the human newborn infant, newborn monkeys of various species, the newborn rat and the kitten. Scattered deposits of brown adipose tissue are also present in other sites in these species. In the human newborn infant the major deposits of brown adipose tissue are in the floor of the posterior triangle of the neck, surrounding the subclavian and carotid vessels, and in the perirenal areas (Aherne and Hull, 1964). The participation of brown adipose tissue in heat production in the human newborn infant has been demonstrated indirectly by a rise in plasma glycerol on exposure to cold, in both mature and premature infants (Dawkins and Scopes, 1965). The newborn seal possesses extensive sheets of brown adipose tissue between skin and muscle, and extending between muscle layers over the whole body. The newborn piglet appears to have virtually no adipose tissue at all, but shivers vigorously when exposed to cold (Mount, 1961). Brown adipose tissue is also present in substantial amounts in the hibernating animal (Johansson, 1958) and in smaller amounts in the cold-adapted rat (Smith, 1962), and plays a major role in heat production during arousal from hibernation (Smith and Hock, 1963; Joel, Treble and Ball, 1964).

Another important aspect of heat production in brown adipose tissue is its topographical anatomy (Smith and Roberts, 1964). Blood returning from head and upper limbs is selectively warmed, so that the body core is protected from a fall in temperature in a cool environment. Blood flow through brown adipose tissue is considerably increased during exposure to cold (Brück, 1964).

Disturbances of heat production in brown adipose tissue may arise in several ways. First, heat production is very sensitive to hypoxia

(Hill, 1959), and at an arterial oxygen tension below 50 mms. the body temperature of newborn infants will fall quite rapidly in a cool environment. The rapid drop of body temperature immediately after delivery into the cold world is probably partly due to transient hypoxia and partly to increased heat loss by evaporation, because the baby is wet. Continuing hypoxia, from post-anoxic apnoea or from the development of atelectasis with hyaline membrane, also leads to a fall in body temperature. Careful control of environmental temperature in an incubator is therefore important for babies with respiratory difficulties. Recently it has been shown that special measures to maintain body and skin temperature as constant as possible result in improvements in mortality from respiratory distress (Day et al., 1964; Buetow and Klein, 1964). This reduction of the thermal load might result in some sparing of both oxygen and glucose for vital functions. Failure of heat production may also occur at the tissue level because of shortage of vital substrates. Starvation of newborn rabbits in a cool environment leads to exhaustion of all the lipid in brown adipose tissue and to loss of the ability to increase oxygen consumption in the cold (Hull and Segall, 1965b). It is an interesting point that the milk of animals which rely largely on brown adipose tissue for heat production has a very high fat content. Prolonged hypoglycaemia might also lead to failure of heat production in brown adipose tissue, since an exogenous source of glucose for conversion to α-glycerol phosphate is required. Heat production depends on the continuous hydrolysis and resynthesis of triglyceride, with simultaneous oxidation of fatty acids. α-glycerol phosphate derived from blood glucose is therefore necessary for the resynthesis of triglyceride since glycerol cannot be phosphorylated directly by brown adipose tissue (Dawkins and Hull, 1964a).

Deficiencies in heat production certainly play a role in perinatal mortality. In addition to the importance of maintaining body temperature in the respiratory distress syndrome, babies may actually die of so-called 'cold injury' (Mann and Elliott, 1957). This condition is usually seen only in winter. Affected babies are very quiet, lethargic and reluctant to feed. The cheeks are bright pink, giving a misleading appearance of well-being. The body temperature may be as low as 25 °C., and the blood glucose is often extremely low. At autopsy these babies show massive haemorrhage into the alveolar spaces of the lung; this is clearly the terminal event. An underlying unrecognized infection may sometimes be present, but most cases seem to result from exposure of normal babies to an environment that is too cold.

The precise relationship between the low body temperature and the low blood glucose is not clear. Perhaps carbohydrate stores become exhausted in an attempt to maintain the body temperature. Measurements of respiratory quotient, however, suggest that fat is the major fuel for heat production in infants, once the first few hours after birth have elapsed (Cross, Tizard and Trythall, 1957). Low blood glucose levels have also been found in the starved newborn pig exposed to cold (Widdowson, 1961), but the pig is exceptional among newborn animals in having little or no store of fat (Widdowson, 1950).

The situation is further complicated by the fact that prolonged hypoglycaemia in babies suffering from intra-uterine malnutrition may lead to death from massive pulmonary haemorrhage (*vide infra*). In this situation body temperature is also low, but because of their low birth weight most of these babies will be kept in incubators at 30–32 °C. Very low body temperatures cannot therefore develop. Most of the cases of massive pulmonary haemorrhage were found in babies which were small for their presumed gestational age (Butler and Bonham, 1963), and were associated with symptoms suggestive of hypoglycaemia. Babies of low birth weight, whether truly premature or small for their gestational age, are also liable to develop a low body temperature, even when the blood sugar is normal. This cannot be due to absence of brown adipose tissue, which appears early in gestation and is present in substantial amounts at 28 weeks. Even very premature babies can increase their oxygen consumption on exposure to cold (Brück, 1961). However, respiratory function is probably not as good in the premature baby without overt respiratory distress as in the mature baby, and this may limit the increase in oxygen consumption on exposure to cold. In any case a larger increase would be necessary because of the larger surface area relative to body mass in the smaller infant.

Babies small for their presumed gestational age also possess brown adipose tissue, but the tissue may contain less lipid than normal. Adipose tissue stores of oxidizable fat are reduced in the runts of rabbit litters (Dawkins and Hull, 1964a).

I. METABOLIC HOMEOSTASIS IN THE NEWBORN

The constancy of the composition of the body fluids demands the integrated activity of many organs, largely controlled by the secretions of the endocrine glands. Before birth, homeostasis is mostly effected by trans-placental exchanges. For this reason gross congenital malformations such as complete absence of the kidneys result in very little disturbance of the foetal internal environment. Immediately after birth, the homeostatic functions of foetal organs are tested for the first time. Of these, the lung is of the first importance in the establishment of gas exchange, and we have seen how failure in this direction is the major cause of neonatal death.

J. LIVER FUNCTION

1. Blood glucose regulation

The regulatory functions of the liver are of considerable interest in the neonatal period and have been extensively investigated. Liver functions are relatively easy to measure and can be related to the underlying activity of liver enzyme systems. The regulation of blood glucose levels by variations in the amount of glucose released from the liver under the stimulation of the hormones adrenaline and glucagon is of great importance, since milk contains relatively small amounts of carbohydrate. In the foetal state, blood glucose levels are a reflection of maternal blood glucose (Shelley, 1960), and therefore probably do not fluctuate very widely. An exception to this may be the foetus of the diabetic woman.

Liver glycogen is present in very large amounts in foetal liver at term, in all species which have been examined, including man (Shelley, 1961). This glycogen disappears from the liver immediately after birth and a reserve of liver glycogen may not be re-accumulated for several days (Shelley, 1961). In the newborn human, blood glucose levels fall in the first few hours of life, often to levels which would cause serious disturbances in the adult, but which do not seem to harm the infant. After six hours blood glucose levels have usually risen again, but tend to be lower than in the adult for the first week or two of life.

Changes in mean blood glucose level during the first 48 hours in newborn babies of various categories are shown in Fig. 4. In all babies there is an immediate fall after birth, probably owing to peripheral utilization of glucose by tissues (principally the brain). In the mature and premature infant the downward trend is halted at about six hours, as a result of the mobilization of liver glycogen. The mechanisms for regulation of blood glucose are apparently not very precise immediately after birth, even in the normal baby. In the

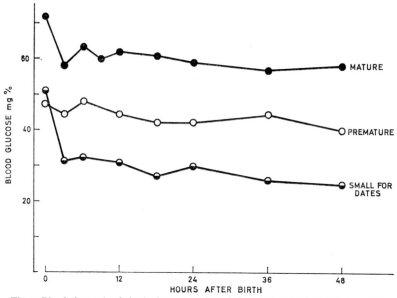

Fig. 4. Blood glucose levels in the human newborn infant during the first 48 hours of life. Mature = heavier than 2.5 Kg.; premature = delivered before 37 weeks' gestation; small for dates = 1 Kg. or more below expected weight for gestation.

'small for dates' baby, which is small for its gestational age, the downward trend continues to considerably lower levels than in the premature baby. This difference may be related to the smaller liver (Gruenwald, 1963) and the smaller glycogen reserve in these babies (Shelley, 1964).

Measurements of the respiratory quotient in newborn infants (Cross, Tizard and Trythall, 1957) suggest that carbohydrate is the major source of fuel immediately after birth, but that oxidation of fat becomes increasingly important after the first few hours. The rise in non-esterified fatty acids in the plasma, from the very low levels present in the foetus, indicates hydrolysis and mobilization of stored triglyceride in adipose tissue (Van Duyne, Parker and Holm, 1965). Since much of the adipose tissue in the newborn is of the brown variety, in which fatty acids are oxidized locally, the rise in free fatty acids in the plasma represents only a small part of the total fatty acids being metabolised. The accumulation of liver glycogen in late foetal life, its utilization immediately after birth and the tendency to low blood glucose levels in the neonatal period, seems to be a common pattern in mammals during the transition from intra-uterine to extra-uterine life.

Hormonal regulation may also contribute to the tendency to low blood glucose levels in the immediate post-natal period. After intravenous glucose loading, insulin levels in the plasma rise sharply and immediately in adult animals, but in the normal newborn baby, although insulin is present in large amounts in the pancreas, there is no immediate response (Baird and Farquhar, 1962). There is however a delayed but prolonged small rise in the level of insulin in the plasma (Milner and Hales, 1965). This prolonged elevation might be related to a slower rate of insulin detoxication by neonatal liver. The half-life of cortisol in the plasma is about three times longer in the newborn than in the adult (Migeon, 1961), because of low activity of the liver enzyme which conjugates cortisol and glucuronic acid to an inactive form.

Mobilization of the large reserve of liver glycogen after birth is probably initiated by the hormones adrenaline and glucagon. However, despite the enormous amount of glycogen present, the hyperglycaemic response to these hormones is small both in the newborn human infant (Desmond, 1953; Cornblath, Ganzon, Nicolopoulos, Baens, Hollander, Gordon and Gordon, 1961), the foetal and newborn lamb (Dawkins, 1964b) and the rat (Dawkins, 1963a). Comparisons of the level of liver glycogen and the response to adrenaline in the newborn lamb have shown that the full response has developed by the time liver glycogen is at its lowest level (Dawkins, 1964b).

Investigation of the cellular mechanisms underlying the synthesis and breakdown of liver glycogen in the foetus and newborn has shown that glycogen synthesis from glucose is very active in the foetus (Dawkins, 1963b). However, glycogen synthesis from pyruvate is very poor in foetal liver (Ballard and Oliver, 1963), and the main precursors of foetal liver glycogen seem to be glucose, galactose and fructose (Ballard and Oliver, 1964). Deposition of glycogen in foetal liver has been shown to be under the control of the pituitary via the adrenal cortex (Jost and Jacquot, 1955). The precise site of control is unknown, but it is probably not by means of the stimulatory effects of adrenal steroids on glycogen synthesis, since the enzymatic pathways involved are of such low activity. The capacity for glycogen synthesis increases very rapidly in the newborn rat, reaching about ten days after birth a maximum several times greater than that of the adult (Ballard and Oliver, 1963). The reaccumulation of a reserve of liver glycogen may be related to this increase.

The enzymes of glycogen breakdown, phosphorylase and glucose-6-phosphatase, are of low activity in foetal liver, but immediately after birth show a very rapid increase in activity to levels as high as or higher than in adult liver (Dawkins, 1963b; Kornfeld and Brown, 1963). The increase in phosphorylase activity measured *in vitro* is accompanied by an increasing hyperglycaemic response to adrenaline and glucagon (Dawkins, 1964b). In a number of species, glucose-6-phosphatase activity may increase to levels 2–5 times higher than in the adult (Dawkins, 1963c). This may be regarded as a true metabolic adaptation, since new enzyme protein has to be synthesized (Dawkins, 1963c). The increase in activity will result in preferential utilization of glucose-6-phosphatase and all its precursors in the direction of glucose release from the liver (Ashmore and Weber, 1959). The alternative metabolic pathways open to glucose-6-phosphate are shown in Fig. 5.

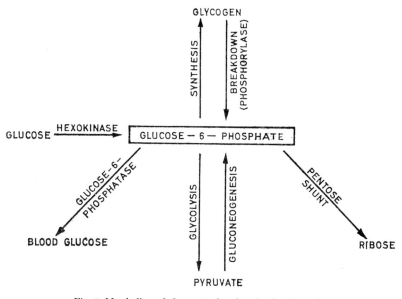

Fig. 5. Metabolism of glucose-6-phosphate by the liver cell.

Low blood glucose levels are common on the first day of life in the normal human baby and do not produce any detectable harm. However, when blood glucose is less than 20 mg.% vague symptoms may occur, consisting of cyanosis, apnoea, lethargy and in some cases convulsions (Cornblath, Wybregt, Baens and Klein, 1964), but they can be relieved immediately by intravenous glucose. Mortality is high, mostly from the syndrome of massive pulmonary haemorrhage described previously in relation to cold injury. The precise relationship between hypoglycaemia and haemorrhage into the alveoli is not known. The syndrome is not part of a generalized bleeding tendency, since bleeding is not seen in other organs. Many of the surviving infants later show gross evidence of damage to the central nervous system. The syndrome is usually found in babies whose birth weight is unexpectedly low for their gestational age (Cornblath et al., 1964; Neligan, 1965) and especially in the smaller of a pair of twins (Reisner, Forbes and Cornblath, 1965). This reduction in birth weight is thought to be the result of intra-uterine malnutrition and these babies have relatively larger brains and smaller livers than normal babies (Gruenwald, 1963; Dawkins, 1964a). In a severely underweight baby the brain may represent as much as 25% of the body weight (average 12% at term). Their livers have also been shown to contain less glycogen than normal (Shelley, 1964). Similar bodily disproportion can be produced by experimental intra-uterine malnutrition (Hammond, 1961). Since the only substrate which the brain can use to any extent is glucose, babies which are small for their gestational age have a greater demand for glucose and a poorer reserve both in terms of glycogen and effective liver mass available for glycogen synthesis than do those of normal weight.

The aetiology of intra-uterine malnutrition is multiple. Known causes include life at high altitude, cyanotic heart disease, multiple pregnancy, maternal starvation in pregnancy and hypertension. Maternal associations are low social class, short stature and elderly primiparity. Foetal abnormalities associated with unexpectedly low birth weight for gestation are single umbilical artery, chorio-angioma of the placenta (a large arterio-venous anastomosis between umbilical artery and vein), chromosomal abnormalities and other foetal malformations. In more than half the cases no obvious cause can be found and a hypothetical 'placental dysfunction' has been suggested as the underlying abnormality.

2. Bilirubin excretion

Another important aspect of liver function at birth is the excretion of bilirubin. The foetus can dispose of free bilirubin derived from the breakdown of haemoglobin across the placenta (Lester, Behrman and Lucey, 1963; Schenker, 1963). After birth it must be conjugated in the liver with glucuronic acid to form the water-soluble glucuronide, and then excreted into the gut via the biliary system. Neonatal jaundice is very common, and is usually due to low activity of the enzyme conjugating bilirubin and glucuronic acid (Dutton, 1963). Free bilirubin consequently accumulates in the blood stream. In normal babies the enzyme increases in activity rapidly after birth and the jaundice disappears after a few days. However, if the jaundice is severe, damage to the nuclei of the brain stem and even death may occur. Bilirubin is a tissue poison (Zetterström and Ernster, 1956) and can damage the central nervous system in the newborn because of functional immaturity of the blood-brain barrier (Driscoll and Hsia, 1958). This picture of damage to the ganglia of the brain stem is known as kernicterus. Excessive jaundice is seen in several situations. It is most commonly associated with haemolytic disease of the newborn due to rhesus incompatibility, with a resulting severe haemolytic anaemia from the transplacental passage of maternal antibodies to foetal red cells. It is also associated with premature delivery, since the postnatal increase in the capacity of the liver to form bilirubin glucuronide develops more slowly after premature delivery than after delivery at term. Bilirubin levels which are not dangerous in the mature infant may be lethal in the premature infant. The combination of hyperbilirubinaemia and birth anoxia may produce more damage than either alone (Lucey, Hibberd, Behrman, Gallardo and Windle, 1964). Other causes of excessive jaundice are neonatal sepsis, and injuries accompanied by haemorrhage into tissues.

The postnatal increase in activity of the enzyme system conjugating bilirubin and glucuronic acid is also a metabolic adaptation requiring synthesis of new protein. It can be greatly reduced in experimental animals by undernutrition in the neonatal period (Flint, Lathe and Ricketts, 1963). Intensive early feeding of the premature human infant has recently been reported to reduce bilirubin levels considerably (Smallpiece and Davies, 1964).

3. Drug metabolism

Another important detoxication function of the liver is the conversion of drugs of many kinds to pharmacologically inactive watersoluble compounds which can be excreted in the bile. The endoplasmic reticulum of the liver cell contains a family of enzymes which detoxicate many drugs by hydroxylation reactions, requiring reduced nicotinamide adenine dinucleotide phosphate and molecular oxygen. Conjugations with glucuronic acid, glycine and sulphate are also important in the detoxication of drugs and hormones. Such drugs as morphia, pethidine and some barbiturates, commonly used during labour, are metabolized by the liver. Their length of action is determined chiefly by the rate at which they are metabolized. The enzymes metabolizing these drugs are virtually absent from the newborn liver (Jondorf, Maickel and Brodie, 1958; Fouts and Adamson, 1959). Consequently drugs administered to the infant, either by transplacental passage from the mother during labour or for deliberate therapeutic reasons, will persist in the blood stream for much longer than in the adult. An excellent correlation exists between the sleeping time after administration of a barbiturate and the activity of the hepatic barbiturate-detoxicating enzyme system in the newborn and young mouse (Yaffe, 1962). This difference in drug detoxication may result in severe and even fatal intoxications in newborn infants given the doses of drugs appropriate for children. Death from chloramphenicol toxicity in newborn infants has recently been recorded (Nyhan, 1961). Chloramphenicol, like bilirubin, is detoxicated by conjugation with glucuronic acid.

A further problem in the administration of drugs to newborn babies is that several drugs increase the severity or toxicity of neonatal jaundice. Vitamin K, for instance, in large doses was found to increase the incidence of kernicterus (Allison, 1955). The mechanism seems to be partly due to increased haemolysis (Zinkham, 1959), leading to higher bilirubin levels, but other factors may play a part (Hsia, Dowben and Riabov, 1963). The antibiotic novobiocin also aggravates jaundice, but in this case by inhibition of the glucuronide-conjugating system of the liver (Hargreaves and Holton, 1962). Exacerbation of jaundice in breast-fed babies has recently been shown to be due to the presence of a progesterone derivative in the milk of some mothers. This hormone also inhibits *in vitro* the glucuronide-conjugating system in the liver (Arias, Gartner, Seifler and Furman, 1964). Sulphonamides increase the toxicity of a given level of plasma bilirubin, probably owing to displacement of bilirubin bound to plasma albumen (Odell, 1959). Therapy in the newborn therefore presents special problems which can only be identified in advance by testing the drugs on appropriate newborn experimental animals.

The relationship between developing liver function and increases in the activity of enzymes associated with these functions is clear in the newborn (Driscoll and Hsia, 1958). These increases in activity can be regarded as metabolic adaptations to the change in environment at birth (Knox, Auerbach and Lin, 1956); some require the synthesis of new enzyme protein (Nemeth and de la Haba, 1962; Dawkins, 1963c) and are reduced by food restriction (Flint *et al.*, 1963). The precise stimuli are not known but they seem to be related to birth itself rather than post-conceptual age. Premature delivery results in immediate increases in the activity of the hepatic enzymes tryptophane pyrollase and glucose-6-phosphatase, whereas artificial prolongation of pregnancy delays the increase until after delivery (Nemeth, 1959; Dawkins, 1961). The rise in activity of these enzymes after premature delivery does not appear to be less than in normal animals delivered at term. However it is clear that in the human new-born infant the enzyme system for the conjugation of bilirubin develops more slowly after premature delivery than after delivery at term. Premature babies are also especially susceptible to the toxic action of chloramphenicol (Nyhan, 1961), which is excreted as a conjugate of glucuronic acid. Thus inadequate metabolic adaptation may be one of the handicaps of premature delivery, although it is not of great importance compared with the pulmonary problems of the premature baby.

K. NEONATAL RESISTANCE TO INFECTION

The foetus *in utero* lives in a bacterially sterile environment. Very rarely bacteria have been shown to cross the placenta but this is usually only in association with maternal septicaemia. Viruses can much more readily cross the placenta, as is shown by the development of characteristic foetal abnormalities when rubella complicates the early months of pregnancy. Rubella virus has now been isolated from the foetus $4\frac{1}{2}$ months after the initial infection (Kay, Peppercorn, Porterfield, McCarthy and Taylor-Robinson, 1964). After birth the alimentary canal of the newborn infant is colonized by bacteria within the first twenty-four hours of life (Hall and O'Toole, 1934). The skin is also rapidly colonized (Hurst, 1960). However, the normal defence mechanisms against bacterial invasion present in the adult are clearly operative. Colonization of the intestinal tract by non-pathogenic viruses may not take place for up to a month after birth (Moscovici and Maisel, 1961).

Immune globulins can be broadly divided into three main fractions. Immune gamma globulins (I.g.G.) include antibodies to the common viruses and to many gram-positive organisms. In the primate these globulins cross the placenta (Bangham, Hobbs and Terry, 1958) mostly during the last part of pregnancy. In the rabbit, antibodies are transferred across the yolk-sac splanchnopleure (Hemmings and Brambell, 1961). Transplacental transfer of antibodies is responsible for the transient passive immunity of the newborn baby to the common infectious fevers. In some animals (especially the calf) large amounts of immune globulins are present in colostrum and are absorbed intact from the intestinal tract (Pierce, 1961). This route exists in the human baby but is probably not very important, although antibodies are present in human colostrum in large amounts (Nordbring, 1957). The capacity to produce I.g.G. in response to antigenic stimulation is virtually absent in newborn babies and is not well developed for several months (see Fig. 6). I.g.G. is probably produced by plasma cells, which are absent in the newborn (Bridges, Condie, Zak and Good, 1959).

Immune macro-globulins (I.g.M.) include the antibodies to gram-negative enteric organisms and anti-spirochaetal antibodies. They do not cross the placenta. When given an antigenic stimulus the newborn baby even if premature can produce I.g.M., but the response is much slower and poorer than in the adult (Smith, 1964). I.g.M. are probably synthesized by lymphocytes.

The third fraction of immune globulins (I.g.A.) is responsible for delayed tissue hypersensitivity, as in the Mantoux reaction. The newborn infant seems to be capable of producing this type of antibody response.

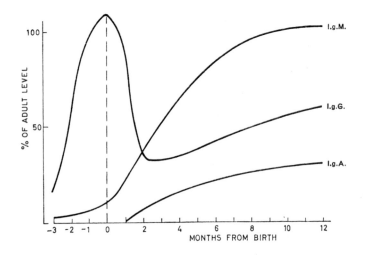

Fig. 6. Changes in immune globulin levels in the blood before birth and during the first year of life.

The changes in the various types of immune globulin levels before and after birth are shown in Fig. 6. These changes represent the response of the normal baby to antigenic stimuli encountered as the result of trivial infections. The fall in I.g.G. after birth is due to the decay in passively acquired I.g.G. At 2-3 months of age, the baby is able to produce its own I.g.G. and the level rises again. Small amounts of I.g.M. are present in the foetus before term, but the amount increases sharply in the neonatal period since I.g.M. is virtually the only immune globulin which the newborn baby can produce in response to an antigenic stimulus (Smith, 1964). I.g.A. cannot be detected at birth, even though the newborn baby can develop a positive Mantoux reaction to immunization with attenuated tubercle bacilli.

The role of the thymus in the development of immunological competence has recently been the subject of much investigation (Miller, 1964). The thymus is very large in newborn animals and its function has until recently been a matter of speculation. Removal of the thymus in newborn mice leads to extreme reduction of circulating lymphocytes, failure of growth and recurrent infections (Miller, 1961). Thymectomy in adult animals produces only a transient drop in the number of circulating lymphocytes (Metcalf, 1960). If thymectomized newborn mice are reared in a germ-free environment, growth is normal (McIntire, Sell and Miller, 1964). Mice thymectomized at birth later show immunological tolerance, and will even accept heterologous tissue grafts. In the human foetus tolerance disappears well before birth (Mitchison, 1961). It is postulated that there is a critical period after birth in the newborn mouse during which the thymus, by some unknown mechanism, is responsible for the development of the lymphoid system (Miller, 1964). Lymphocytes are probably concerned in the production of macroglobulin antibodies (I.g.M.). It may be significant that babies which are small for their gestational age show marked atrophy of the thymus and are particularly liable to infections in the neonatal period (Butler, 1965).

Infections in the neonatal period in this country are now almost entirely confined to the lung, although formerly umbilical sepsis was an important cause of perinatal mortality. Gastro-enteritis is fortunately also now rare, though formerly a major cause of mortality in the first week of life. Lung infections are still an important cause of neonatal death, accounting for nearly as many deaths as hyaline membrane (Table III). Neonatal pneumonia can be divided into two broad clinical categories. The first occurs in babies born at term who have shown signs of anoxia during delivery. These babies have often inhaled meconium, and the combination of meconium and focal collapse seems to be a very good medium for bacterial invasion. Where the membranes have been ruptured and labour has been prolonged, the amniotic cavity can become invaded by bacteria and a true intra-uterine pneumonia may develop (Benirschke, 1960). Bacterial invasion may also occur after birth. The usual organism is of the gram-negative enteric group, against which the newborn baby has no passive immunity and can make only a poor antibody response.

The second large group of babies dying of pneumonia in the neonatal period are babies of very low birth weight. The infecting organisms may be of any type, and measurement of immune globulin concentration in these babies has shown that the I.g.G. fraction is very low. These babies may well have missed the transplacental donation of I.g.G. by being born too early (*see* Fig. 6). Babies of very low birth weight who are not premature are also especially liable to pneumonia in the neonatal period, but so far no information is available on their immune globulin levels.

ACKNOWLEDGEMENTS

Table I is reproduced by permission of the National Birthday Trust and E. and S. Livingstone Ltd., Edinburgh. I am grateful to Dr. G. S. Dawes for the data shown in Fig. 1, to Dr. W. W. Payne for the data in Fig. 4 and to Dr. J. Hobbs for the data shown in Fig. 6.

REFERENCES

Adams, F. H. and Fujiwara, T. (1963) Surfactant in fetal lamb tracheal fluid. *J. Pediat.*, **63**, 537–42.

Adams, F. H., Fujiwara, T. and Rowshan, G. (1963) The nature and origin of the fluid in the fetal lamb lung. *J. Pediat.*, **63**, 881–8.

Adamsons, K., Behrman, R., Dawes, G. S., Dawkins, M. J. R., James, L. S. and Ross, B. B. (1963) The treatment of acidosis with alkali and glucose during asphyxia in foetal rhesus monkeys. *J. Physiol., Lond.*, **169**, 679–89.

Adamsons, K. Jr., Behrman, R., Dawes, G. S., James, L. S. and Koford, C. (1964) Resuscitation by positive pressure ventilation and Tris-hydroxy methyl aminomethane of rhesus monkeys asphyxiated at birth. *J. Pediat.*, **65**, 807–18.

Aherne, W. and Dawkins, M. J. R. (1965) Removal of fluid from the pulmonary airways after birth in the rabbit and the effects on this of prematurity and prenatal hypoxia. *Biol. Neonat.* In press.

Aherne, W. and Hull, D. (1964) Site of heat production in the newborn infant. *Proc. Roy. Soc. Med.*, **57**, 1172–3.

Allison, A. C. (1955) Danger of Vitamin K to the newborn. *Lancet, i,* 669.

Arias, I. M., Gartner, L. M., Seifler, S. and Furman, M. (1964) Prolonged neonatal unconjugated hyperbilirubinaemia associated with breast feeding and a steroid Pregnane—3(α), 20(β)—Diol, in maternal milk that inhibits glucuronide formation *in vitro. J. Clin. Invest.*, **43**, 2037–8.

Ashmore, J. and Weber, G. (1959) The role of glucose-6-phosphatase in the regulation of carbohydrate metabolism. *Vitamins and Hormones*, **17**, 91–132.

Assali, N. S., Holm, L. and Parker H. (1961) Regional blood flow and vascular resistance in response to oxytocin in the pregnant sheep and dog. *J. Applied Physiol.*, **16**, 1087–92.

Assali, N. S., Holm, L. W. and Sehgal, N. (1962) Hemodynamic changes in fetal lamb *in utero* in response to asphyxia, hypoxia and hypercapnia. *Circ. Res.*, **11**, 423–30.

Avery, M. E. (1964) *The lung and its disorders in the newborn infant.* Saunders.

Avery, M. E. and Mead, J. (1959) Surface properties in relation to atelectasis and hyaline membrane disease. *Amer. J. Dis. Child.*, **97**, 517–23.

Baird, D. (1964) The epidemiology of prematurity. *J. Pediat.*, **65**, 909–24.

Baird, J. and Farquhar, J. W. (1962) Insulin secreting capacity in newborn infants of normal and diabetic women. *Lancet, i,* 71–4.

Baker, J. B. E. (1960) The effects of drugs on the foetus. *Pharmacol. Rev.*, **12**, 37–90.

Ballard, F. J. and Oliver, I. T. (1963) Glycogen metabolism in embryonic chick and neonatal rat liver. *Biochem. Biophys. Acta*, **71**, 578–88.

Ballard, F. J. and Oliver, I. T. (1964) Ketohexokinase, isoenzymes of glucokinase and glycogen synthesis from hexoses in neonatal rat liver.*Biochem J.*,**90**,261–8.

Bangham, D. R., Hobbs, K. R. and Terry, R. J. (1958) Selective placental transfer of serum proteins in the rhesus. *Lancet, ii,* 351–4.

Barcroft, J. (1946) *Researches on prenatal life.* Blackwells, Oxford.

Benirschke, H. (1960) Route and types of infection in the fetus and newborn. *Amer. J. Dis. Child.*, **99**, 714–21.

Born, G. V. R., Dawes, G. S., Mott, J. C. and Rennick, B. R. (1956) Constriction of the ductus arteriosus caused by oxygen and by asphyxia in newborn lambs. *J. Physiol., Lond.*, **132**, 304–42.

Bridges, R. A., Condie, R. H., Zak, S. J. and Good, R. A. (1959) The morphological basis of antibody formation during the neonatal period. *J. Lab. Clin. Med.*, **53**, 331–57.

Brown, E. S. (1965) *J. Appl. Physiol.* In press.

Brück, K. (1961) Temperature regulation in the newborn infant. *Biol. Neonat.*, **3**, 65–119.

Brück, K. (1964) General aspects of temperature regulation of small subjects. pp. 229–47 in Nutrica symposium, '*The adaptation of the newborn infant to extra-uterine life*'. Ed. J. Jonxis, H. Visser and J. Troelstra. Stenfert Kroese. Leiden.

Buetow, K. C. and Klein, S. W. (1964) Normal skin temperature and survival of prematures. *Pediatrics*, **34**, 163–70.

Burns, B. D. (1963) The central control of respiratory movements. *Brit. med. Bull*, **19**, 7–9.

Butler, N. (1965) *Causes of neonatal death in the dysmature infant.* Little Club Clinic. In press.

Butler, N. R. and Bonham, D. G. (1963) *Perinatal Mortality.* E. and S. Livingstone Ltd., Edinburgh.

Campiche, M. A., Gautier, A., Hernandez, G. I., and Reymond, A. (1963) Electron microscope studies of fetal development of human lung. *Pediatrics*,**32**, 976–94.

17

Carone, F. A. and Spector, W. G. (1960) Formation of pulmonary hyaline membranes. *J. Path. Bact.*, **80**, 63–71.

Carr, D. H. (1963) Chromosome studies in abortuses and stillborn infants. *Lancet*, **2**, 603–6.

Cassin, S., Dawes, G. S., Mott, J. C., Ross, B. B. and Strang, L. B. (1964) The vascular resistance of the foetal and newly ventilated lung of the lamb. *J. Physiol., Lond.*, **171**, 61–79.

Chinard, E. P., Enns, T, and Nolan, M. F. (1962) Permeability characteristics of the alveolar capillary barrier. *Trans. Ass. amer. Physic.*, **75**, 253–61.

Clements, J. A., Brown, E. S. and Johnson, R. P. (1958) Pulmonary surface tension and the mucous lining of the lungs: some theoretical considerations. *J. Appl. Physiol.*, **12**, 262–8.

Cohen, E. N. (1962) Placental transmission of anaesthetic agents. pp. 26–31 in 41st Ross Conference 'Perinatal Pharmacology'. Ed. C. May. Columbus Ross Laboratories.

Comline, R. S. and Silver, M. (1958) Response of the adrenal medulla of the sheep foetus to asphyxia. *Nature, Lond.*, **181**, 283.

Cornblath, M., Ganzon, A., Nicolopoulos, D., Baens, G. S., Hollander, R., Gordon, M. and Gordon, H. (1961) Studies of carbohydrate metabolism in the newborn infant. *Pediatrics*, **27**, 378–89.

Cornblath, M., Wybregt, S. H., Baens, G. S. and Klein, R. I. (1964) Symptomatic neonatal hypoglycaemia. *Pediatrics*, **33**, 388–402.

Craig, J. M., Fenton, K. and Gitlin, D. (1958) Obstructive factors in the pulmonary hyaline membrane syndrome in asphyxia of the newborn. *Pediatrics*, **22**, 847–56.

Cross, K. W., Dawes, G. S., Hyman, A. and Mott, J. C. (1964) Hyperbaric oxygen and intermittent positive pressure respiration in resuscitation of asphyxiated newborn rabbits. *Lancet*, ii, 560–2.

Cross, K. W., Klaus, M., Tooley, W. H. and Weisser, K. (1960) The response of the newborn baby to inflation of the lungs. *J. Physiol., Lond.*, **151**, 551–65.

Cross, K. W., Tizard, J. P. M. and Trythall, D. A. H. (1957) The gaseous metabolism of the newborn infant. *Acta Paediat., Uppsala.*, **46**, 265–85.

Darling, R. C., Smith, C. A., Asmussen, E. and Cohen, F. M. (1941) Some properties of human fetal and maternal blood. *J. Clin. Invest.*, **20**, 739–47.

Davis, J. A. and Moore, M. (1965) *J. Appl. Physiol.* In press.

Dawes, G. S. (1961) Changes in the circulation at birth. *Brit. med. Bull.*, **17**, 148–53.

Dawes, G. S. (1965) Circulation, respiration and metabolism of newborn. *Recent Advances in Paediatrics*, 3rd Ed. pp. 1–35. Ed. D. Gairdner. Churchill, London.

Dawes, G. S., Hibberd, E. and Windle, W. F. (1964) The effect of alkali and glucose infusion on permanent brain damage in rhesus monkeys asphyxiated at birth. *J. Pediat.*, **65**, 801–6.

Dawes, G. S., Jacobson, H. N., Mott, J. C., Shelley, H. J. and Stafford, A. (1963) The treatment of asphyxiated mature foetal lambs and rhesus monkeys with intravenous glucose and sodium carbonate. *J. Physiol., Lond.*, **169**, 167–84.

Dawes, G. S. and Mott, J. C. (1962) The vascular tone of the foetal lung. *J. Physiol., Lond.*, **164**, 465–77.

Dawes, G. S. and Mott, J. C. (1964) Changes in O_2 distribution and consumption in foetal lambs with variations in umbilical blood flow. *J. Physiol., Lond.*, **170**, 524–40.

Dawes, G. S., Mott. J. C. and Shelley, H. J. (1959) The importance of cardiac glycogen for the maintenance of life in foetal lambs and new-born animals during anoxia. *J. Physiol., Lond.*, **146**, 516–38.

Dawes, G. S., Mott, J. C., Shelley, H. J. and Stafford, A. (1963) The prolongation of survival time in asphyxiated immature foetal lambs. *J. Physiol., Lond.*, **168**, 43–64.

Dawes, G. S., Mott, J. C., Widdicombe, J. G. and Wyatt, D. G. (1953) Changes in the lungs of the newborn lamb. *J. Physiol., Lond.*, **121**, 141–62.

Dawkins, M. J. R. (1961) Changes in glucose-6-phosphatase activity in liver and kidney at birth. *Nature, Lond.*, **191**, 72–3.

Dawkins, M. J. R. (1962) Effect of drugs used in labor and delivery. 41st Ross Conference '*Perinatal Pharmacology*', pp. 33–4. Ed. C. May. Columbus Ross Laboratories.

Dawkins, M. J. R. (1963a) Discussion workshop on neonatal hypoglycaemia in Fetal and Infant Liver Function and Structure. *Ann. N.Y. Acad. Sci.*, **111**, 538–42.

Dawkins, M. J. R. (1963b) Glycogen synthesis and breakdown in rat liver at birth. *Quart. J. exp. Physiol.*, **48**, 265–72.

Dawkins, M. J. R. (1963c) Glycogen synthesis and breakdown in fetal and newborn rat liver. *Ann. N.Y. Acad. Sci.*, **111**, 203–11.

Dawkins, M. J. R. (1964) Hypoglycaemia in childhood. *Proc. Roy. Soc. Med.*, **57**, 1063–4.

Dawkins, M. J. R. (1964b) Changes in blood glucose and non-esterified fatty acids in the foetal and newborn lamb after injection of adrenaline. *Biol. Neonat.* **7**, 160–166.

Dawkins, M. J. R. and Hull, D. (1963) Brown fat and the response of the newborn rabbit to cold. *J. Physiol., Lond.*, **169**, 101.

Dawkins, M. J. R. and Hull, D. (1964a) Brown adipose tissue and the response of newborn rabbits to cold. *J. Physiol., Lond.*, **172**, 216–38.

Dawkins, M. J. R. and Hull, D. (1964b) Brown adipose tissue and non-shivering thermogenesis in newborn animals. Pp. 269–80 in Nutricia Symposium '*The adaptation of the newborn infant to extra-uterine life*'. Ed. J. Jonxis, H. Visser and J. Troelstra. Stenfert Kroese. Leiden.

Dawkins, M. J. R. and Scopes, J. W. (1965) Non-shivering thermogenesis and brown adipose tissue in the human newborn infant. *Nature, Lond.*, **206**, 201.

Day, R. L., Caliguiri, L., Kamenski, C. and Ehrlich, F. (1964) Body temperature and survival of premature babies. *Pediatrics*, **34**, 171–81.

Desmond, M. (1953) Observations related to neonatal hypoglycemia. *J. Pediat.*, **43**, 253–62.

Dixon, H. G., Browne, J. C. Mc. and Davey, D. A. (1963) Choriodecidual and myometrial blood flow. *Lancet*, ii, 369–73.

Dixon, H. G. and Robertson, W. B. (1958) A study of the vessels of the placental bed in normotensive and hypertensive women. *J. Obstet. Gynaec., Brit. Emp.*, **65**, 803–15.

Drillien, C. M. (1965) The effect of obstetrical hazard on the later development of the child. *Recent Advances in Paediatrics*. 3rd Ed. pp. 82–109. Ed. D. Gairdner, Churchill. London.

Driscoll, S. G. and Hsia, D. Y-Y. (1958) Development of enzyme systems during early infancy. *Pediatrics*, **22**, 785–845.

Dutton, G. J. (1963) Comparison of glucuronide synthesis in developing mammalian and avian liver. *Ann. N.Y. Acad. Sci.*, **111**, 259–72.

Editorial (1954) Blindness and oxygen. *Lancet*, **266**, 86–7.

Farquhar, J. W. (1962) Birth weight and survival of babies of diabetic women. *Arch. Dis. Childh.*, **37**, 321–9.

Fazekas, J. R., Alexander, F. A. D. and Himwich, H. E. (1941) Tolerance of the newborn to anoxia. *Amer. J. Physiol.*, **134**, 281–7.

Flint, M., Lathe, G. M. and Ricketts, T. R. (1963) Effect of undernutrition and other factors on the development of glucuronyl transferase activity in the newborn rabbit. *Ann. N.Y. Acad. Sci.*, 111, 295–301.

Fouts, J. R. and Adamson, R. H. (1959) Drug metabolism in the newborn rabbit. *Science*, 129, 897–8.

Fujiwara, T., Adams, F. H. and Scudder, A. (1964) Fetal lamb amniotic fluid. Relationship of lipid composition to surface tension. *J. Pediat.*, 65, 824–30.

Gairdner, D. (1965) Respiratory distress in the newborn. *Recent Advances in Paediatrics*, 3rd Ed. pp. 54–81. Ed. D. Gairdner. Churchill, London.

Gitlin, D. and Craig, J. M. (1956) Nature of hyaline membrane in asphyxia of the newborn. *Pediatrics*, 17, 64–71.

Gribetz, I., Frank, N. R. and Avery, M. E. (1959) Static volume-pressure relations of excised lungs of infants with hyaline membrane disease, newborn and stillborn infant. *J. Clin. Invest.*, 38, 2168–75.

Gruenwald, P. (1947) Surface tension as a factor in the resistance of neonatal lungs to aeration. *Amer. J. Obstet. Gynec.*, 53, 996–1007.

Gruenwald, P. (1963) Chronic fetal distress and placental insufficiency. *Biol. Neonat.*, 5, 215–65.

Gruenwald, P. (1964a) The fetus in prolonged pregnancy. *Amer. J. Obstet. Gynec.*, 89, 503–9.

Gruenwald, P. (1964b) Pulmonary surface forces as affected by temperature. *Arch. Path.*, 77, 568–74.

Hall, I. C. and O'Toole, E. (1934) Bacterial flora of first specimens of meconium passed by 50 newborn infants. *Amer. J. Dis. Child*, 47, 1279–85.

Hammond, J. (1961) Nutrition and development of animals at birth. Ciba symposium '*Somatic Stability in the Newly Born*'. Pp. 5–9. Ed. G. Wolstenholme and M. O'Connor. Churchill, London.

Hargreaves, T. and Holton, J. B. (1962) Jaundice of the newborn due to novobiocin. *Lancet*, i, 839.

Harned, H. S., Jr., Rowshan, G., MacKinney, L. G. and Sugioka, K. (1964) Relationships of pO_2, pCO_2 and pH to onset of breathing of term lamb as studied by a flow-through cuvette electrode assembly. *Pediatrics*, 33, 672–81.

Hart, J. S. and Fisher, H. D. (1964) The question of adaptations to polar environments in marine animals. *Fed. Proc.*, 23, 1207–14.

Hemmings, W. A. and Brambell, F. W. R. (1961) Protein transfer across foetal membranes. *Brit. med. Bull.*, 17, 96–101.

Hertig, A. T., Rock, J., Adams, E. C. and Menkin, M. C. (1959) Thirty-four fertilized human ova, good, bad and indifferent, recovered from 210 women of known fertility. A study of biological wastage in early human pregnancy. *Pediatrics*, 23, 202–11.

Hill, J. (1959) The oxygen consumption of newborn and adult mammals. Its dependence on the oxygen tension in the inspired air and on the environmental temperature. *J. Physiol., Lond.*, 149, 346–73.

Himwich, H. E., Bernstein, A. O., Herrlich, H., Chester, A., and Fazekas, J. F. (1942) Mechanisms for the maintenance of life in the newborn during anoxia. *Amer. J. Physiol.*, 135, 387–91.

Hsia, D. Y-Y., Dowben, R. M. and Riabov, S. (1963) Inhibitors of glucuronyl transferase in the newborn. *Ann. N.Y. Acad. Sci.*, 111, 326–32.

Hull, D. and Segall, M. (1964) The effect of removing brown adipose tissue on heat production in the newborn rabbit. *J. Physiol., Lond.*, 175, 58.

Hull, D. and Segall, M. (1965a) The effect of sympathetic denervation and stimulation on brown adipose tissue in the newborn rabbit. *J. Physiol., Lond.* 177, 63P–64P.

Hull, D. and Segall, M. (1965b) *J. Physiol., Lond.* In press.

Hurst, V. (1960) Transmission of hospital staphylococci among newborn infants. II. Colonisation of skin and mucous membranes of infants. *Pediatrics*, **25**, 204–14.

James, L. S. (1960) Acidosis of the newborn and its relation to birth asphyxia. *Acta paediat., Uppsala*, **49**. Suppl. 122, 17–28.

James, L. S., Apgar, V., Moya, F., Kvisselgard, N., Burnard, E., Brady, J., Tuchman, W., Crawford, J. and Holaday, D. (1963) Intragastric oxygen: experimental observations in newborn puppies. *Acta paediat., Uppsala*, **52**, 241–4.

James, L. S. and Burnard, E. (1961) Changes occurring during asphyxia at birth. Ciba symposium '*Somatic Stability in the Newly Born*', pp. 75–91. Ed. G. E. W. Wolstenholme and M. O'Connor. Churchill. London.

Joel, C. D., Treble, D. H. and Ball, E. G. (1964) On a major role for brown adipose tissue in heat production during arousal from hibernation. *Fed. Proc.*, **23**, 271.

Johannson, B. (1958) Brown fat—a review. *Metabolism*, **8**, 221–40.

Jondorf, W. R., Maickel, R. P. and Brodie, B. B. (1958) Inability of newborn mice and guinea-pigs to metabolise drugs. *Biochem. Pharmacol.*, **1**, 352–4.

Jost, A. and Jacquot, R. (1955) Recherches sur les facteurs endocriniens de la charge en glycogène du foie fétal chez le lapin (avec des indications sur le glycogène placentaire). *Ann. Endocr. (Paris)*, **16**, 849–72.

Karlberg, P., Adams, F. H., Geubelle, F. and Wallgren, G. (1962) Alteration of the infant's thorax during vaginal delivery. Physiological studies. *Acta. obstet. gynec, Scand.*, **41**, 223–9.

Karlberg, P. and Celander, O. (1965) Respiratory and circulatory adaptation in the newborn. *Recent Advances in Paediatrics*, 3rd ed., pp. 36–53. Ed. D. Gairdner. Churchill, London.

Karlberg, P. and Koch, G. (1962) Respiratory studies in newborn infants. III. Development of mechanics of breathing during the first week of life. A longitudinal study. *Acta paediat.*, **51**, Suppl. No. 135, 121–9.

Kay, H. E. M., Peppercorn, M. E., Porterfield, J. S., McCarthy, K. and Taylor-Robinson, C. H. (1964) Congenital Rubella infection of a human embryo. *Brit. med. J.*, **2**, 166–7.

Knox, W. E., Auerbach, V. H. and Lin, E.C.C. (1956) Enzymatic and metabolic adaptations in animals. *Physiol. Rev.*, **36**, 164–254.

Kornfeld, R. and Brown, D. H. (1963) The activity of some enzymes of glycogen metabolism in fetal and neonatal guinea-pig liver. *J. Biol. chem.*, **238**, 1604–7.

Kovalcík, V. (1963) The response of the isolated ductus arteriosus to oxygen and anoxia. *J. Physiol., Lond.*, **169**, 185–97.

Kupferberg, H. J. and Way, E. L. (1963) Pharmacologic basis for the increased sensitivity of the newborn rat to morphine. *J. Pharmacol. Exp. Ther.*, **141**, 105–12.

Laws, R. M. (1953) Falkland Islands Dependency Scientific Surveys. Report No. 8.

Lester, R., Behrman, R. and Lucey, J. F. (1963) Transfer of bilirubin-C^{14} across monkey placenta. *Pediatrics*, **32**, 416–19.

Lucey, J. F., Hibberd, E., Behrman, R. E., Gallardo, F. O. E. and Windle, W. F. (1964) Kernicterus in asphyxiated newborn rhesus monkeys. *Exper. Neurol.*, **9**, 43–58.

Mann, T. P. and Elliott, R. I. K. (1957) Neonatal cold injury due to accidental exposure to cold. *Lancet*, i, 229–34.

McIntire, K. R., Sell, S. and Miller, J. F. (1964) Pathogenesis of the post-neonatal thymectomy wasting syndrome. *Nature, Lond.*, **204**, 151–5.

Metcalf, D. (1960) Effect of thymectomy on the lymphoid tissues of the mouse. *Brit. J. Haemat.*, **6**, 324–33.

Migeon, C. J. (1961) Endocrine function of the newborn. Ciba symposium '*Somatic Stability in the Newly Born*', pp. 215–37. Ed. G. Wolstenholme and M. O'Connor. Churchill. London.

Miller, J. F. (1961) Immunological function of the thymus. *Lancet*, ii, 748–9.

Miller, J. F. (1964) The thymus and the development of immunologic responsiveness. *Science*, 144, 1544–50.

Milner, R. D. G. and Hales, C. N. (1965) Effects of intravenous glucose on concentration of insulin in maternal and umbilical cord plasma. *Brit. med. J.*, 1, 284–6.

Misrahy, G., Behran, A., Spradley, J. and Garwood, V. (1960) Fetal brain oxygen. *Amer. J. Physiol.*, 199, 959–64.

Mitchison, N. A. (1961) Immunological tolerance and immunological paralysis. *Brit. med. Bull.*, 17, 102–6.

Moscovici, C. and Maisel, J. (1961) Intestinal viruses of newborn and older prematures. *Amer. J. Dis. Child.*, 101, 771–7.

Moss, A. J., Emmanouilides, G. C., Adams, F. H. and Chang, K. (1964) Response of the ductus arteriosus and pulmonary and systemic arterial pressure to changes in oxygen environment in newborn infants. *Pediatrics*, 33, 937–44.

Mott, J. C. (1961) Ability of young mammals to withstand total oxygen lack. *Brit. med. Bull*, 17, 144–7.

Mount, L. E. (1961) Metabolic rate and body temperature of pigs. Ciba symposium '*Somatic Stability in the Newly Born*', pp. 117–30. Ed. G. Wolstenholme and M. O'Connor. Churchill. London.

Neligan, G. (1965) Idiopathic hypoglycaemia in the newborn. *Recent Advances in Paediatrics*, 3rd ed. pp. 110–20. Ed. O. Gairdner. Churchill, London.

Nemeth, A. M. (1959) Mechanisms controlling changes in tryptophan peroxidase activity in developing mammalian liver. *J. Biol. Chem.*, 234, 2921–4.

Nemeth, A. M. and de la Haba, G. (1962) The effect of puromycin on the developmental and adaptive formation of tryptophan pyrollase. *J. Biol. Chem.*, 237, 1100–93.

Nordbring, F. (1957) Failure of newborn premature infants to absorb antibodies from heterologous colostrum. *Acta. paediat. Uppsala*, 46, 569–78.

Nyhan, W. L. (1961) Toxicity of drugs in the neonatal period. *J. Pediat.*, 59, 1–20.

Odell, G. B. (1959) Studies in Kernicterus. 1. The protein binding of bilirubin. *J. Clin. Invest.*, 38, 823–33.

Pattle, R. E. (1955) Properties, function and origin of the alveolar lining layer. *Nature, Lond.*, 175, 1125–6.

Pattle, R. E., Claireaux, A. E., Davies, P. A. and Cameron, A. H. (1962) Inability to form a lung lining film as a cause of the respiratory distress syndrome in the newborn. *Lancet*, ii, 469–73.

Pierce, A. E. (1961) Ciba symposium '*Somatic Stability in the Newly Born*', pp. 49–52. Ed. G. Wolstenholme and M. O'Connor. Churchill, London.

Prechtl, H. F. R. (1960) The long term value of the neurological examination of the newborn infant. In '*Child Neurology and Cerebral Palsy*', pp. 69–74. Little Club Clinic in Developmental Medicine No. 2.

Prod'hom, L. S. (1964) Pulmonary and circulatory patho-physiology of respiratory distress. Nutricia symposium '*The adaptation of the newborn infant to extrauterine life*', pp. 174–84. Ed. J. Jonxis, H. Visser and J. Troelstra. Stenfert Kroese, Leiden.

Registrar General (1964) *Quarterly Returns for England and Wales*. Her Majesty's Stationery Office, London.

Reisner, S. H., Forbes, A. E. and Cornblath, M. (1965) The smaller of twins and hypoglycaemia. *Lancet*, i, 524–6.

Schenker, S. (1963) Disposition of bilirubin in the fetus and newborn. *Ann. N.Y. Acad. Sci.*, **111**, 303–5.

Seller, M. J. and Spector, R. G. (1964) Effects of anoxia on the newborn and adult rat lung. *J. Path. Bact.*, **88**, 309–11.

Shelley, H. J. (1960) Blood sugars and tissue carbohydrate in foetal and infant lambs and rhesus monkeys. *J. Physiol., Lond.*, **153**, 527–52.

Shelley, H. J. (1961) Glycogen reserves and their changes at birth. *Brit. med. Bull.*, **17**, 137–43.

Shelley, H. J. (1964) Carbohydrate reserves in the newborn infant. *Brit. med. J.*, **1**, 273–5.

Smallpiece, V. and Davies, P. (1964) Immediate feeding of premature infants with undiluted breast milk. *Lancet*, ii, 1349–52.

Smith, R. E. (1962) Thermoregulation by brown adipose tissue in cold. *Fed. Proc.*, **21**, 221.

Smith, R. E. and Hock, R. J. (1963) Brown fat: thermogenic effector of arousal in hibernators. *Science*, **140**, 199–200.

Smith, R. E. and Roberts, J. C. (1964) Thermogenesis of brown adipose tissue in cold-acclimated rats. *Amer. J. Physiol.*, **206**, 143–8.

Smith, R. T. (1964) Immunologic tolerance: developmental phenomenon. *Pediatrics*, **34**, 14–22.

Stafford, A. and Weatherall, J. A. C. (1960) The survival of young rats in nitrogen. *J. Physiol., Lond.*, **153**, 457–72.

Stahlman, M., LeQuire, V. S., Young, W. C., Merrill, R. E., Birmingham, R. T., Payne, G. A. and Gray, T. (1964) Pathophysiology of respiratory distress in newborn lambs. *Amer. J. Dis. Child.*, **108**, 375–93.

Strang, L. B. (1963) Respiratory distress in newborn infants. *Brit. med. Bull.*, **19**, 45–8.

Sutherland, E. W. and Rall, T. W. (1960) The relation of adenosine 3^1, 5^1 phosphate and phosphorylase to the action of catecholamines and other hormones. *Pharmacol. Rev.*, **12**, 265–99.

Sutnick, A. I. and Soloff, L. A. (1964) Pulmonary surfactant and atelectasis. *Anaesthesiology*, **25**, 676–81.

Tierney, D. F. and Johnson, R. P. (1961) Factors in tension area relationships of pulmonary surface films. *Physiologist*, **4**, 122.

Tooley, W. H., Gardner, R., Thing, N. and Finlay, T. (1961) Factors affecting the surface tension of lung extracts. *Fed. Proc.*, **20**, 428.

Usher, R., McLean, F. and Maugham, G. (1964) Respiratory distress syndrome in infants delivered by cesarean section. *Amer. J. Obstet. Gynec.*, **88**, 806–15.

Van Duyne, C., Parker, H. R. and Holm, L. W. (1965) Metabolism of free fatty acids during perinatal life of lambs. *Am. J. Obstet. Gynec.*, **91**, 277–85.

Vest, M. F. and Salzberg, R. (1965) Conjugation reactions in the newborn infant: The metabolism of para-aminobenzoic acid. *Arch. Dis. Child.*, **40**, 97–105.

Vitsky, M. (1964) Cesarean section on the dead and critically injured. *Amer. J. Obstet. Gynec.*, **90**, 17–24.

Wagenvoort, C. A., Neufeld, H. N. and Edwards, J. E. (1961) The structure of the pulmonary arterial tree in fetal and early postnatal life. *Lab. Invest.*, **10**, 751–62.

Widdowson, E. M. (1950) Chemical composition of newly born mammals. *Nature, Lond.*, **166**, 626–8.

Widdowson, E. M. (1961) Metabolic effects of fasting and food. Ciba symposium 'Somatic Stability in the Newly Born', pp. 39–49. Ed. G. Wolstenholme and M. O'Connor. Churchill, London.

Yaffe, S. J. (1962) Strain variation in drug response. 41st Ross Conference 'Perinatal Pharmacology', pp. 48–53. Ed. C. May. Columbus Ross Laboratories.

Zetterström, R. and Ernster, L. (1956) Bilirubin: an uncoupler of oxidative phosphorylation in isolated mitochondria. *Nature, Lond.*, **178**, 1335–7.

Zinkham, W. H. (1959) An *in vitro* abnormality of glutathione metabolism in erythrocytes from normal newborns: mechanisms and clinical significance. *Pediatrics*, **23**, 18–32.

9

HUMAN FERTILITY AS A WORLD PROBLEM

G. R. Venning

G. D. Searle & Co. Ltd., High Wycombe,
Buckinghamshire, England

A. INTRODUCTION

Accelerating population growth is interfering to an increasing extent with efforts at economic progress in Asia and many other parts of the world. As each year goes by, new data necessitate repeated upward revision of the demographers' most pessimistic population forecasts. The only compensating good news is that an increasing number of foundations, semi-official bodies, and even Governments are recognizing the problem and a few are making a small start at doing something about it. In January, 1965, the U.N. set up a Commission to give advice on population problems in India at the request of Mr. Shastri. The question will be how to tackle the problem. Experience in other fields has already shown that major foreign investment in the developing countries can easily be wasted, and that pre-investment research is essential (Hoffman, 1963).

Governments that have decided to adopt a policy of population control by family planning may be tempted to start large-scale programmes, using particular contraceptive methods and particular administrative procedures, without knowing what return can be expected in terms of reduction in the birth rate. Finding the right answer will be difficult as the problem is a complex one. To understand it fully it is necessary to consider many different aspects—demographic, geographical, historical, economic, religious, sociological and cultural, medical (including the technical problem of contraceptive methods) and finally the logistic problems involved in any deliberate attempt at population control.

B. THE DEMOGRAPHIC PROBLEM

In a sense the entire problem is demographic, and all other aspects are related to this. Death rates are falling, largely as a result of the control of diseases, particularly smallpox and malaria. As long as this trend continues, the rate of population growth will increase, as birth rates in many developing countries are stationary or rising; and, where the trend is downwards, the rate of decrease tends to be slower than the reduction in death rates. Modern methods of malaria control rapidly reduce the death rates at all ages, including perinatally; hence malaria control may lead directly to a rise in the birth rate, quite apart from the indirect rise resulting from improved survival of children to reproductive age. The changing age structure which can be expected as a result of death control leads to a spurt in overall birth rate in the next generation. This is the stage which is now being reached as the aftermath of DDT. In Central and Latin America crude death rates have fallen to levels below 10 per 1,000 per annum, lower than those existing in fully industrialised societies such as the U.K. and the U.S.A. Age-specific death rates may still be higher in Latin America, the low figure for crude death rate reflecting a different age structure of the population. A developing country with a crude death rate of 15 per 1,000 can expect the problem of population growth to get more acute, since the death rate is likely to fall further. This is almost certainly applicable to many Asian countries.

There is another disturbing feature about the short term prospects which may be relevant to the demographers' under-estimates. When population growth is accelerating because of a falling death rate, the population will contain a disproportionate number of young children. The present crude birth rates in a number of countries therefore give a falsely low picture of reproductive capacity (Florence, 1964, 1965). After an interval of fifteen or twenty years, the large new generation will reach maturity. Population growth can then be expected to accelerate, as a result of a rising crude birth rate in addition to the still declining death rate. This is happening in many parts of Central and Latin America. Costa Rica, for instance, has a crude birth rate of over 50 per 1,000, with a death rate of less than 10 and a population growth rate of over 4% (Population Reference Bureau, 1964). The population of Costa Rica can therefore be expected to double within about sixteen years, and to quadruple by the turn of the century. The simple arithmetic of demography makes it inevitable that a similar situation will develop in those Asian countries which at present enjoy the relatively easy conditions of a modest population growth rate of 2.5% per annum, unless effective action is taken to bring about a reduction in the birthrate. Every year of delay makes the problem more urgent, as so many millions pass through puberty and enter reproductive life.

C. THE GEOGRAPHICAL PROBLEM

The striking differences between the present demographic situation in Asia and Latin America have arisen because the reduction in death rates occurred at an earlier stage in Latin America. Africa presents yet a different problem as the demographic transition is even less advanced than in Asia. Another aspect of the geographical problem relates to shortage of land in use for agricultural purposes. In some parts of Latin America there is no problem of this kind. But in many parts of Asia and elsewhere, population growth has led to progressive reduction in the size of agricultural holdings, so that surplus young men are driven to the outskirts of the cities in a search for work. One result is what is described as a 'population implosion', namely, a progressive concentration of people around the large cities. It has been estimated, for instance, that by the end of the century the population of Calcutta will rise to 66 million, and the number of migrants to

Indian cities may be between 100 and 200 million (Davis, 1963). This migration towards the cities obviously leads to specific problems in the field of public health, but at the same time it appears to be associated with a realization of the need for family planning. Rice-Wray (1963) and Rice-Wray, Cervantes, Gutierrez, Rosell and Goldzieher (1965) have shown that migrants around the outskirts of Mexico City are aware of the problem, even though many of them are illiterate; they have also shown that these people can effectively solve their own problem by the use of oral contraceptive pills.

In the past, large-scale migration has itself provided a solution to the problem. In classical times there was a land shortage in Ancient Greece, and migration throughout the Mediterranean provided an answer to the problem of population growth. Migration to the New World provided a solution to population growth in Europe; at the present time large-scale movements of people into Siberia and Central Asia are taking place, so that no urgent problem is recognized in the U.S.S.R. Migration can, however, contribute little if anything to the problem confronting most parts of the world today.

Successful family planning would solve the problem of additional unwanted pregnancies, but might still leave a population growing at a slower rate than at present. This assumes that couples would continue on average to want about three children. The stage would eventually be reached where the physical dimensions of the Earth's surface would impose a limitation to further population growth; one may speculate whether migration through space would then be a more acceptable solution to the problem than the limitation of families to a smaller size, appropriate for maintenance of a steady state. The only other option would be a rising death rate, whether from famine, war or stress disorders.

D. ECONOMIC ASPECTS

The economic aspects of population growth have been reviewed in detail by Coale (1963), Harkavy (1964) and Enke (1960). Apart from the simple arithmetic of food supply and mouths to feed, population growth may interfere in many ways with economic progress. For example, the changing age structure means that there is a greater burden of dependency; savings which are required for capital investment have to be diverted to extra housing and education. As recently as the last decade it was widely considered that gradual economic progress was a real possibility in India and other Asian countries.

More recent experience has however shown that the rate of increase of population is exceeding the rate of increase of the national product. Population growth is thus contributing to the widening gap between the 'have' and 'have not' countries (Theobald, 1961). The economic value of effective family planning has been discussed by Shepherd (1964). In North Carolina an investment of 10,000 dollars yielded a saving of 250,000 dollars. Enke (1960) has calculated that an investment of 125 dollars would be worthwhile for the prevention of each birth in a family planning programme in India.

E. HISTORICAL ASPECTS

1. *Western Europe and the United States*

We know surprisingly little about the factors which have determined transition from a high birth-rate to a low birth-rate in Western countries during the last two centuries. There are five reasons for rejecting the apparently obvious explanation that the use of contraceptive appliances was responsible:

(i) Studies of failure rates with the old contraceptive methods (Venning, 1961) indicate that these could not have produced the change in birth-rate that has occurred, even if they had been more widely used than surveys suggest. Participants in clinical trials and surveys tend, however, to be couples of greater than average fecundity; calculations based on such surveys would therefore tend to underestimate the demographic effectiveness of the old methods. The relationship between effectiveness of contraceptive methods and changes in the birth-rate has been studied by Tietze (1962) and by Sheps & Perrin (1963).

(ii) The use of contraceptives in the U.K. developed almost entirely after 1910, whereas the fall in the birth-rate began in 1870 and was virtually complete by 1930 (Pierce & Rowntree, 1961; Lafitte, 1963).

(iii) Marked changes in birth-rate followed the Great Depression in the 1930s, without any evidence of sudden change in contraceptive usage.

(iv) The fall in birth-rate occurred earlier in France than in England. Although I do not know of any valid survey of contraceptive usage in France, the more effective mechanical and chemical methods were probably used less, not more, than in England.

(v) There is good evidence of a high incidence of induced abortion in the United States (Calderone, 1958; Gebhard, Pomeroy, Martin and Christenson, 1958). The frequency has been estimated as one for every four or five live births. Though valid evidence is lacking, an incidence of one induced abortion for every live birth has been claimed for France (Venning, 1964); this frequency is approximately the same as that reported in many countries where legal induced abortion is freely available. Induced abortion on this scale must surely have had a significant impact upon birthrates.

Abstinence alone is unlikely to have been important; a degree of abstinence may however have increased the effectiveness of coitus interruptus and the rhythm method, which by themselves have such poor practical effectiveness that their demographic effect would be negligible. When the incentive to avoid pregnancy is powerful enough, men and women are afraid to sleep together; this may have had an important influence upon the birthrate in the West, especially at the time of the Great Depression in the early 1930s. In view of the concomitant development of psychoneurotic disorders as the major single cause of morbidity in Western countries, it is obviously important that nations now entering upon the era of demographic transition should find some happier method of solving the problem.

2. Ireland

One unique achievement in the demographic field has been the limitation of population growth in Ireland. This appears to have taken place largely as a result of a late average age of marriage, combined with a tendency for young men to emigrate and leave an excess of women who may never get married. The situation has apparently developed as a result of unusually strict adherence to the Roman Catholic doctrine, together with a socio-political background that is peculiar to Ireland.

3. Japan

In the post-war period the birth-rate in Japan has fallen rapidly, with the result that the problem of population growth has to a great extent been solved. This has undoubtedly contributed to the remarkable economic progress which has taken place during this time. As far as birth rate is concerned, Japan achieved in ten years a transition which took over 100 years in Western Europe. The deliberate adoption of a policy of legalized abortion appears to have been the main factor in this achievement, as the contraceptive programme met with difficulties (Koya, 1963).

Abortion, however, may well be unacceptable in other countries.

The mortality and morbidity of legal abortion in Japan and Eastern Europe are low, and the same is probably true of much illegal abortion in Western countries; but it is not a practical proposition at the present time for the rural communities in Asia, where facilities for safe aseptic surgery are only available to a minority.

F. SOCIOLOGICAL ASPECTS

Berelson (1964) has recently reviewed the experience of the Population Council in the introduction of birth control to people who have not previously attempted to limit family size. Surveys from four different countries have shown that increasing motivation for family planning brings in its wake an increasing incidence of induced abortion. This has proved equally true in Lebanon (Yaukey, 1961), Turkey (Tucker, Stycos, Angell and Berelson, 1964), U.K. (Lewis-Faning, 1949) and U.S.A. (Gebhard et al., 1958). Berelson has warned that governments embarking upon national family planning campaigns should be aware of this risk. Induced abortion is a problem mainly attributable to contraceptive failure (Venning, 1964); with oral contraception, unplanned pregnancies seldom if ever occur, and induced abortion is therefore virtually unknown.

One problem for the future is whether modern methods of education and communication can make possible a rapid spread of effective family planning in rural areas. Many writers have taken the pessimistic view that motivation is lacking, and that the best that can be expected is a very gradual adoption of family planning *pari passu* with the spread of education and with rising standards of living. This point of view seems to me to be based on a failure to appreciate that the inefficacy and inconvenience of the methods available in the past has had a serious adverse effect upon their acceptability. Surveys in the U.K. (Royal Commission on Population, 1949; Pierce & Rowntree, 1961) have shown that people who have attempted to practise some method of family planning have often given up after failure or through dislike of the method.

In rural communities, where the dwellings may be over-crowded, privacy is frequently lacking, and the cultural background usually militates against the success of any method which calls for restraint and for the application of contraceptive measures at the time of intercourse. In the United Kingdom only a minority of couples use the effective mechanical and chemical methods such as the male condom and the female cap and jelly (Lafitte, 1963). The use of appliance methods was more widespread in the United States before the advent of oral contraceptives, but failures were frequent, mainly because of poor acceptability and hence ineffective and irregular use. Since these methods have only gained partial acceptance in fully industrialized modern societies in the West, it is hardly surprising that attempts to spread their use in the East have been with few exceptions unsuccessful. Attempts to persuade people to use these methods when they do not have the necessary privacy, educational background, skill and restraint, may not merely be unsuccessful but may be positively harmful to a family planning programme. Suppose that a hundred women are offered a vaginal contraceptive device; twenty or thirty may, with luck, become successful users and will tell their friends and thus spread the practice of family planning, but the other 70 or 80 will recognize quite quickly that the method is entirely inappropriate. They will discard it and will tell their friends that this family planning idea is a fiasco. When this situation exists, the more effort that is made to spread family planning, the bigger will be the resistance of the people. The figures quoted for successful usage are those actually encountered in Ceylon, amongst an urban population many of whom were literate, including some who had reached a good standard of school education. The situation in rural communities might well be even worse. The condom seems to be clearly superior to the vaginal methods of mechanical and chemical contraception. The reasons for failure can be easily understood by the couple, whereas failures with the vaginal contraceptives are more likely to be blamed, rightly or wrongly, on the method. An additional advantage of the condom in a public health programme is, of course, protection against venereal disease. The disadvantage is low effectiveness in use (Table I).

Table I

CONTRACEPTIVE FAILURE RATES

Pregnancies per Thousand Woman Years	Rhythm	Withdrawal	Jelly, etc.	Diaphragm	Condom	Intra-uterine Device (I.U.D.)	Oral Contraceptive
Due to Incorrect Use ..	Yes	Yes	Yes	Yes	140	? No	0–3
In Spite of Correct Use ..	Yes	?	200	Yes	? No	26–50	? No
TOTAL ..	240	180	200+	120	140	26–50	0–3

For these reasons, the experiences of contraceptive programmes using the old methods have been disappointing. In India, for instance, the India-Harvard-Ludhiana Population Study (1963) yielded very little if any result. Motivation was good in the opinion survey, but was not good enough in practice for successful family planning with inappropriate methods. A similar project at Singur (1963), in a rural community with higher than average educational status, achieved a significant reduction in birth-rate, after a major and sustained effort of education and propaganda. This success has however been the exception, and the overall result of India's major birth control programme, which has had Government support on a large scale since 1951, has been extremely discouraging.

Male sterilization by vasectomy has however achieved a considerable measure of success in Southern India. In Bombay, these operations have been carried out at mobile camps, whereas in Madras the operations are being performed at centres in the main cities, and also at smaller hospitals in the rural areas and even at primary health centres. An encouraging feature of the success achieved in Madras has been the way in which the programme has accelerated. Acceptance of vasectomy in Madras was rapid, and satisfied customers were quick to spread the news to their friends, so that the greater the effort made, the more success was achieved, in contrast with the unhappy situation when unsuitable methods are offered. The method snowballed between 1959 (3,343 operations) and 1962 (47,886 operations), but in 1963 there was a serious setback. The reason for this is of interest. The Madras State Government offered financial incentives both to men undergoing the operation and to those (already operated upon) who assisted the programme by recruiting further volunteers. In 1963 the allowance paid to volunteers remained unchanged at ten rupees, but the fee paid to canvassers was reduced from Rs. 10 to Rs. 3 per volunteer recruited. This clearly had a serious adverse effect upon recruitment. At the present time a new system of financial incentive has been initiated. Each primary health centre serves a population of 50,000—100,000 people of an administrative district. Each district has now been set a target of 400 vasectomy operations per annum, and a financial grant has been offered of Rs. 100 for every operation in excess of 200 up to the limit set by the target. This makes it possible for each district to earn a useful sum of money for improvements to the local health centre and medical service facilities. It will be interesting to see whether an incentive at community level will be as effective as the personal incentive scheme.

18

With increasing spread of contraceptive practices there is a tendency not only for more people to limit their family size, but for use of contraceptives to begin earlier in marriage. This pattern of development may have accounted for the slow and gradual reduction of the birth-rate in Western countries. If in the early stages contraceptive methods tend to be employed by women with completed families of three or more children in an attempt to avoid larger families, the impact on the birth-rate may be slight. Owing to the high fertility which exists in the younger age groups, reproductive performance early in marriage has an important effect upon birth-rate. Even in India, for instance, where large families are the rule, 21 % of births in a recent survey were first order births (Chandrasekaran, personal communication). Although in the long run population trends depend upon average completed family size, the speed of transition may be to a great extent influenced by the pattern of family spacing. If this family spacing can include delay in first pregnancy, the experience from the history of Ireland indicates that this may have a particularly useful effect on the birth-rate.

Of the two available effective methods of family planning suitable for developing countries, only the oral contraceptives are applicable to nulliparous women, as the incidence of unpleasant complaints with intra-uterine devices is inescapably high in this group (Landesman, 1964).

In the nationwide programme now in progress in Taiwan (Population Council, 1965), the main method used has been the intra-uterine device (Guttmacher, 1964). Since most of the women coming forward for contraceptive advice have been women of high parity with completed families, it will be interesting to observe the influence of this programme upon the birth-rate.

G. MEDICAL ASPECTS

The old methods of contraception offer little prospect for any acceleration of the demographic transition in developing countries. Any decision to proceed with newer methods on a large scale must involve a consideration of the long term effects of oral contraception and of the newer plastic intra-uterine devices (I.U.D.s).

There is now extensive scientific literature on matters relating to the long term safety of progestin/oestrogen combinations. The most up-to-date reviews available at present include the March 1965 issue of *Metabolism, Clinical and Experimental* devoted to this subject, and the April 1965 issue of the *Practitioner*. The subject was previously reviewed at the 2nd Symposium of the International Fertility Association, Brussels, 1963. In summary, oral contraceptives have been in widespread use throughout the world during the last ten years, and similar hormonal substances have been in clinical use for twenty years previously. Five million women are using oral contraceptives at the present time, and there is no evidence of any long-term hazard.

In discussing the safety of oral contraceptives, Fox (1965) pointed out that 'older methods are less effective and sometimes less acceptable and if they did not take oral contraceptives many women would have less protection from pregnancy and some would have none at all. If there are risks in taking the pill they seem to be small; and for these women the risk of not taking it might even be greater, for the unwanted pregnancy has its own hazards for mother and for child.'

Although there is less long-term information about the I.U.D.s, preliminary studies were reviewed by the Population Council (1962), and extensive and thorough studies during the last three years have been reported at the Second International Conference on Intra-Uterine Contraception in New York (Population Council, 1964). With this information and that previously available on the Gräfenberg ring (Oppenheimer, 1959), there is no evidence of any serious long-term hazard. The chief source of anxiety relates to methods of sterilisation of plastic introducers. The device most widely used in national programmes is the Lippes Loop, at present in use in Taiwan and South Korea. The only available introducer for this is made of Teflon, a high quality plastic which cannot be adequately sterilized for repeated use. The biggest problem relates to the risk of transmitting hepatitis virus, the causative agent of homologous serum jaundice. Cheap plastic introducers which might be used once and thrown away have not been satisfactory owing to the high friction which makes it difficult to thread the device into the introducer. Metal introducers, which can be sterilized by autoclaving, also offer too much frictional resistance for the Lippes Loop (McBride, 1965).

The hazards of inadequate contraceptive practice are less often appreciated (Venning, 1965). Women who rely on the older, less effective methods of contraception are exposed to avoidable morbidity and mortality even in Western countries where medical care is almost universally available. In developing countries where medical services are less generally available, the morbidity and mortality associated with unwanted pregnancies may be many times greater;

the hazards of inadequate contraceptive practice are thus far more serious than any long-term hazards which may be associated with the newer methods. Maternal mortality is still the major cause of death amongst women of reproductive age in Ceylon, in spite of the fact that there is an island-wide medical service almost universally available. In other Asian countries where this is not so, satisfactory data on maternal morbidity and mortality are not available for the rural areas. Even in a city survey, however, maternal mortality has been found to be approximately 100 times greater than in the West (Pandit, 1948). In rural areas where people may live and die without ever seeing a doctor it is probably even higher: mortality in pregnancy may then represent a risk in excess of 2 %.

In addition to these general considerations of avoidable maternal mortality and morbidity, there are specific medical problems associated with inadequate contraceptive practice. Apart from hunger and malnutrition due to inadequate food supplies, which affect the entire population, there are special hazards affecting young children. Protein and calorie malnutrition, or kwashiorkor, is now one of the major public health problems in the world. In the absence of adequate food supply the children may thrive, possibly at the expense of the mothers' nutrition, during lactation. After weaning, however, there may be deterioration in child health: the main incidence of kwashiorkor falls upon children in this age group. In many instances the transition from a healthy breast-fed infant to a malnourished child takes place as a result of another pregnancy.

Anxiety has sometimes been expressed that oral contraception might interfere with lactation. Female sex hormones have been used for the inhibition of lactation; but in this situation the child is not put to the breast. The administration of female hormones in high dosage will then be expected to have a dose-dependent inhibitory effect (Toaff and Jewelewicz, 1963). Even under these circumstances, however, inhibition can only be relied upon when treatment is given before lactation is established, or at a late stage when lactation may in any case be on the decline. When the baby is sucking, the administration of hormones even at high dosage may not inhibit lactation. Evidence from the use of oral contraceptives is available from unpublished studies of Dr. Satterthwaite of Puerto Rico, who has collected data on the duration of lactation in women taking various doses of norethynodrel for oral contraception in the dose range 2.5 to

20 mg. daily. The duration of lactation has been compared with that on previous occasions when oral contraception was not used. The results are shown in Table II.

Table II

EFFECTS OF ENVOID (NORETHYNODREL WITH MESTRANOL) ON THE DURATION OF LACTATION IN WOMEN (HUMACAO)

Dosage mg./day	Total no. followed up	% lactating less long than previously	% lactating same as previously	% lactating longer than previously
20	22	77	18	5
18	37	38	57	5
5	84	45	45	10
2.5	34	15	70	15

Data from Dr. A. P. Satterthwaite, Humacao, Puerto Rico
(*for explanation see text*)

H. FAMILY PLANNING PROGRAMMES TODAY

In Western countries that have already passed through the demographic transition, the major contraceptive development in the last few years has been the increasingly widespread use of oral contraceptives, particularly in the U.S. and in Australia and to a lesser extent in Europe. It is estimated that approximately five million women are using oral contraceptives at the present time, almost four million in the U.S. alone (Sadusk, 1965). In the U.S. the crude birth rate has been declining during the last decade. Until 1961 this reflected a change in the age structure of the U.S. population, with relatively small numbers of women entering the period of reproductive life as an aftermath of the reduced fertility in the 1930s. During the 1950s the fall in the crude birth rate in the U.S. was not associated with any change in age-specific birth rates. Since 1961, however, there has been a reduction in the age-specific birth rates in the U.S.; this may well be related to the widespread use of oral contraception. In Australia also, the recent decline in the birth rate has been attributed to the fact that oral contraceptives are now being used by a significant proportion of women of reproductive age. In contrast with the U.S. and Australia, the number of women using oral contraceptives in Europe is still only a relatively small minority. According to the most recent estimate there are now approximately 400,000 women on oral contraceptives in the U.K.

It has often been said that uneducated women could never be taught to use oral contraception, and that this method will therefore not contribute to the solution of the problem of population growth in many of the developing countries. Abundant evidence is now available to the contrary. After the initial trials in the U.S., large-scale studies were carried out in Puerto Rico and in Haiti (Pincus, Garcia, Rock et al., 1959). These studies, and further studies in Puerto Rico (Satterthwaite, 1963), have involved several thousand women; many of these have been illiterate and uneducated, particularly in Haiti, but in spite of this there have been no problems in explaining the method, which has provided virtually complete protection against pregnancy. In Mexico Rice-Wray (1963) and Rice-Wray et al. (1965) have confirmed that oral contraception is a simple and effective method for uneducated people, including many migrants to the city from rural areas. Further confirmation on a large scale has come from Ceylon, where Chinnatamby (1963) has found the method satisfactory in a group of over 1,000 women during the last four years. Studies in India and Pakistan have been on a smaller scale but have also provided confirmation (Shah and Cobb, 1963; Shah, 1963; Kanitkar, 1963). Sodhy (1965) has reported that this method has proved satisfactory for routine use in the clinics of the Malayan Family Planning Association, and there have been similar reports from the Singapore Family Planning Association (1963) and the Hong Kong Family Planning Association (1963).

In considering different methods of contraception, effectiveness may be measured in three ways: theoretical effectiveness allowing for correct use, practical effectiveness allowing for normal conditions of use, and demographic effectiveness allowing for the percentage of women of reproductive age who will be willing to use a method and succeed in using it effectively. There is little valid evidence on the demographic effectiveness of any methods of contraception. Investigators who have reported that oral contraception is simple and satisfactory amongst uneducated and illiterate women, have for the most part been concerned with studies carried out at clinics, and it could be argued that the people coming to the clinics for advice represent an intelligent or enlightened minority of the female population. It is therefore important to know whether a significant percentage of an unselected population in a developing country could be expected to use oral contraceptives effectively. Preliminary information is extremely encouraging. Rao (1965) has carried out a major study involving Indian Tamil tea estate labourers in Ceylon. In an area with a total population of 10,000 with approximately 1,000 women of reproductive age in the community, there have been 300 women using oral contraceptives effectively since September 1963. The impact on the birth rate of the community can therefore be judged from the number of births during the period June 1964 to March 1965. The birth rate in these and other estates was 32 per thousand per annum before the use of oral contraception; the birth rate in other estates in Ceylon has remained unchanged since then. On the experimental estates, however, the birth rate has fallen to 19 per thousand per annum. The reduction is greater than might be expected from the use of an effective contraceptive by this number of women had they been selected at random, and can only be accounted for by assuming that the most fertile women have in fact been involved in the project. Evidence that this may be so comes from a simultaneous survey of the incidence of lactational amenorrhoea in other women on these estates, not using oral contraceptives. The group on oral contraceptives included fewer women showing lactational amenorrhoea, and a relatively greater number of menstruating women; the likelihood of pregnancy is of course greater amongst menstruating women than amongst those with lactational amenorrhoea.

Up to the present time, the main information on the use of I.U.D.s has come from two relatively advanced countries, namely South Korea and Taiwan (Berelson and Freedman, 1964). I.U.D. projects in these countries have been successful, as judged by the number of insertions, but the expulsion and pregnancy rates have been higher. The devices have been inserted by doctors who have received from gynaecologists a three-day period of special training in the necessary technique. In less advanced countries the problem will clearly be to find a sufficient number of people with the necessary skill available in the rural areas.

In the developing countries there has been a rapidly expanding interest at a national level in the problem of family planning. The first country to give official recognition to the problem in the form of a family planning programme was India, where there has been an official programme during the first three 5-year plans. In spite of this effort the evidence from the 1961 census indicates that there has been no significant effect upon the birth rate. Nor has there been any significant reduction in high order births, or change in the age structure of the population, such as one might expect during the early stage of an effective programme, before the apparent reduction in overall birth rate. What has been achieved, however, is an increasing number of clinics and an enlarging framework which could form the basis of a successful programme in due course (Raina, 1964). Up to the present time the actual usage of contraception in India's programme has been low, probably to a great extent because of the unsatisfactory and inappropriate nature of the methods offered. As far as other countries are concerned, major Government-sponsored programmes have been initiated in Pakistan, South Korea and Tunisia, but these have been too recent to draw any conclusions on their effectiveness. In addition, as has already been mentioned, there has been a major programme supported by the Population Council in Taiwan, in which emphasis has been placed on the use of I.U.D.s, and a programme in South Korea which was originally initiated with the older contraceptive methods, but has recently incorporated emphasis on I.U.D.s. Within the next few years evidence should be available on the effectiveness of this method from a demographic point of view. There has also been a United Nations enquiry on the attitude of Governments to the relationship between population growth and economic progress, while the need for Government family planning programmes has been recognized in many countries in Asia, Africa and America, including several of the Roman Catholic countries of Latin America (Chile, Guatemala and Panama) (Harkavy, 1964).

There has been consistent opposition in the past to the inclusion of family planning in the activities of the World Health Organisation (W.H.O.). This has come primarily from Roman Catholic countries. As a result of this, the contributions of W.H.O. to world population control have been largely confined to aggravation of the problem through successful work in the field of malaria control. The changing attitude of many Catholic countries in Latin America at the present time, and the visit of the Pope to Bombay, may therefore be of great importance. There is general awareness now in Latin American countries of the growing and serious problem posed by illegal abortions. As a result of this, Government supported action in the family planning field is already being taken in several countries, particularly in Chile.

I. TECHNICAL ASPECTS – METHODS OF FAMILY LIMITATION

1. Contraceptive methods

In considering sociological aspects of the population problem and the attitudes of people to family planning, it has been apparent that attitudes and motivation cannot be considered independently of the methods available. Until quite recently it has been commonplace for writers on the population problem to adopt a pessimistic attitude, based on the idea that women living in poverty in rural areas prefer large families, and that no reduction in the birth rate is likely until such time as education and economic progress have taken place. From discussion with people in many different countries the author has reached an opposite conclusion. In the past women in peasant communities have wanted large numbers of children, because they knew that many would fail to survive. It was necessary to have 8 or 10 children to ensure the survival of 3 or 4. Now that death rates are much lower this is no longer necessary. Uneducated women in rural areas are of normal intelligence, and are in general aware of the change in circumstances and would prefer to have smaller families of 3 or 4 living children. Confirmation of this has come from family planning surveys in many countries throughout the world (see Berelson 1964).

With unsatisfactory methods, motivation for family planning needs to be strong before any action is taken; indeed, the use of unsatisfactory methods may have an adverse effect upon the problem. In addition, the failure rates with the old methods of contraception have been such that they could have little impact on birth-rates. In the well known Singur study, a major effort using the old methods resulted in only a small, though significant, reduction in the birth-rate. The major programme of family planning in South Korea, also using the old methods, achieved considerable success as judged by the numbers of couples using contraceptive appliances (chiefly the condom). Although there was a significant reduction in the birth-rate, this occurred equally in the experimental area where contraceptive usage was high and in a control area where usage was much lower. There was thus no significant demographic effect from the greater spread of contraceptive usage in the experimental area (Yang, 1965).

Similarly, in Ceylon, a reduction in birth rate has been reported in a pilot study carried out by the Sweden/Ceylon Family Planning Project (Kinch, 1963). Even in this study, however, the pregnancy rates amongst contraceptive users were high, and there appears to have been little significant effect which could be attributed to the methods used, of which the least ineffective was the condom.

The evidence suggests that the old methods, involving precautions at the time of intercourse, may all be regarded as of little or no value from a demographic point of view. It has been pointed out that 50 % of the population using a 90 % effective method will give a much greater reduction in the birth rate than 90 % of the population using a 50 % effective method. A high degree of effectiveness of the methods used is clearly of paramount importance in any family planning programme. Table I shows the pregnancy rates with a variety of methods; an attempt has been made to distinguish between failures in spite of correct use and failures due to errors in use.

It seems that only two contraceptive methods deserve serious consideration for effective programmes aiming to speed up a reduction in the birth rate in developing countries. These are oral contraception and intra-uterine devices. Before considering non-contraceptive methods of family limitation such as sterilization and induced abortion, we may consider further the specific characteristics and implications of the two new methods of contraception. These two methods share one important characteristic, namely that the need for precautions at the time of intercourse has been eliminated, and it is this above all which has conferred on these methods an overwhelming advantage. There are, however, significant differences which can now be considered.

(a) ORAL CONTRACEPTION

As shown in Table I this method has the lowest failure rate of any method of contraception. Against this, there is a need for continuing motivation and continuing supplies. Experience has shown that amongst women of all types in many different countries, including illiterate women and others of low educational status, there is a minority who may lose interest and fail to continue using the method. Psychological factors are undoubtedly important in the acceptance of this as of any method of family planning, acceptance being higher in those projects where medical and other staff are familiar with the method and provide an efficient service. Where this is the case it has generally been found that the oral method of contraception is medically acceptable to approximately 95–97 % of women and continuing effective usage can be expected from 70–

80%. The need for continued motivation and supplies does not therefore constitute a major disadvantage in areas where the population live within reach of a clinic or other centre of distribution, though in inaccessible rural areas it may prove a major problem. In Western countries, oral contraceptives are available only on a doctor's prescription, and women normally receive a medical examination before using this method. Opinions differ concerning the need for precautions or contra-indications to the use of the pill. The most widely recognized contra-indication is the existence of cancer of the breast, the incidence of which, in women of child-bearing age, is extremely low. It is clear that any programme using oral contraception should be under the control of the medical profession and that medical examination and advice should be available when necessary. Instruction in this method of family planning, however, can be undertaken by people with little training; this may prove to be a major advantage in countries where there is a serious shortage of medical and nursing staff.

In the early days of oral contraception, the method was only used by women of proven fertility. Since it is now universally recognized that oral contraceptives have no adverse effect upon subsequent fertility, there need no longer be any restriction of this kind. Women of high fertility below the age of 30, and particularly in the 20–25 age group, make a major contribution to the birth rate in any community; even in countries such as India where large families are the rule, one in five of all births are first children. A fully effective programme for reduction of the birth rate must therefore include provision for contraception by nulliparous women. Oral contraception may prove to be the only satisfactory method for this group of women.

(b) INTRA-UTERINE DEVICES

The intra-uterine devices have one major advantage over the pill. Once inserted the I.U.D. may be expected to provide continued effective contraception for some women without the need for return visits for further supplies. This is a particularly important advantage for two groups of people. First, in inaccessible rural areas this may be the only satisfactory method of contraception; the only problem is to find the trained staff. Secondly, for women whose motivation is weak and who might otherwise discontinue contraceptive practice through disinterest or laziness, the I.U.D. may be the most satisfactory method, as a positive act of will is required to have the device removed, otherwise continued contraceptive effectiveness can normally be expected. An additional major advantage of the I.U.D.s is the extremely low cost, so low that it is likely to make a negligible contribution to the cost of a family planning programme. From an economic point of view there may perhaps have been too much emphasis on this advantage. Enke (1960) has pointed out that the Government of India could profitably spend 125 dollars for each birth prevented in a family planning programme, as it has been calculated that each extra person contributes a liability of 200 dollars and an asset of only 75 dollars to India's economy. In any realistic assessment of the costs of a family planning programme, therefore, the cost of even the most expensive methods, such as oral contraception and the condom, should be regarded as negligible in relation to the economic benefits of an effective family planning programme. At the present time, however, few if any Governments are giving adequate financial support to family planning. Even in India, for instance, where there has been Government support for over ten years, the budget is no more than 1c per head of population, or about 8% of the total budget for health services. In South Korea, Government spending has reached levels of about 4.5c per head, but it may well be that expenditure on a substantially larger scale will be necessary if effective results are to be achieved.

Against the striking advantages of the I.U.D.s there are certain disadvantages in comparison with oral contraception. As will be seen from Table I, the I.U.D.s have a failure rate of approximately 5% (Population Council, 1964, Tietze & Lewit, 1964). This means that, for most people, the method is several times more effective than are conventional contraceptive appliances. However, pregnancy rates of only 4% have been achieved with condoms and vaginal methods of contraception in studies involving selected couples of high educational status. For women in Western countries, therefore, the I.U.D.s have little if any advantage to offer. In Western countries up to the present time, I.U.D.s have been little used, and the main interest is centred on their use for women in problem families for whom the old contraceptive appliances have proved of no value, and for whom the only alternative method is oral contraception. For many women of this type, oral contraceptives also have proved satisfactory (Shepherd, 1964; Flowers, 1964; Morgan, 1964). Problem families may, however, include mental defectives, psychopaths and alcoholics (Peberdy, 1963 and 1964), and for these even oral contraceptives cannot be expected to provide complete protection against pregnancy. Although comparative studies have not yet been reported, the possible advantages of the intra-uterine method for such people are clear.

The main difficulty with intra-uterine devices up to now has been the high incidence of unpleasant side effects during the first two or three months. Most women experience excessive and irregular bleeding after first insertion of an I.U.D., and pain due to uterine cramping is also extremely common. When the method is offered with appropriate reassurance, many women will apparently put up with these discomforts and inconveniences, and the method has proved to be medically acceptable for about 70 % of people. The main reasons for drop-out, apart from pain and bleeding, are pregnancy and repeated expulsion of the device. In South Korea and Taiwan, intra-uterine devices are being increasingly used. The demographic impact cannot yet be assessed, as the numbers of people involved still represent only a small minority of women of child-bearing age. Those who have accepted this device may represent an enlightened majority. The real test of the effectiveness, as with any other method, will depend upon the percentage acceptance among women of reproductive age in the community. Up to the end of 1964 there had been over 100,000 insertions in South Korea, Taiwan and Hong Kong; these countries have a total population of 44 million.

Up to now, insertion of I.U.D.s has been virtually confined to doctors with a gynaecological training. With the original Gräfenberg ring, dilatation of the cervix is necessary, which normally calls for general anaesthesia. The modern plastic devices can be inserted through an introducer without dilatation of the cervix; this is a simple procedure which can be carried out under direct vision with a speculum inserted in the vagina. Paramedical personnel could perhaps be trained to undertake insertions. However, the training required for the insertion of intra-uterine devices will necessitate a higher minimum standard of background knowledge and education than is necessary for giving instruction on the use of oral contraceptives.

The original Gräfenberg ring fell into disrepute for reasons which in retrospect seem to have been totally inadequate (Oppenheimer, 1959). Fears that there might be an increased incidence of pelvic infection following the insertion of I.U.D.s appear to have been unfounded. Any risk that exists may be related primarily to spread of infection through the cervix when devices are used with a protruding tail. But any such hazard is a small one, and as with oral contraception the hypothetical risks are trivial in relation to the real hazards of unwanted pregnancy.

The problem in India and Pakistan, and other countries where medical services in the rural areas are not yet generally available, is clearly a very different one from the problem in Korea and Taiwan, and the usefulness of the I.U.D. will to a great extent depend upon the feasibility of a programme of insertions carried out by non-medical people, under medical supervision. Even under these conditions the hazard of insertion into a normal non-pregnant uterus is probably very small; the main problem is likely to arise from insertion into the softened uterus of a woman who is pregnant but in whom pregnancy is not detected. The other problem which is likely to arise is that in many developing countries there is a high incidence of inflammatory disease of the genital tract, and there may be special hazards with the insertion of I.U.D.s in women with pelvic inflammatory disease. For women with existing pregnancy or pelvic inflammatory disease, oral contraception may be safer than insertion of an I.U.D. by someone whose training has been inadequate to detect these conditions.

One final limitation of the intra-uterine method is its unsuitability for the nulliparous woman: the incidence of expulsion and of side effects necessitating rejection is extremely high in this group (Landesman, 1964).

To summarize the pros and cons of the modern contraceptive methods, the new I.U.D.s have two obvious advantages, firstly low cost and secondly continued effectiveness without the need for repeated visits for supplies. Against these advantages the oral contraceptive pill provides greater effectiveness (virtually 100% as against 95%), greater acceptability (95–97% against 70%) and finally, suitability for use by special groups such as nulliparous women and women with pelvic inflammatory disease. The logistic problems of carrying out a family planning programme with these methods in countries where there is a shortage of medical staff have not been adequately studied. No programme relying on only one of these methods is likely to be as successful and effective as a programme in which both methods are used, as it is clear that neither method is suitable for all women.

2. Non-contraceptive methods

The technical methods for consideration are those of sterilization (male and female) and legalized abortion. Other factors may influence the birth rate through effects upon the age of marriage and upon economic, cultural and other incentives to restrict the size of the family.

It might be assumed that sterilization, through its permanence and effectiveness, would have a major influence upon the birth rate. But the influence is probably limited, and will depend upon the lower limits of family size set as criteria for permitting sterilization. In the programme already discussed for sterilization (chiefly of the male) in Southern India, operations have been limited to men with at least three living children. The effect of this programme on the birth rate has unfortunately not been studied. The 400,000 sterilizations carried out have been spread over a wide area, and there is no published information on the demographic effect on a test community. As the average age of the men was 37, their wives, as a group, will have been well past the age of maximum fertility, so that the contribution of these couples to the birth rate might in any case have been a minor one. Any programme of sterilization can therefore only play an ancillary part in a population control programme.

In the short term, the failure rates are somewhat higher than those of oral contraception, though lower than those of any other contraceptive method; while the long continued effectiveness is advantageous within the demographic limitations already discussed. The fact that sterilization is normally irreversible is a major disadvantage, but one which may be regarded as acceptable in areas where the population problem is an urgent one and where adequate family planning services with effective methods are not at present available. In India the sterilisation programme in the South has probably achieved more than the whole of the rest of the family planning programme, which has been based on old contraceptive methods.

From a practical point of view the usefulness of female sterilization is limited by the fact that full hospital services are necessary for aseptic surgery and anaesthesia; this method is therefore unlikely to contribute to the problems of the rural areas in Asia. However, female sterilization still plays an important role in family limitation in many Western countries. Sir Dugald Baird has pioneered this approach to family planning in Scotland, thus drawing attention to the inadequacy of the older methods of contraception and to the importance of effective family planning in the public health field. Female sterilization has also been widely practised in many other countries including Puerto Rico.

Quite apart from the planned operations of tubal section and ligation, hysterectomy has in the past been carried out very frequently for a variety of menstrual disorders, even in the absence of demonstrable objective disease or abnormality of the uterus. It has been estimated that one woman in six in the United States is sterilized by tubal operation or by hysterectomy during reproductive life. Many women seeking a gynaecologist's advice for menorrhagia are worried about their menstrual periods as constant reminders of fertility and the likelihood of pregnancy. The haemoglobin level and blood count are often normal in patients with 'functional uterine bleeding', and objective studies of menstrual losses have shown poor correlation with subjective complaints of excessive bleeding. The popularity of hysterectomy for menorrhagia may have been due in part to the large number of satisfied women who are thus relieved of the fear and anxiety of an unwanted pregnancy late in married life.

Male sterilization is such a simple procedure that it can be carried out by a doctor after a very short period of training in this particular technique. It would therefore be quite feasible for young doctors working in primary health centres to take part in this programme, as is happening to some extent in Madras. The operation can be carried out in 5 or 10 minutes under local anaesthesia on an out-patient basis, and the man can expect to return to work the same day or the following day. Although vasectomy is reversible in most instances, the reconstruction operation requires a high degree of skill and full aseptic surgical facilities. From a practical point of view, therefore, the procedure is irreversible for the majority of men who have this operation in rural areas of South India.

The contribution of legalized abortion to the decline in the birth rate in Japan has already been considered. The disadvantage of this method of family limitation from a demographic point of view is that repeated abortions may be necessary in the same patient. The other disadvantages are well known, and in many societies the whole idea of adopting a deliberate policy of legalized abortion as a method of family planning may be unacceptable. There is undoubtedly an adverse psychological effect in many women, and apart from this the medical hazards are likely to be substantial in rural areas where full hospital facilities are not available. Although the mortality from legalized abortion carried out under satisfactory conditions is low (probably somewhat lower than the mortality from full-term normal delivery), the morbidity associated with abortion on a large scale may be of significance. In spite of the success of the abortion programme

TABLE III: FACTORS AFFECTING DEMOGRAPHIC EFFICACY OF DIFFERENT METHODS

	Male Sterilization	Female Sterilization	Abortion	Oral Contraception	I.U.D.	Condoms	Diaphragm (and Jelly)	Foam tablets, etc.	Abstinence and Withdrawal	Withdrawal	Rhythm	Abstinence
Practical Effectiveness ..	++++	++++	++++	++++	+++	++	++	++	++	+	+	+
Personal and cultural ..	++	+++	++			+	+	+	++	++		
Need for special medical facilities ..	+	+++	++	+	+		+					
Need for repeat supplies ..			+	+		+	+	+				
Need for high motivation ..	+	+	+			+	+	+	+	+	+	+
Need for higher education ..						+	+	+			+	
Religious (R.C.) ..	++	++	+++	+	++	++	++	++	++	++		
Unsuitable for nulliparous ..	+	+			+							
Unsuitable for low parity ..	+	+										
Unsuitable when menstrual irregularity ..											+	
Troublesome side effects ..	+	+	+	c.3%	c.15—20%	+	+	+	+	+	+	+
Demographic utility ..	+		+	+	+							

LIMITATIONS

authorities in Japan are making a major effort to introduce contraceptive practices and to discourage reliance upon abortion for family planning (Koya, 1963). An important consideration for any country contemplating a policy of legalized abortion for family limitation concerns the role of the doctor. In Japan, the financial incentive to doctors who carry out this operation acts as a disincentive to contributing to the contraceptive programme. Another consideration is that the incidence of illegal abortion is not necessarily reduced by the introduction of legalized abortion. It is obviously difficult to obtain valid information on this subject. Experiences in Eastern Europe have, however, been reviewed by Tietze and Lehfeldt (1961) and Tietze (1963).

In summary, legalized abortion can contribute effectively to a population control programme, but many people would consider that the disadvantages outweigh the advantages. An attempt has been made in Table III to summarise the characteristics of all the various methods of family limitation including contraceptive methods, sterilization and abortion. From a demographic point of view only four methods are likely to contribute to an accelerated reduction of the birth rate in developing countries in which medical services in the rural areas are not fully developed. These methods are oral contraception, I.U.D.s, legalized abortion and male sterilization by vasectomy. In view of the reservations about legalized abortion, the practical procedures which are likely to be of value are oral contraception, I.U.D.s and vasectomy.

J. AGE OF MARRIAGE AND INCENTIVES TO FAMILY PLANNING

The influence of age of marriage and age of first childbirth upon the birth rate of a community is extremely difficult to evaluate. Early age of marriage is correlated in a number of surveys with a larger average completed family size. It is, however, not necessarily valid to conclude from this that a deliberate policy of delaying marriage and first childbirth (whether by exhortation or by law) would necessarily result in smaller completed families. One may argue that the correlations observed in surveys may simply indicate that age of marriage and completed family size are both subject to influences by other factors, rather than that there is a cause-and-effect relationship. These considerations apply, however, to the long-term influence of age of marriage upon the birth-rate. The problem in developing countries is an immediate one, as economic progress is being hindered by the birth-rate now; even a temporary reduction in the birth-rate through a change in the age of marriage could be of great importance and value in many countries. The average age of first childbirth in India at the present time is 16½ years. If this could be raised to 20 there would probably be an immediate beneficial effect. To bring about a change in national customs is difficult. The remarkable achievement of Westernization in Turkey brought about by Kemal Ataturk shows that rapid cultural metamorphosis is possible. In that instance the main changes related to the written language, customs of dress, and the emancipation of women; age at marriage was not specifically selected as a target for reform (though Turkey has recently recognized the existence of a serious problem of population growth). The problem of introducing new ideas in the age-old pattern of life in Indian villages is a complex one, and has been described in vivid detail by Wiser and Wiser (1963) and Nair (1962), who have shown that the problems, although difficult, are by no means insuperable.

Financial incentives to childbirth exist in many countries through family allowances and patterns of taxation. Other factors also contribute in the general sociological, cultural and economic background of the community. No serious attempt has ever been made to influence the birth-rate by such methods.

K. SUMMARY

The problem of human fertility is complex; an attempt has been made to review the present status of progress (or lack of progress) in the field of fertility control and the evidence available concerning the nature of the problem, including demographic, historical, geographical, economic, sociological and medical aspects. In many of these areas the data available are inadequate for valid conclusions to be drawn, and further information is still needed on the nature of the problem before any assumptions can be made concerning the best methods of solution. The technical problem of bringing about a more rapid decline in the birth-rate has been considered from the point of view of contraceptive methods, and other methods of family limitation such as sterilization and abortion; other factors which may influence the birth-rate have also been discussed. It is concluded that oral contraceptives and the new plastic intra-uterine devices provide the only two contraceptive methods available today that are likely to be of any value in this context. Male sterilization and legalized abortion are potentially effective from a demographic point of view, but legalized abortion may be unacceptable for other reasons. In practice, we are therefore left with the situation that a population control programme should be based on oral and intra-uterine contraception for family spacing, with male sterilization as an additional method for family limitation.

The two contraceptive methods both have their own advantages and disadvantages; these have been reviewed. The main advantages of the I.U.D.s are their low cost, and the continuing protection provided without the need for repeated motivation and contraceptive supplies. The main limitations are related to the medical skill necessary for insertion and the fact that this method is unsuitable for nulliparous women. The other disadvantage of the intra-uterine method is that approximately 30% of women find the method unacceptable on account of repeated spontaneous expulsion of the device or persistent pain or bleeding, and the pregnancy rate with this method is approximately 5 per 100 woman years. For the substantial minority of people for whom this method is unsuitable or unacceptable, oral contraception will often be satisfactory. The main advantages of oral contraception are that it is virtually 100% effective, and the simplicity and acceptability are such that this method has proved satisfactory for illiterate women and others of low educational status in rural communities throughout the world. The main disadvantage is that repeated contraceptive supplies are necessary. With this method also there are a minority of women (3 – 5%) who find the method unacceptable.

Doubts have been expressed about the long-term safety of oral contraceptives and I.U.D.s. Oral contraceptives have been studied as thoroughly and extensively as any available drugs and have been widely used for 10 years; 5 million women are using the method regularly at the present time and there is no evidence of any long-term hazard. There is less evidence concerning the long-term safety of the new plastic intra-uterine devices. These have, however, been very thoroughly investigated during the last three years, and this experience, together with evidence from the older Gräfenberg ring studies, has given no indication of any long-term hazard. If there are any long-term hazards with either of these methods, they are likely to be substantially less than the long-term hazards of the inadequate protection from unwanted pregnancy provided by all other methods of contraception. This is particularly true in the developing countries.

The limitations of each method are such that any programme relying upon one only is unlikely to be as effective as a programme in which both are employed.

REFERENCES

Berelson, B. (1964) National family planning programs: a guide. *Studies in Family Planning.* **5,** 1. (Supp.).

Berelson, B. and Freedman, R. (1964) A study in fertility control. *Scientific American.* **210,** 29.

Calderone, M. S. ed. (1958) *Abortion in the United States.* Hoeber-Harper, New York.

Chinnatamby, S. (1963) Clinical trial of oral contraceptives (Enovid and Conovid-E). In Proceedings of a Symposium on *Oral Contraception,* Colombo, Ceylon, February. G. D. Searle & Co. Ltd., High Wycombe, England.

Coale, A. J. (1963) The economic effects of fertility control in under-developed areas, in *Human Fertility and Population Problems.* Schenkman, Cambridge, Mass.

Davis, K. (1963) *Scientific American.*

Enke, S. (1960) The economics of government payments to limit population, in *Economics Development and Cultural Change,* p.339, cited by Harkavy, 1964.

Florence, P. S. (1964) in *Biological Aspects of Social Problems.* Lancet ii, 856.

Florence, P. S. (1965) The public cost of large families. *The Eugenics Review.* **56,** No. 3.

Flowers, C. (1964) Effects of new low-dosage form of norethynodrel-mestranol. *J. Amer. Med. Assn.* **188,** 1115.

Fox, Sir T. (1965) B.M.A. Annual Clinical Meeting, April 1–3, Dundee.

Gebhard, P. H., Pomeroy, W. B., Martin, C. E., and Christenson, C. V. (1958) *Pregnancy, birth and abortion.* Harper, New York.

Guttmacher, A. F. (1964) *The Intra-uterine Contraceptive Device (I.U.C.D.).* The Eighth Oliver Bird Lecture, 23 Nov. 1964, London.

Harkavy, O. (1964) *Economic problems of population growth.* The Ford Foundation, New York.

Hoffman, P. G. (1963) *World without want.* Chatto and Windus, London.

Hong Kong Family Planning Association (1963) *12th Annual Report.*

India-Harvard-Ludhiana Population Study (1963) *Studies in Family Planning.* **1,** 4.

Kanitkar, S. D. (1963) Acceptability of oral contraceptives by Indian women – a preliminary report. In Proceedings of a Symposium on *Oral Contraception,* Colombo, Ceylon.

Kinch, A. (1963) The Sweden–Ceylon Family Planning Pilot Project. *Studies in Family Planning,* **2,** 9.

Koya, Y. (1963) *Pioneering in family planning.* Population Council, New York.

Lafitte, F. (1963) *Family planning in the sixties.* Birmingham University.

Landesman, R. (1964) Second International Conference on *Intra-Uterine Contraception.* Population Council, New York.

Lewis-Faning, E. (1949) *Report of Royal Commission on Population.* H.M.S.O. London.

McBride, W. G. (1965) International Seminar on Modern Contraception, Indian Federation of Obstetrics and Gynaecology, Bombay, July.

Morgan, D. (1964) in Biological aspects of social problems. *Lancet,* ii, 858.

Nair, K. (1962) *Blossoms in the dust; the Human element in Indian development.* Duckworth, London.

Oppenheimer, W. (1959) Prevention of pregnancy by the Graefenberg ring method. *Amer. J. Obstet. Gynec.* **78**, 446.

Pandit, S. (1948) *Summary of the findings of investigation into the causes of maternal mortality in India.* India Research Fund Association, Kanpur.

Peberdy, M. (1963) Oral contraceptive trials in problem families in Newcastle-upon-Tyne. In Proceedings of a Symposium on *Oral Contraception*, Colombo, Ceylon.

Peberdy, M. (1964) in *Biological Aspects of Social Problems*, Lancet, ii, 858.

Pierce, R. M. and Rowntree, G. (1961) Birth control in Britain. *Population Studies*, **15**, 1.

Pincus, G., Garcia, C. R., Rock, J., Paniagua, M., Pendleton, A., Laraque, N. R., Borno, R. and Pean, V. (1959) Effectiveness of an oral contraceptive. *Science*, **130**, 81.

Population Council (1962) Proceedings of the conference on Intra-Uterine Contraceptive Devices. *Excerpta Medica*, Amsterdam.

Population Council (1964) Second International Conference on Intra-Uterine Contraception, New York, October 2–3.

Population Council (1965) Korea and Taiwan: Two national programs. *Studies in Family Planning*, **6**, 1.

Population Reference Bureau, Inc., December 7th. World Population 1964: 3.3 billion.

Raina, B. L. (1964) The family planning programme in India. *Studies in Family Planning*, **3**, 1.

Rao, P. V. (1965) International Seminar on Modern Contraception, Indian Federation of Obstetrics and Gynaecology, Bombay, July.

Rice-Wray, E. (1963) The acceptability of oral contraceptives by women of the low income group. Proceedings of the 91st Annual Meeting of the American Public Health Association, Kansas City, Missouri.

Rice-Wray, E., Cervantes, A., Gutierrez, J., Rosell, A. A. and Goldzieher, J. W. (1965) The acceptability of oral progestagens in fertility control. *Metabolism*, **14**, 451–456.

Sadusk, J. F. (1965) Food and Drug Committee Reports, **27**, No. 15, p.9.

Satterthwaite, A. P. (1963) Experience with multiple contraceptive methods in Puerto Rico, April 1957 – March 1963. Paper presented at the School of Public Health, University of North Carolina, Chapel Hill, N.C. May 1963.

Second Symposium of the International Fertility Association (1963) Brussels, March 2–3. *Internat. J. Fertil.* **9**, No. 1.

Shah, N. A. and Cobb, J. C. (1963) A preliminary report on the use of oral contraceptive pills synchronised with the phases of the moon. Proceedings of the Seventh Conference of the International Planned Parenthood Federation, Singapore, Feb. 1963. *Excerpta Medica*, Amsterdam.

Shah, P. N. (1963) Some experiments with norethynodrel in Indian women. Analysis of 276 cycles in 38 women. *J. Obst. & Gyn.* India **13**, 255.

Shepherd, J. (1964) Birth control and the poor: A solution. *Look*, April 7th.

Sheps, M. C. and Perrin, E. B. (1963) Changes in birth rates as a function of contraceptive effectiveness: Some applications of a stochastic model. *Amer. J. Public Health*, **53**, 1031.

Singapore Family Planning Association (1963). *14th Annual Report.*

Singur Study (1963) *Studies in Family Planning*, **1**, 1.

Sodhy, L. S. (1965) Family Planning administration in the State of Malaysia with special reference to oral contraception. Proceedings of Symposium on Oral Progestins in Gynaecology and Contraception. Bangkok.

Theobald, R. (1961) *The Rich and the Poor*. New American Library (Mentor), New York.

Tietze, C. (1962) Pregnancy rates and birth rates. *Population Studies*, **16**, 31.

Tietze, C. (1963) The demographic significance of legal abortion in Eastern Europe. Paper presented at the Annual Meeting of the Population Association of America, April 25–27, Philadelphia.

Tietze, C. and Lehfeldt (1961) Legal abortion in Eastern Europe. *J. Amer. Med. Assn.* **175**, 1149.

Tietze, C. and Lewit, S. (1964) Second International Conference on Contraception, New York, October 2–3, p.46.

Toaff, R. and Jewelewicz, R. (1963) Inhibition of lactogenesis by combined oral progestagens and oestrogens. *Lancet*, ii, 322.

Tucker, J., Stycos, J. M., Angell, G. W. and Berelson, B. (1964) Turkey: National Survey on Population. *Studies in Family Planning*, **5**, 1.

Venning, G. R. (1961) The Contraceptive Pill. *Brit. Med. J*. **2**, 899.

Venning, G. R. (1964) The abortion problem. *Family Planning*, **13**, 8.

Venning, G. R. (1965) The influence of contraceptive practice upon maternal and child health. *Metabolism*, **14**, 457–464.

Wiser, W. H. and Wiser, C. V. (1963) *Behind Mud Walls*. University of California Press, Berkeley and Los Angeles.

Yang, J. M. (1965) Paper submitted to U.N. Population Conference, Belgrade.

Yaukey, D. (1961) *Fertility differences in a modernizing country; a survey of Lebanese couples.* Princeton University Press, Princeton, New Jersey.